MODERN PRACTICAL BOTANY

VOLUME – III

INCLUDING SIX UNITS

1. *Plant Physiology;* 2. *Biochemistry;* 3. *Ecology;* 4. *Biotechnology;*
5. *Utilization of Plants : Economic Botany;* 6. *Plant Breeding and Crop Improvement.*

(As per UGC Model Curriculum and Syllabi of other Indian Universities)

Dr. B.P. PANDEY

M.Sc., Ph.D., FPSI

Reader and Head
Department of Botany, J.V. College, Baraut (Retd.)
Convener, Board of Studies and Research Degree Committee
C.C.S. University, Meerut

S. CHAND & COMPANY LTD.

(AN ISO 9001 : 2000 COMPANY)
RAM NAGAR, NEW DELHI-110 055

S. CHAND & COMPANY LTD.

(An ISO 9001 : 2000 Company)

Head Office: 7361, RAM NAGAR, NEW DELHI - 110 055
Phone: 23672080-81-82, 9899107446, 9911310888
Fax: 91-11-23677446

Shop at: **schandgroup.com**; e-mail: **info@schandgroup.com**

Branches :
AHMEDABAD : 1st Floor, Heritage, Near Gujarat Vidhyapeeth, Ashram Road, **Ahmedabad** - 380 014,
Ph: 27541965, 27542369, ahmedabad@schandgroup.com
BENGALURU : No. 6, Ahuja Chambers, 1st Cross, Kumara Krupa Road, **Bengaluru** - 560 001,
Ph: 22268048, 22354008, bangalore@schandgroup.com
BHOPAL : Bajaj Tower, Plot No. 243, Lala Lajpat Rai Colony, Raisen Road, **Bhopal** - 462 011,
Ph: 4274723. bhopal@schandgroup.com
CHANDIGARH : S.C.O. 2419-20, First Floor, Sector - 22-C (Near Aroma Hotel), **Chandigarh** -160 022,
Ph: 2725443, 2725446, chandigarh@schandgroup.com
CHENNAI : 152, Anna Salai, **Chennai** - 600 002, Ph: 28460026, 28460027, chennai@schandgroup.com
COIMBATORE : No. 5, 30 Feet Road, Krishnasamy Nagar, Ramanathapuram, **Coimbatore** -641045,
Ph: 0422-2323620 coimbatore@schandgroup.com **(Marketing Office)**
CUTTACK : 1st Floor, Bhartia Tower, Badambadi, **Cuttack** - 753 009, Ph: 2332580; 2332581,
cuttack@schandgroup.com
DEHRADUN : 1st Floor, 20, New Road, Near Dwarka Store, **Dehradun** - 248 001,
Ph: 2711101, 2710861, dehradun@schandgroup.com
GUWAHATI : Pan Bazar, **Guwahati** - 781 001, Ph: 2738811, 2735640 guwahati@schandgroup.com
HYDERABAD : Padma Plaza, H.No. 3-4-630, Opp. Ratna College, Narayanaguda, **Hyderabad** - 500 029,
Ph: 24651135, 24744815, hyderabad@schandgroup.com
JAIPUR : A-14, Janta Store Shopping Complex, University Marg, Bapu Nagar, **Jaipur** - 302 015,
Ph: 2719126, jaipur@schandgroup.com
JALANDHAR : Mai Hiran Gate, **Jalandhar** - 144 008, Ph: 2401630, 5000630,
jalandhar@schandgroup.com
JAMMU : 67/B, B-Block, Gandhi Nagar, **Jammu** - 180 004, (M) 09878651464 **(Marketing Office)**
KOCHI : Kachapilly Square, Mullassery Canal Road, Ernakulam, **Kochi** - 682 011, Ph: 2378207,
cochin@schandgroup.com
KOLKATA : 285/J, Bipin Bihari Ganguli Street, **Kolkata** - 700 012, Ph: 22367459, 22373914,
kolkata@schandgroup.com
LUCKNOW : Mahabeer Market, 25 Gwynne Road, Aminabad, **Lucknow** - 226 018, Ph: 2626801,
2284815, lucknow@schandgroup.com
MUMBAI : Blackie House, 103/5, Walchand Hirachand Marg, Opp. G.P.O., **Mumbai** - 400 001,
Ph: 22690881, 22610885, mumbai@schandgroup.com
NAGPUR : Karnal Bag, Model Mill Chowk, Umrer Road, **Nagpur** - 440 032, Ph: 2723901, 2777666
nagpur@schandgroup.com
PATNA : 104, Citicentre Ashok, Govind Mitra Road, **Patna** - 800 004, Ph: 2300489, 2302100,
patna@schandgroup.com
PUNE : 291/1, Ganesh Gayatri Complex, 1st Floor, Somwarpeth, Near Jain Mandir,
Pune - 411 011, Ph: 64017298, pune@schandgroup.com **(Marketing Office)**
RAIPUR : Kailash Residency, Plot No. 4B, Bottle House Road, Shankar Nagar, **Raipur** - 492 007,
Ph: 09981200834, raipur@schandgroup.com **(Marketing Office)**
RANCHI : Flat No. 104, Sri Draupadi Smriti Apartments, East of Jaipal Singh Stadium, Neel Ratan
Street, Upper Bazar, **Ranchi** - 834 001, Ph: 2208761,
ranchi@schandgroup.com **(Marketing Office)**
SILIGURI : 122, Raja Ram Mohan Roy Road, East Vivekanandapally, P.O., **Siliguri**-734001,
Dist., Jalpaiguri, (W.B.) Ph. 0353-2520750 **(Marketing Office)**
VISAKHAPATNAM: Plot No. 7, 1st Floor, Allipuram Extension, Opp. Radhakrishna Towers, Seethammadhara
North Extn., **Visakhapatnam** - 530 013, (M) 09347580841,
visakhapatnam@schandgroup.com **(Marketing Office)**

First Edition 2010
Reprint 2012

ISBN : 81-219-3508-3   **Code : 03 386**

PRINTED IN INDIA
By Rajendra Ravindra Printers Pvt. Ltd., 7361, Ram Nagar, New Delhi -110 055
and published by S. Chand & Company Ltd., 7361, Ram Nagar, New Delhi -110 055.

PREFACE TO THE FIRST EDITION

The practical study of the subject is of immense value. The theoretical classroom knowledge remains meaningless and incomplete unless and until is supplemented with the practical work either in the field or inside the laboratory. The laboratory work always adds to the knowledge and discipline. The practical work develops confidence and scientific outlook which makes the most essential part of life. The science subjects can only be understood well when a student works in the laboratory and makes the rational approach based on the facts and figures. Laboratory is the only place where a student learns and makes clear cut demarcation between right and wrong. A student always needs some guide lines to facilitate his work in the laboratory. The present text will fulfil this need. The first edition of **'Modern Practical Botany'** Volume III is just published and it is hoped that this will serve those well for whom it is intended.

The Modern Practical Botany, Volume III includes *six* units naming *1. Plant Physiology, 2. Biochemistry, 3. Ecology, 4. Biotechnology, 5. Utilization of Plants (Economic Botany), 6. Plant Breeding and Crop Improvement.*

In subsequent chapters, the 'laboratory exercises' are given, and in some chapters the 'terms to remember' are being given, that help in *viva-voce*. This Practical Manual covers the syllabi of all Indian Universities and UGC Model Curriculum.

My sincere thanks are due to Dr. S. Kumar, Dr. J. Mohan, Dr. Rajeshwari Sharma and Dr. Ashok Kumar of J.V. College, Baraut, and Dr. S.S. Sharma and Dr. Shashi, of H.P. University, Shimla (H.P.). Sanjeeva Pandey, I.F.S., Rahul Pandey, I.F.S and Shanti Priya, I.F.S. deserve special thanks for their valuable suggestions. I also express my deep sense of gratitude to my friends, botanists, and educationists who have accorded their full co-operation and well wishes during preparation of this Practical Manual.

I am really grateful to Mrs. Nirmala Gupta, CMD, Mr. Navin Joshi, Vice-President (Publishing), Mr. R.S. Saxena, Advisor and Mr. Shishir Bhatnagar, Pre-Press Manager, S. Chand and Company Ltd., New Delhi, who have brought the book in this shape and fine get up. Mr. Bhagirath Kaushik, the Branch Manager of Nagpur Branch deserves my special thanks for his very special co-operation.

The healthy suggestions and criticisms from all corners of country are invited for the improvement of subsequent editions.

'Neelkanth Karteer'   **Dr. B.P. PANDEY**
Subhash Nagar, Baraut - 250611   Department of Botany,
January, 1, 2010   J.V. College, Baraut-250611

CONTENTS

Genetic Engineering-**174**, Applications of Recombinant DNA Technology-**178**, Diagnosis of Human Diseases-**180**, Cloning-**182**, Plant Cloning and Genetic Engineering-**187**, Animal Cloning and Genetic Engineering-**187**, DNA Fingerprinting-**191**, Genomics-**195**, Transgenics-**197**, Gene Libraries and Gene Banks-**198**, Terms to Remember-**199**.

UNIT 5 : UTILIZATION OF PLANTS : ECONOMIC BOTANY

UNIT 6 : PLANT BREEDING AND CROP IMPROVEMENT

PLANT PHYSIOLOGY

Plants germinate from seeds, grow, develop, mature, reproduce and die. Plant physiology is the study of these processes. In other words, plant physiology deals with how plants function. Plants are autotrophs (chlorophyllous plants) and make their own food by utilising carbon dioxide, water and sunlight.

But before plants become photosynthetically competent after the emergence of the leaves, the germinating plants get their food from reserves in the cotyledons as in peas and beans. As the plant grows, the role of food production is shifted from cotyledons to fully exposed leaves, which take a variety of shapes and sizes and carry out the process of photosynthesis.

It is said that "only the sun gives without taking", and plants play a big role in this process. The sun energy is converted to ATP which is necessary for conversion of carbon dioxide to carbohydrates. The carbohydrates (glucose, sucrose or starch) are utilized in respiration by plants themselves (and also by animals which eat plants) to form ATP that provides the energy necessary for life's function.

The process of respiration that produces ATP uses oxygen that is released during photosynthesis. It is this oxygen that changed the atmosphere from one full of hydrogen to one rich in oxygen.

Plants possess the capability of taking up nitrogen and other nutrients, along with water, from the soil through an elaborate root system. The inorganic and organic nutrients act as building blocks and help plants grow and reproduce. All these activities in plants, like any other living organism, follow the known chemical and physical laws.

CHAPTER 1

Plant Physiology : Laboratory Exercises

GENERAL ASPECTS

EXERCISE 1

Object : To prepare suspension.

Requirements : $BaCl_2$ solution, H_2SO_4, test tube.

Experiment : In a test tube the solution of $BaCl_2$ is taken and then some amount of H_2SO_4 is added to it. On shaking the suspension of fine particles of $BaSO_4$ is obtained. Now the test tube is left as such for a little while.

Observation : The precipitate gradually settles down. In the suspension the particles remain dispersed.

EXERCISE 2

Object : To prepare suspensoid.

Requirements : Sulphur, 95% ethyl alcohol, water bath and a conical flask.

Experiment : Take about 25 ml. 95% alcohol in a conical flask and add a small pinch of sulphur to it. Now boil this mixture on the water bath and then cool it.

Observation : The suspensoid of sulphur is formed. Here the solid phase of sulphur acts as dispersion medium.

EXERCISE 3

Object : To prepare emulsion.

Requirements : Olive oil, water and a test tube.

Experiment : Take water in the test tube and add three or four drops of olive oil to it. Now shake it vigorously and then put it as such undisturbed.

Observation : After shaking the test tube the particles of olive oil get dispersed in the water and form an emulsion.

EXERCISE 4

Object : To prepare an emulsoid.

Requirements : Castor oil, 90% ethanol, water and a test tube.

Experiment : Take a few drops of castor oil in a test tube and add some 90% ethanol to it and shake vigorously. Now pour this solution in a flask of water.

Observation : Here a fine emulsion is formed in which the two liquid phases cannot be separated. It is called an emulsoid.

EXERCISE 5

Object : To prepare a reversible gel.

Requirements : Agar-agar, conical flask, water, spirit lamp.

Experiment : Take some water in the conical flask and add a little agar-agar powder to it. Now put this solution on the spirit lamp with a continuous stirring. After some time a fine homogeneous solution is obtained.

Observation : This experiment suggests that on boiling the agar-agar with water a solution is formed which on cooling sets to the gel form. If this gel is warmed again it will get converted into sol and this sol on cooling will get converted to gel. Therefore this change is termed as a reversible one.

EXERCISE 6

Object : To demonstrate the Tyndall Phenomenon.

Requirements : Glass tank or beaker, arsenious sulphide solution, condensing lens and a candle.

Experiment : The solution of arsenious sulphide is taken in a glass tank or beaker. Now a source of light is placed at a distance from it. The light rays are focussed through a condensing lens. This whole experiment is done in a dark room.

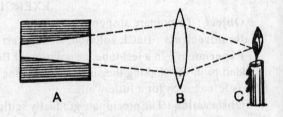

Observation : When the light falls through a condensing lens on the beaker of arsenious sulphide solution, a cone-like structure is formed. It is known as Tyndall cone (Fig. 1.1).

Fig. 1.1. Showing Tyndall phenomenon

Explanation : This is due to scattering of light by the particles of the dispersed phase. These particles thus visible and appear in the form of a bright cone.

Note : This phenomenon may easily be seen in a closed room when a beam of light is passed through a small hole.

EXERCISE 7

Object : To demonstrate Brownian movement.

Requirements : Latex of any plant, water, slide.

Experiment : Take a drop of latex on the slide and dilute it with the addition of few drops of water. Now place a cover slip on it and observe under microscope.

Observation : Under the high power of microscope it is observed that there are rapid, oscillatory movements performed by solid colloidal particles in the *zig zag* direction. Robert Brown (1827) first told about this movement so it is termed as Brownian movement (Fig. 1.2).

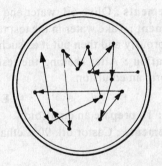

Fig. 1.2. Showing Brownian movement.

EXERCISE 8

Object : To demonstrate surface tension.

Requirements : Petridish, water, needle, forceps.

Experiment : 1. Take a petridish full of water.

2. Place a clean needle on the surface of the water with the help of a forceps (avoid touching of water with the fingers).

Observations : The needle begins to float on the water surface. If the water surface is touched by the pointed end of the needle, a small cavity or depression is observed as if a membrane is pressed.

Result : This floating of the needle on the water surface is because of the phenomenon of surface tension.

EXERCISE 9

Object : To demonstrate streaming movement of protoplasm.

Requirements : Fresh *Hydrilla* or Moss plant, microscope with light arrangement.

Experiment : 1. Select young leaves of Moss or *Hydrilla.*

2. Mount a leaf on slide and see it under the microscope.

Observations : The chloroplasts move continuously along with the cell wall.

EXERCISE 10

Object : To demonstrate importance of living membrane.

Requirements : Epidermis of *Rhoeo discolor* or onion, water, any hypertonic solution, microscope, alcohol.

Experiment : 1. Put a piece of epidermis in concentrated salt solution (hypertonic) for about 5 minutes.

2. Boil another piece of epidermis in water or alcohol.

3. Now transfer this piece to hypertonic solution for 5 minutes.

4. See both the pieces under the microscope.

Observation. The first peeling shows plasmolysis when kept in hypertonic solution. In this case the cells were living. In second case the peeling is boiled in water or alcohol and in this process the cells are dead. This membrane, therefore, when transferred to the salt solution, does not show any plasmolysis.

Result : It shows the importance of living membrane.

PLANT WATER RELATIONS

The plants absorb water and soluble mineral salts from the soil by their root system. This function of absorption is facilitated by the unicellular root hairs present on the roots. These unicellular root hairs enter in the interspaces of the soil particles, irregularly. These root hairs absorb the water found in the form of thin films around these soil particles.

Cell as a physiological unit. Cells are the building blocks from which living things are made. A single cell may make up an entire organism, or groups of cells may be loosely organised and live together.

Scientists have known about cells for a long time. About two hundred years back biologists realised that 'the cell is the basic unit of all living organisms', hence **cell theory** was proposed by two German scientists, 'Schleiden and Schwann'.

The major ideas of cell theory are:

1. Living things are made up of cells and cell products.

2. Cells are very much alike in their structure and composition.

3. Cells have a set of functions that they carry out in order to stay alive.

4. New cells arise from old cells by cell reproduction.

However, plant cells are composed of cell wall and protoplast.

The term **protoplast** is generally used to refer collectively to the **plasma membrane and protoplasm.**

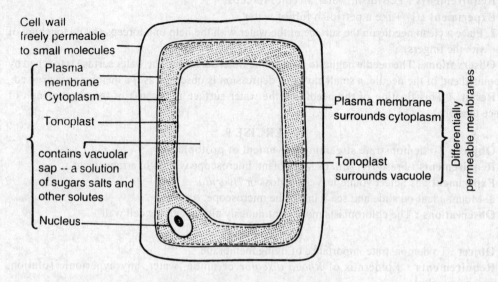

Fig. 1.3. Structure of a plant cell.

The protoplasm refers to the living contents of the cells and consists of **cytoplasm** and **nucleus.** Generally, the plant cell possesses three compartments :

(*i*) Vacuole, (*ii*) protoplasm and (*iii*) cell wall. These compartments are separated from each other by **plasma membranes,** *i.e.*, the tonoplast is found in between the vacuole and the protoplasm, while plasmalemma between the protoplasm and the cell wall. Plasmodesmata connect the protoplasm of one cell to that of other cell.

The plasma membrane is **selectively permeable.** This means, it allows some materials to pass through and not others.

The plasma membrane is made up almost of protein and lipid molecules.

Protoplasm. According to modern view, the protoplasm is a colourless, semi-transparent and viscous substance. It is considered as complex colloidal system of many phases.

However, it is well established that water is chief component of all physiologically active protoplasm and in such cases may constitute up to 90% of the protoplasm and in cases of hydrophytes even more. In dry seeds where the protoplasm is rather inactive, water may be less than 10% of the total protoplasm.

The Water

Importance of water. The water is the most important factor for the vital functions of the plants. The plants cannot survive in its absence. Water is a very important solvent, and usually consists most of the part of the protoplasm. Many biochemical reactions going on in the plants are catalysed by many enzymes, formed in the protoplasm. Usually 75% quantity of water is found in the cytoplasm. Usually in the leaves, the quantity of water is 75%, whereas in the stems it is 60%. In several hydrophytes, *e.g.*, algae, etc., this quantity exceeds up to 98%. In the same way, the quantity of water in the xerophytes is usually 60% or less than this. In the dormant seeds, this quantity of water is only about 10%. This is, of course, very much less for any vital function, and therefore, the germination of these seeds is only then possible, when they get sufficient moisture. The cytoplasm can remain viable only in the presence of sufficient amount of water. In the scarcity of water, it dies.

The water also plays an important role in the function of photosynthesis. The water is a good solvent, the minerals cannot be absorbed unless they are not soluble in water. The cell of the plants remain turgid by water; and give temporary mechanical support to the young plants.

The water found in the plants is a very small part of the water absorbed by the plants, rest of the larger part of the water goes out from the surface of the plants, by a vital process, called **transpiration.**

Availability of water in the soil. About three forms of water are found in the soil. Just after the rains, because of gravitation some amount of water

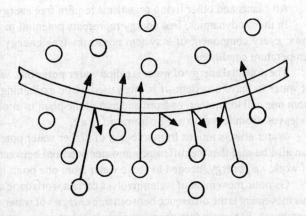

Fig. 1.4. Passage of molecules of different substances through a selectively permeable membrane.

along with some mineral salts goes in the lower strata of the earth. This is called **gravitational** or **free water** and cannot be used by the plants. Besides this, every particle of soil holds some imbibed water in it. This water is held up in the soil particle with such a great imbibition force, that it cannot be separated from it for the use of the plant. This is called **hygroscopic water,** which also cannot be absorbed from the soil by the plants. Besides these, each soil particle is surrounded by a loose film of water; this film is attracted by the capillary force to the soil particle, and such water film is called **capillary water.** Now it is to be noticed that only this capillary water may be absorbed by the root hairs of the plants. The mineral salts are also found in this water in soluble state, and are absorbed by the plants along with water. If soil lacks this capillary water, the plants very soon begin to wither and ultimately die.

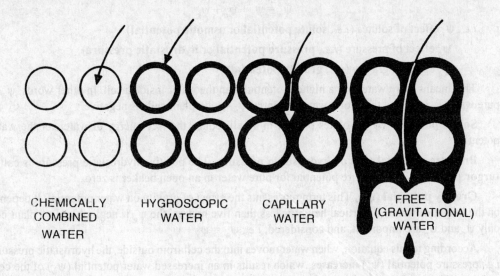

CHEMICALLY COMBINED WATER   HYGROSCOPIC WATER   CAPILLARY WATER   FREE (GRAVITATIONAL) WATER

Fig. 1.5. Types of soil water.

WATER POTENTIAL ψ (Psi)

All plants and other living organisms require free energy to grow and reproduce.

In thermodynamics, free energy represents potential to do work. According to thermodynamic laws, every component of a system possesses **free energy** capable of doing work under constant temperature conditions.

The potential energy of water is called **water potential**. Water potential is regarded as the tendency of water to leave a system. It is often used while explaining the direction in which water will flow from one cell to another, or from one part of the plant to another such as from soil to root, from root to leaves, from leaves to air, or from soil to air.

Water always moves from a region of higher water potential to that of lower water potential. It can also be said that the difference in water potential between two points is a measure of the amount of work, *i.e.*, energy, needed to move water from one point to the other.

Osmotic movement of water involves certain work done and in fact the main driving force behind this movement is the difference between free energies of water on two sides of the selectively permeable membrane. For water free energy molecule is known as water potential (ψ_w).

Water potential is measured in terms of pressure. Common measurement unit of water potential is **Pascal**, *Pa*; *I* Megapascal represents 10 bars, *i.e.*, 1 **Megapascal** = **10 bars**. One bar is close to one atmosphere of pressure, *i.e.*, 1 bar = 0.987 atmosphere of pressure.

At atmospheric pressure water potential of pure water is zero, and therefore, all solutions at atmospheric pressure have lower water potentials than water, *i.e.*, they have a negative value.

Water potential ψ_w is measured in relative quantity, and expressed as the difference between the potential of a solution in a given state and the potential of the same solution in a standard state.

Water potential is lowered by the addition of solutes and as water potential value is zero for pure water, all other water potential values will be negative. Thus, the movement of water will take place in osmotic or other systems from a region of **higher water potential** (*i.e.*, less negative) to a region of **lower water potential** (*i.e.*, more negative).

Water potential of any solution (ψ_w) is influenced by three factors: (*i*) concentration, (*ii*) pressure and (*iii*) gravity. This can be represented by following equation:

$$\psi_w = \psi_s + \psi_p + \psi_g$$

i.e., ψ_s effect of solutes (*i.e.*, **solute potential or osmotic potential**)

ψ_p effect of pressure (*i.e.*, **pressure potential or hydrostatic pressure**)

ψ_g effect of gravity (*i.e.*, **gravity potential**)

This means, pure water has a higher potential than the water inside a cell. In other words, ψ_w of pure water is zero, and therefore, water potential ψ_w inside plant cells is negative.

Solute potential (ψ_s). Solutes present in a cell reduce the free energy of water, or the water potential.

Pressure potential (ψ_p) or hydrostatic pressure. The positive hydrostatic pressure is called **turgor pressure**. The pressure potential for pure water in an open beaker is zero.

Gravity potential (ψ_g). This term represents the effect of gravity on water potential. It depends on the height of water. If vertical height is less than five metres, the ψ_g is negligible. In a plant cell only ψ_s and ψ_p are important, and considered, *i.e.*, $\psi_w = \psi_s + \psi_p$.

According to this equation, when water moves into the cell from outside, the hydrostatic pressure, *i.e.*, pressure potential (ψ_p) increases, which results in an increased water potential (ψ_w) of the cell, and the difference between the inside and outside ψ_w ($\Delta \psi_w$) is reduced.

On the other hand, when concentration of solute is increased in the cell, the solute potential (ψ_s) is lowered, and therefore, water potential (ψ_w) is decreased.

Table 1.1. Differences Between DPD and Water Potential

Diffusion Pressure Deficit (DPD)	Water Potential ψ (Psi)
1. It is measure of actual pressure.	1. It is measure of free energy.
2. It is measure of decrease in diffusion pressure of water (pure solvent) due to addition of solute molecules.	2. It is measure of difference of energy of pure water and an aqueous solution.
3. It is equal in magnitude and opposite in direction to water potential (ψ Psi).	3. It is equal in magnitude and opposite in direction to diffusion.

Thus, water moves into the cell from outside due to a water potential gradient. If a pressure is created on the cell, water moves out of it. Here, external pressure raises the water potential (ψ_w) of the cell, and thus the difference in water potential (ψ_w) inside and outside ($\Delta \psi_w$) will be such that water will flow out of cell.

There are two basic factors that affect the water potential : (i) amount of solute and (ii) external pressure.

(i) **Amount of solute.** Pure water at atmospheric pressure has a zero water potential. An addition of solutes lowers the water potential (ψ_w), i.e., it becomes negative in value.

(ii) **External pressure.** Effect of pressure on water potential is just opposite to the effect of solutes, i.e., the increase in pressure increases the water potential (ψ_w).

STOMATAL MECHANISM

The stomata are very minute apertures, usually found on the epidermis of the leaves, Each stoma is surrounded by two kidney-shaped special epidermal cells, known as **guard cells.** The stomata may be found in all the aerial parts of the plant. They are never found on its roots. The epidermal cells surrounding the guard cells of the stoma are known as **accessory** or **subsidiary cells.** Usually the term stoma stands for the stomatal opening and the guard cells. The guard cells are always living and contain chloroplasts. These cells, however, contain much amount of protoplasm than the other ordinary cells. Usually the stomata are found scattered on the dicotyledonous leaves whereas they are arranged in parallel rows in the case of monocotyledonous leaves. The number of stomata may range from thousands to lacs per square centimeter on the surface of the leaf. The stomata may be found on both the surfaces of the leaf, but their number is always greater on the lower surface. However, the upper surface of the leaves of banyan and rubber trees lack stomata. The upper surface of the leaves of several xerophytes also lack the stomata. The free floating leaves of the water plants bear stomata only on their upper surface. In normal condition the stomata remain closed in the absence of light. They are always open in the day time or in the presence of light.

Table 1.2. Number of Stomata on Upper and Lower Surfaces of Leaves

Plants	Number of Stomata/mm²	
	Upper surface	Lower surface
Monocot		
Wheat	50	40
Barley	70	85
Onion	175	175
Dicot		
Sunflower	120	175
Alfalfa	169	188
Geranium	29	179

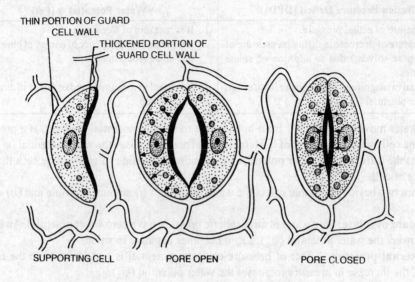

THIN PORTION OF GUARD
CELL WALL
THICKENED PORTION OF
GUARD CELL WALL

SUPPORTING CELL   PORE OPEN   PORE CLOSED

Fig. 1.6. Opening and closing of stomata.

Stomatal Opening and Closing

Each stoma is surrounded by two guard cells. The kidney-shaped guard cells contain chloroplasts. A respiratory cavity or chamber is found under each stoma. The mechanism of the closing and opening of the stomata depends upon the presence of sugar and starch in the guard cells. During day time or in the presence of light, the guard cells of the stomata contain sugar synthesized by their chloroplasts. The sugar is soluble and increases the concentration of the sap of guard cells. Due to higher concentration of the cytoplasm of guard cells, the water comes to them from the neighbouring cells by osmosis and they become turgid. With the result the stomata remain open. In the night or in the absence of light the sugar present in guard cells converts into the starch. The starch is insoluble, and this way the cell sap of the guard cells remains of much lower concentration than those of neighbouring cells, and the neighbouring cells take out the water from the guard cells by osmosis making them flaccid and the stomata closed. The conversion of sugar into starch during night and vice-versa in day time depends upon the acidity (pH) and alkalinity of the cell sap of guard cells. During night there is no photosynthesis and the carbon dioxide accumulates in the guard cells., converting the cell sap into weak acidic starch. During day time the carbon dioxide is used in the process of photosynthesis, the cell sap becomes alkaline and the starch converts into sugar.

During photosynthesis, the density of carbon dioxide remains .03%, the guard cells remain flaccid and the stomata closed.

Active potassium (K⁺) theory (Levitt, 1974). Role of potassium K^+ in stomatal opening is now universally accepted. This was observed for the first time by Fujino (1967) that opening of stomata occurs due to the influx of K^+ ions into the guard cells. The source of K^+ ions are nearby subsidiary and epidermal cells, thereby increasing the concentration from 50 mM to 300 mM in guard cells. The increase in K^+ ions concentration increases the osmotic concentration of guard cells thus leading to stomatal opening. The uptake of potassium K^+ controls the gradient in the water potential. This in turn triggers osmotic flow of water into the guard cells raising the turgor pressure. ATP helps in entry of K^+ ions into the guard cells. Levitt (1974) observed that proton (H^+) uptake by guard cell's chloroplasts takes place with the help of ATP. This leads to increase in value of pH in guard cells. Rise in pH converts starch into organic acid, such as malic acid.

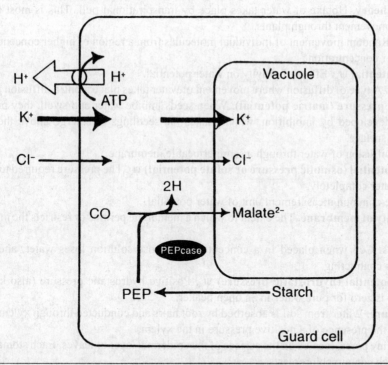

Fig. 1.7. Role of potassium K+ ions in stomatal opening.

$$\text{Starch} \rightarrow \text{phosphoglyceric acid} \xrightarrow{\text{carboxylase}} \text{Phosphophenol pyruvic acid} + CO_2$$
$$\downarrow$$
$$\text{Oxaloacetic acid}$$
$$\downarrow$$
$$\text{Malic acid}$$

Malic acid further dissociates to form H^+ and malate anion. The uptake of potassium K^+ ions is balanced by one of the following :

   (*i*) uptake of Cl

   (*ii*) transport of H^+ ions from organic acids, such as malic acid

   (*iii*) by negative charges of organic acids when they lose H^+ ions.

The accumulation of large amounts of K^+ ions in guard cells is electrically balanced by the uptake of negatively charged ions, *i.e.*, chloride and malate. The high amount of malate in guard cells of open stomata accumulates by hydrolysis of starch.

The stomatal closure is considered to be brought about by a passive or highly catalysed excretion of K^+ and Cl^- from the guard cells to the epidermal tissue in general and subsidiary cells in particular. It is thought that subsidiary cells have an active reabsorption mechanism of K^+.

TERMS TO REMEMBER

Absorption of water. Roots absorb water in plants. From root hair, water moves through the root cortex and to the xylem elements.

Apoplast pathway. The movement of water occurs exclusively through the cell wall without crossing any membranes.

Capillarity. Rise in water in tubes of small diameter (capillaries) kept in a vessel containing water.

Cohesion theory. Uptake of water takes place by transpirational pull. This is most accepted theory of water movement through plants.

Diffusion. Random movement of individual molecules from a region of higher concentration to a region of lower concentration.

Gravity potential ψ_g. Effect of gravity on water potential.

Imbibition. A type of diffusion where movement of water takes place along a diffusion gradient.

Imbibition pressure (matric potential). When seeds imbibe water and swell, they produce a large pressure developed by imbibition, which makes the seedlings to emerge above the ground through the soil surface.

Osmosis. Diffusion of water through a semipermeable membrane.

Osmotic potential (osmotic pressure or solute potential) ψ_s. The pressure required to stop the movement of water completely.

Pascal. The common measurement unit of water potential.

Permeability of membrane. The extent to which a membrane permits or restricts the movement of a substance.

Plasmolysis. Cell when placed in a concentrated sucrose solution loses water, and plasma membrane starts contracting.

Pressure potential (hydrostatic pressure) ψ_p. Positive hydrostatic pressure (also known as turgor pressure) is zero for pure water in an open beaker.

Root pressure. Water from soil is absorbed by root hairs and conducted through xylem vessels, which indicates the presence of a positive pressure in the xylem.

Stomata. Tiny pores, located on the surface of the epidermal layer of leaves. Each stoma has two guard cells, which contain chloroplasts.

Suberin. A wax-like substance.

Symplast pathway. Movement of water occurs from cell to cell through the plasmodesmata.

Transmembrane pathway. Movement of water through the cell membrane.

Transpiration. Loss of water in the form of water vapour from the plant to the atmosphere.

Water potential ψ_w. The potential energy of water.

DIFFUSION, PLASMOLYSIS, OSMOSIS AND IMBIBITION EXERCISES

DIFFUSION

EXERCISE 11

Object : To demonstrate diffusion.

Requirements : Beaker, water, copper sulphate crystals.

Method : Take a clean beaker and fill it completely with water. Place a big crystal of copper sulphate on one side of the beaker as in Fig. 1.8.

Observations : After some time, crystal of copper sulphate dissolves and its particles get equally distributed throughout the water.

Results : Molecules of the copper sulphate move from the region of higher concentration, *i.e.* crystal, to the region of lower concentration, *i.e.* water, thus showing the phenomenon of diffusion.

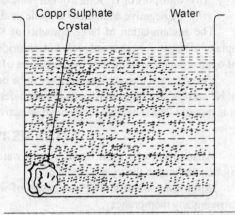

Fig. 1.8. Diffusion.

PLASMOLYSIS

EXERCISE 12

Object : To demonstrate plasmolysis.

Requirements : Red coloured *Tradescantia* leaves. Water, sugar solution, slide and microscope.

Experiment : To demonstrate plasmolysis, red coloured *Tradescantia* leaves are taken. With a sudden jerk a small segment can be peeled off from the lower surface of leaf. Cut this piece of peel into two parts. First part is put in a drop of water on a slide, second part is put in a drop of sugar solution on another slide. Now both slides are observed under the microscope respectively.

Observation : In first slide the cell structure is seen clearly. Almost most of the cells are turgid. Another slide shows that the cell contents have been separated from their cell walls and so a space is being formed nearer the cell wall.

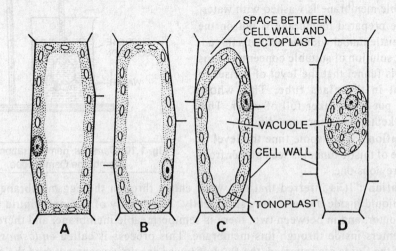

Fig. 1.9. Plasmolysis, a, turgid cell; b-d, successive stages in the shrinkage of protoplasm from the cell wall.

If the sugar solutions are used with higher concentrations, then the cell contents of the cells will shrink continuously.

Explanation : First slide represents the normal condition. Only a slightly inflated condition may be observed after a considerable time.

The second slide shows the separation of cell contents from the cell wall. It is due to loss of water from the cell. Here so-called space shows the beginning of the plasmolysis and so it is called as incipient type of plasmolysis.

When the concentration of outer medium is increased, the space becomes more wider due to complete loss of water from the cell. This condition is of complete plasmolysis.

Note : Here in the fully plasmolysed cell the hypertonic solution, *i.e.*, the sugar solution, fills the space formed between cell wall and cell contents.

If the first slide in which incipient plasmolysis has been completed is provided by pure water or hypotonic solution, the cell will attain its normal position of turgidity. This process is known as *deplasmolysis.*

OSMOSIS

EXERCISE 13

Object : Demonstration of osmosis by Egg Membrane Osmoscope.

Requirements : An egg, thistle funnel, dil. HCl, water beaker, sugar (sucrose) solution, stand, etc.

Experiment : To set this experiment, an egg is taken. One small hole is made at one end of the egg. The yolk and albumen are taken out of the egg shell through this hole. Now the egg shell is kept in dil. HCl for some time, with the result the hard egg shell of calcium carbonate dissolves in the dil. HCl and the semipermeable egg membrane adhering to the shell remains unaffected. Now this semipermeable membrane is washed with water.

Thus the prepared membrane is put on the mouth of a thistle funnel with the help of a thread. Now a sugar solution of suitable concentration is poured in this funnel that the level of it rises to some extent in the glass tube. This whole apparatus is put in a beaker full of water. This apparatus is kept as such for some time.

Observation : After some time the level in the glass tube of thistle funnel is seen higher from that of the previous one.

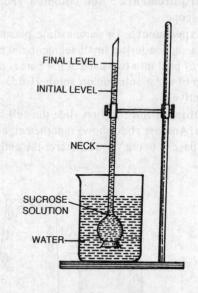

Fig. 1.10. *Osmosis,* demonstration by Egg Membrane Osmoscope.

Explanation : It is inferred that the water enters through the egg membrane, and the level of the liquid inside the tube rises sufficiently. The density of the inner liquid is greater than that of outer, and in between two, there is semipermeable membrane, and therefore, the outer fluid enters inside through this membrane. This process is called *endosmosis.* In the same way, if the fluids are reversed, the fluid of lower density sweeps out, and the process is called *exosmosis.*

EXERCISE 14

Object : Demonstration of Osmosis by Potato Osmoscope.

Requirements : Potato, sugar solution, water and beaker.

Experiment : A peeled potato is made flat on its one end, and towards the other end a cavity is made. This cavity must be sufficiently deep and broad, so that this may reach to the bottom, and the walls may not remain thick. Now, fill up this cavity with concentrated sugar solution and place this potato in a beaker filled up with water. The level of the outer and inner solutions must be same. After some time it is observed that the level of the fluid inside the potato cavity rises sufficiently.

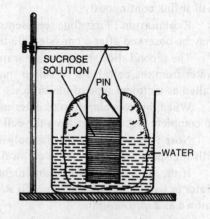

Fig. 1.11. *Osmosis,* demonstration by Potato Osmoscope.

Explanation : This happens because of *endosmosis*. The density of the sugar solution is greater than that of water, and the potato tissues collectively act as semipermeable membrane, and thus the water moves in from outside.

Note : If sugar solution is placed in the beaker and water is placed in the cavity of potato, the result will be reversed. It happens because of *exosmosis, i.e.*, water moves out from the inside.

EXERCISE 15

Object : To demonstrate osmosis by using goat bladder/parchment paper.

Requirements : Sugar solution, water, thistle funnel, parchment paper or membrane from goat's bladder, thread, beaker, stands, razor or safety blade, etc.

Experiment : Fill the beaker with water. Tie a piece of parchment paper or membrane from goat's bladder to the broad mouth of the thistle funnel. Fill the thistle funnel with concentrated sugar solution. Mark the level of sugar solution in the funnel. Dip the funnel into the beaker containing water. Allow the experiment to stand for some time.

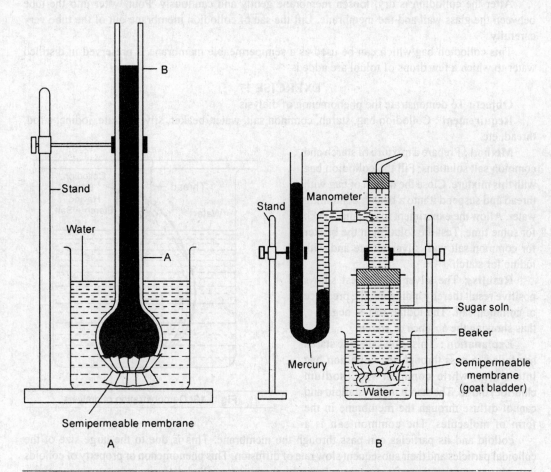

Fig. 1.12. Apparatus A and B. Demonstration of osmosis by using goat bladder.

Results : There is an increase in the level of sugar solution in the thistle funnel.

Explanation : The rise is due to entry of water into the thistle funnel (the region of low conc. of water molecules) from the beaker (the region of high conc. of its molecules) through the cell membrane.

The movement of solvent molecules (water) from its region of higher conc. to its region of lower conc. (sugar soln.) through a semipermeable membrane (cell membrane) is known as osmosis.

After allowing the experiment to remain as such, watch the rise in the level. It does not change at all, indicating that the concentration of water molecules in the beaker and inside the thistle funnel is equal.

EXERCISE 16

Object : To prepare a semipermeable membrane — collodion bag.

Requirement : Wide-mouthed tube, collodion (cellulose nitrate dissolved in alcohol and ether), water, toluol, etc.

Method : Take a wide-mouthed tube. Clean and dry it thoroughly. Pour a small amount of collodion solution into the tube. Gradually pour back collodion while revolving the tube gently so that the liquid gets evenly spread over the inner wall. Invert the tube and allow the contents to dry for about 10-15 minutes. Another layer of collodion is formed inside the tube in the same fashion. The tube with collodion layer is now allowed to dry for about 5-7 hours.

After the collodion is dry, loosen membrane gently and cautiously. Pour water into the tube between the glass wall and the membrane. Lift the sac of collodion membrane out of the tube very carefully.

This collodion bag which can be used as a semipermeable membrane is preserved in distilled water to which a few drops of toluol are added.

EXERCISE 17

Object : To demonstrate the phenomenon of dialysis.

Requirement : Collodion bag, starch, common salt, water, beaker, silver nitrate, iodine, a rod, thread, etc.

Method : Prepare a mixture of starch and common salt solutions. Fill the collodion bag with this mixture. Close the mouth of bag with thread and suspend it into a beaker containing water. Allow the experiment to remain as such for some time. Test the solution in the beaker for common salt with silver nitrate and with iodine for starch.

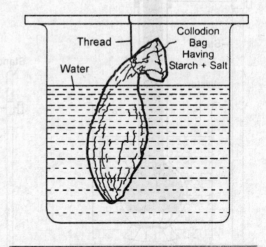

Results : The silver nitrate test shows positive result thereby indicating the presence of common salt. The iodine test is negative, thus showing the absence of starch.

Explanation : This shows that the starch has failed to pass through the collodion bag into water, while common salt (sodium chloride) did so. The starch is a crystalloid and cannot diffuse through the membrane in the form of molecules. The common salt is a

Fig. 1.13. Demonstration of dialysis.

colloid and its particles can pass through the membrane. This is due to the large size of the colloidal particles and their subsequent slow rate of diffusion. This phenomenon or property of colloids is used in separating them from a true solution by the process called dialysis.

EXERCISE 18

Object : To demonstrate exosmosis and endosmosis.

Requirements : Potato tubers (2), knife, conc. sugar solution, water, pin, beakers (2).

Experiment : 1. Remove the outer skin of the tubers and cut their one end flat with a sharp knife.

2. Scoop out a cavity from the other end of the tuber running almost up to the bottom as in experiment No. 14.

3. Fill the concentrated solution of sugar in the cavity of one tuber, and water in the other.

4. Mark the level of the sugar solution and water in the cavities with the help of pins.

5. Place the potato containing sugar solution in a beaker containing water, and the other potato containing water in its cavity in the beaker containing sugar solution (Fig. 1.14).

6. Keep and observe experiments for some time.

Observations : The level in the cavity containing sugar solution increases while the level decreases in the other tuber, *i.e.* the cavity filled with water.

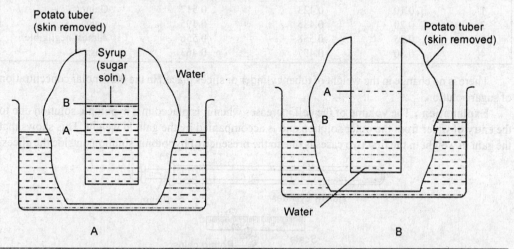

Fig. 1.14. Potato osmoscopes to demonstrate. A—endosmosis (note rise in level),
B—exosmosis (note fall in level).

Explanation : The level of the sugar solution in the first tuber increases because of the fact that water moves from the beaker into the cavity through the semipermeable membrane of potato. Thus it shows the phenomenon of *endosmosis*.

The level of the water in the second tuber decreases because of the fact that water moves from the cavity into the beaker through the semipermeable membrane of potato tuber. Thus it shows the phenomenon of *exosmosis*.

Some Modifications

(*a*) Place the raisins in water for some time. They will swell up, thus showing endosmosis.

(*b*) Place some grapes in water and some in concentrated salt solution. They show the exosmosis and endosmosis, respectively.

(*c*) Place one potato slice in water and another of the same thickness in concentrated salt solution. The former slice becomes comparatively stiffer and the latter, *i.e.*, slice in the salt solution, will become very soft.

EXERCISE 19

Object : Measurement of Diffusion Pressure-Deficit (Suction pressure) of plant cells.

Requirements : Sugar, water, cork borer (hollow cylinder with piston), petri dishes, pipette, scale, watch glasses, balance with weighing box, etc.

Method : Take a potato tuber and remove the skin. Then bore a hollow cylinder into the tuber and with the piston take out a cylinder of tissue. Cut the cylinder into about 20 equal-sized slices.

Also prepare the molar solutions of sugar of different concentrations, *e.g.* 0.10M, 0.20M, 0.25M and 0.30M. Pour approximately equal quantity of each solution into four different petri dishes.

Weigh the cylinders of slices of tuber to be placed in each of the petri dishes. Now place the slices into the petri dishes containing different molar concentrations of sugar solutions. Cover the petri dishes.

After some time (preferably 24 hours), remove the cylinders from each of the solution, blot away the excess solution and reweigh. Record the gain or loss of weight.

Results :

S.No.	Conc. of the soln. M	Initial wt. of the potato slices	Final wt. of the potato slices	Loss/Gain
		(in grams)		
1.	0.10	0.423	0.517	Gain
2.	0.20	0.435	0.495	Gain
3.	0.25	0.558	0.556	Almost negligible.
4.	0.30	0.497	0.463	Loss

There is no change in the weight of tuber cylinder or slices placed in the 0.25 molar concentration of sugar solution.

Explanation : The volume of the cell increases when it is placed in a hypotonic solution due to the entry of water from the outer solution and is accompanied by the gain in weight. This shows that the gain in weight in the first two cases is due to the presence of hypotonic solution outside the slices.

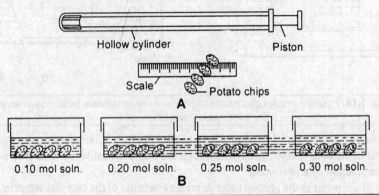

Fig. 1.15. Measurement of DPD. A — Cylinder and potato slices.
B — Potato slices in different solutions.

The volume of the cell decreases (and thus weight) when water moves from inside to the outside, solution outside being hypertonic (*i.e.* concentration of water molecules in the solution outside is less than in the cell sap).

In the third case, however, there is no change in the weight (the loss shown in observations being taken as negligible). This can happen only if there is no movement of water molecules from inside the cell or into the cell. Thus, the sugar solution (0.25 molar) should be isotonic with the cell sap. This indicates that the osmotic concentration of the cell sap is equal to 0.25 molar.

The osmotic pressure of the solution, in which no gain or loss of weight occurs, is considered to be equal to the diffusion-pressure deficit of the cells of the potato tuber (DPD = OP). Therefore, the DPD is 0.25 M.

IMBIBITION EXERCISES

EXERCISE 20

Object : Demonstration of phenomenon of imbibition.

Requirements : Gram seeds, water and watch glasses.

Experiment : Take some gram seeds in the water in the water glasses. Keep them for some time.

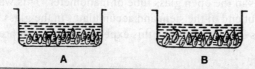

Fig. 1.16. *Imbibition*, demonstration of the phenomenon.

Observation : After some time the seeds get swollen.

Explanation : Here no cell membrane is involved in this process. The pectic or proteinaceous surface attracts the water molecules by intermolecular forces. These pectic substances are hydrophilic in nature. As the diffusion pressure of dry seeds is zero, therefore, the water is absorbed in the seeds. This process remains continued till the diffusion pressure of the seeds and water becomes equal. Thus the seeds get swollen here.

EXERCISE 21

Object : Demonstration of developing pressure during imbibition.

Requirements : A corked jar, a disc fitting in it, a round scale and a pointer attached with the disc, stand, experimental gram seeds and water.

Experiment : Take seeds and water in the jar as directed in Fig. 1.17. Fit the disc over these seeds. To this disc attach the pointer indicating initial reading at zero on the round scale. The whole apparatus should be airtight. Let this adjustment be as such for few hours.

Observation and explanation : After few hours the pointer moves down showing an upward movement of disc in the jar. Here the gram seeds swell considerably due to imbibition process. These seeds cause a pressure known as imbibition pressure.

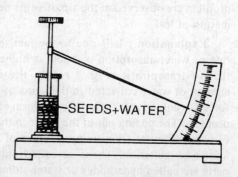

SEEDS+WATER

Fig. 1.17. Demonstration of developing pressure during imbibition.

ROOT PRESSURE

EXERCISE 22

Object : Demonstration of root pressure.

Requirements : A potted balsam plant, a rubber tubing, a glass tube and a U-shaped manometer.

Experiment : The stem of a healthy balsam plant is cut a few inches above the ground level in the morning time and set up the apparatus as shown in the figure. With the help of rubber tubing a glass tube is fitted just above the stem which is not dried up. A U-shaped manometer, partially filled up with mercury, is connected to the glass tube. The whole apparatus must be airtight.

Observation : When again observed the apparatus after few hours, the mercury is found on the higher level in the open tube of the manometer, and simultaneously the quantity of water is also increased in the glass tube.

Explanation : Due to accumulation of water in the glass tube, the pressure is exerted on the mercury,

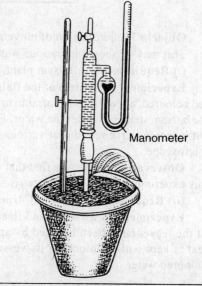

Manometer

Fig. 1.18. Demonstration of root pressure.

and it is pushed upwards in the open glass tube of manometer. This water exudates, because of root pressure from the cut end of the stem and accumulates in the glass tube fitted just above the cut end of the stem. This is also proved by this experiment that root pressure helps the ascent of sap.

GUTTATION

EXERCISE 23

Object : Demonstration of phenomenon of Guttation.

Requirements : Well developed potted plant of Garden nasturtium, bell jar, cork, a glass tube.

Experiment : Put the watered plant under the bell jar for some time (as shown in the figure).

Observation : After some time water droplets are observed at the tip of veins near the margin of leaf.

Explanation : It is due to the fact that the rate of water absorption by roots is higher than that of transpiration. As a result, the excess amount of water collected in the veins of leaf is forced to come out at their tip in the form of water droplets. The oozing out of the water in the form of water droplets from uninjured part of leaf is known as guttation. These so-called uninjured parts are called hydathodes or water stomata.

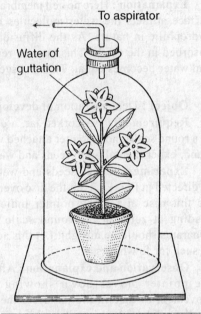

Fig. 1.19. *Guttation,* demonstration of the phenomenon.

MOVEMENT OF WATER IN PLANTS

EXERCISE 24

Object : Demonstration of movement of water through xylem.

This may be shown in various ways. Some important ones are given here.

(i) Requirements : Balsam plant, water safranin, microscope.

Experiment : The stem of the Balsam plant is cut under the water. Now, to make the water red coloured, a few drops of safranin or euosine are added in the beaker full of water. Thereafter, the balsam stem, cut under the water, is kept in this coloured water. After some time the stem is cut into transverse sections at various levels, and the sections are studied under the lens of the microscope.

Observation : Here, we find that only the vessels and tracheids are red stained. This way, this experiment proves that water rises in the stem through the vessels and tracheids only.

(ii) Requirements : Plant of *Arundo donax,* vegetable ghee, coloured water in a beaker.

Experiment : Two white and linear leaves of *Arundo donax* are taken. The vessels of one of the leaves have been blocked by applying the melted vegetable ghee at its base ; the other leaf is kept without blocking its vessels. Now, both the leaves are kept in the beaker full of coloured water.

Observation : After a few hours, it is observed that the leaf with blocked base is as before, and the veins of the leaf with unblocked base have become coloured. This indicates the rising of water through the veins (xylem vessels).

(*iii*) **Requirements** : Two twigs of a plant, vegetable ghee, two beakers of water, etc.

Experiment : We take the two twigs of plant cut under water. The base of one of the twigs is blocked with melted vegetable ghee whereas of the other twig is not blocked. These twigs are kept in two separate beakers full of water.

Observation : After a sufficiently long time, it is observed that the leaves of the twig with blocked end have been wilted and drooped whereas the leaves of the other twig are turgid and fresh. In the second twig, the water rises through the vessels, as they are not blocked by melted vegetable ghee.

(*iv*) **The Ringing Experiment :**

Requirements : A twig, a sharp scalpel, beaker full of water, etc.

Experiment : A twig with few leaves cut under the water is taken. In the middle part of the twig, with the help of a sharp scalpel, the cortex and phloem are removed, and a ring is formed. The central xylem strand is kept intact. This twig is kept in a beaker full of water.

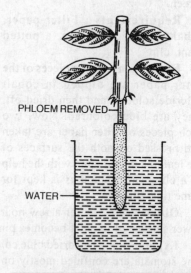

Observation : It is observed, even after a long time, that the leaves of the twig are turgid and fresh. The water supply of the leaves is not cut as the xylem strand is intact. This experiment proves that the water rises in the plant through xylem vessels.

Fig. 1.20. *Movement of water through xylem,* demonstration of phenomenon.

The above given experiments indicate clearly that the pathway of the ascent of sap in the plants is through the xylem vessels and the tracheids.

TRANSPIRATION EXERCISES

EXERCISE 25

Object : Demonstration of transpiration by keeping a plant under a bell jar.

Requirements : A potted plant, rubber sheet, water, bell jar, glass plate, vaseline.

Experiment : A healthy potted plant is taken for this purpose. Now, the soil surface of the pot is being covered by the rubber sheet so that there is no evaporation of water from the moist surface of the soil. Thereafter the potted plant is kept on a glass plate being covered over by a bell-jar. The margins of the bell-jar are vaselined, so that the atmospheric air may not enter the bell-jar. Now the covered potted plant is kept at room temperature.

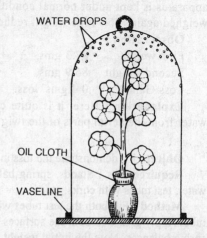

Observation : After some time, the droplets of water appear on the inner surface of bell-jar.

Explanation : As all the precautions have been taken for checking the entrance of any moisture from

Fig. 1.21. *Transpiration,* demonstration of the phenomenon.

outside, and the release of moisture from the soil surface, these droplets of water adhered to the inner surface of the bell-jar are definitely given off from the aerial parts of the plant by means of transpiration.

EXERCISE 26

Object : Demonstration of transpiration by cobalt-chloride screen.

Requirements : Filter paper, cobalt-chloride solution, a potted plant, clip.

Experiment : Some pieces of the filter paper are dipped in cobalt chloride solution and then dried off. They are blue coloured. Now, two such pieces of filter paper are taken and pressed on both the surfaces of the leaf of a potted plant with the help of a clip. This apparatus is kept for some time this way.

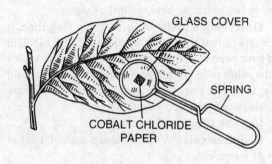

Fig. 1.22. *Transpiration,* demonstration of phenomenon. (Cobalt-chloride method).

Observation : After a few hours, when it is observed, the cobalt chloride paper of the lower surface of the leaf becomes pink coloured.

Explanation : The dried blue coloured cobalt-chloride paper turns red as it becomes moist. The stomata are confined mostly on the lower surface of the leaf, and therefore the cobalt-chloride paper of that surface becomes moist and turns red. The paper of the upper side of the leaf may also become pink to some extent, as few stomata are found on this side.

EXERCISE 27

Object : Demonstration of transpiration by weighing method.

Requirements : A wide-mouthed bottle, a twig, rubber cork, melted wax, balance, etc.

Experiment : A wide-mouthed bottle is taken. A twig with few leaves cut under the water is entered into the bottle through the hole of the rubber cork. With the help of melted wax the apparatus is made airtight. Now, this apparatus is weighed on a pan balance. Thereafter the apparatus is kept under normal conditions for transpiration. After few hours, the apparatus is weighed again. This time weight reduces to some extent.

Observation :

First weight   = 87.3 gms.
Second weight = 86.9 gms.
Loss/Gain   = 0.4 gms. loss.

Explanation : Here, it is quite clear that the weight reduces, because of the transpired water from the aerial parts of the twig.

EXERCISE 28

Object : To demonstrate the loss in the total weight of the plant (leaf) during transpiration.

Requirements : Stands, spring balances, two leaves of almost equal sizes and ages, grease, water, test tubes with corks, etc.

Method : Fill both the test tubes with water. Insert a fresh leaf through the cork hole into each tube. Apply grease to both the surfaces of leaf B, leaving leaf A as such. Hang the tubes on to the spring balances. Note the initial weight of the tubes. Make sure at the beginning of the experiment that both the corks are made airtight and the petiole of the leaf is dipped in the water.

Keep the apparatus in open air and then note the weight once again after a few hours.

Results :

Leaves	Initial weight	Final weight	Loss/Gain
A	26.3 gm	25.9 gm	0.4 gm loss.
B	30.4 gm	30.4 gm	No change.

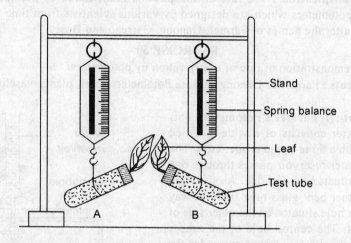

Stand

Spring balance

Leaf

Test tube

A   B

Fig. 1.23. Experiment to demonstrate the loss of weight during transpiration.

Explanation : Leaf B being greased does not show any transpiration. The loss of weight of the tube A is due to loss of water during transpiration, leaf being non-greased. The water is absorbed by the leaf which is lost during transpiration. The loss of the tube A indicates the amount of water lost by the leaves. The experiment, therefore, shows that there is a loss in the total weight during transpiration.

EXERCISE 29

Object : Demonstration of transpiration by Four Leaves Experiment.

Requirements : Four leaves, vaseline and a string.

Experiment : To demonstrate the transpiration from the leaf surface, four banyan leaves are taken. Both the surfaces of the A leaf, lower surface (with stomata) of B leaf, upper surface (without stomata) of C leaf are vaselined. The vaseline is not applied on the D leaf. Now, as shown in the figure, the leaves are hanged so that they may transpire freely.

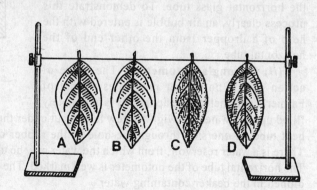

A   B   C   D

Fig. 1.24. *Comparison of Transpiration,* demonstration by four leaves.

Observation and Explanation : When the observations are taken after a day or two, they are as follows - The A leaf, which is vaselined on its both the surfaces, looks fresh and green, as no surface transpires. The B leaf is vaselined on its lower surface (with stomata), and transpiration takes place only from the upper surface which is negligible. This leaf also remains turgid and green like the A leaf. If few stomata are present on the upper surface of the leaf, then it shrivels to some extent. The C leaf is vaselined on its upper surface, which contains less number of stomata or no stomata. The transpiration takes place from the lower stomatal surface, and the leaf shrivels to a large extent. The D leaf is not vaselined and both the surfaces transpire freely releasing much water. The leaf wilts completely in this case. This experiment proves that the rate of stomatal transpiration is fairly higher than the cuticular transpiration.

Rate of Transpiration : The rate of transpiration is measured by potometer. There are many types of potometers which are designed by various scientists from time to time. These potometers are after the names of Farmer, Ganong, Garreau and Bose.

EXERCISE 30

Object : Demonstration of rate of transpiration by potometers.

Requirements : Farmer or Ganong or Bose Potometer, water, plants, vaseline, stop watch, etc.

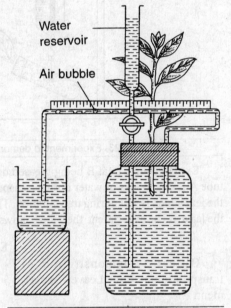

Experiment : (*i*) Farmer's Potometer - This type of potometer consists of a wide-mouthed bottle, fitted with a three-holed rubber cork. The glass tube of water reservoir passes through one of these holes situated on one side. As shown in the figure, another bent glass tube finds its way through another hole situated on the other side of the rubber cork. The central hole of the rubber cork bears a twig with few leaves cut under the water. The apparatus is completely filled up with water, and as shown in the figure, the other end of the horizontal glass tube is dipped in the beaker full of water. The complete apparatus is airtight. The apparatus is kept in this position for some time. The water transpires from the surface of leaves, and to fulfil the vacuum the water rises in the horizontal glass tube. To demonstrate this process clearly, an air bubble is entered with the help of a dropper from the other end of the horizontal tube.

Fig. 1.25. *Rate of Transpiration, Demonstration by Farmer's Potometer.*

(*ii*) Ganong's Potometer - The mode of action of this potometer resembles to that of Farmer's potometer. The apparatus is completely filled up with water. A twig with few leaves cut under the water is entered in the wide-mouthed bent tube on one side through the hole of the rubber cork, like that of Farmer's potometer. There is a water reservoir, from which the water may be taken inside the apparatus when needed. The horizontal tube of the potometer is well marked. The bent end of the horizontal tube remains dipped in the beaker containing water.

(*iii*) Bose's Potometer - We set the apparatus as shown in the figure. The water-filled wide-mouthed bottle fitted with three holed cork is taken. A twig with few leaves or a long petioled leaf cut under the water is inserted in the bottle through the central hole. In one hole of the cork the glass tube of water reservoir is inserted and in the other hole the U-tube with two bulbs is inserted as shown in the figure. A drop of oil is put in the U-tube. Now, the apparatus is kept in such condition so that the aerial parts of the twig transpire freely.

Observation : (*i*) As water transpires, the air-bubble moves towards the bottle along with water. This air bubble may be brought back by adding the water in the bottle from the reservoir which is controlled by a stop cock. There is a scale behind the horizontal tube. With the help of a stop watch, the time may be noted, which is consumed in the travelling of the air bubble from one particular mark to another particular mark on the scale. Several readings may be taken in different conditions. The rate of transpiration may easily be calculated, if one knows the actual volume of water in between two particular points on the horizontal tube.

(ii) As the leaves transpire, the water flows towards the twig in the horizontal tube. At the end of the bent horizontal tube there is a sub-terminal hole. With the help of a dropper or otherwise an air bubble is entered through this hole in the tube. As the leaves transpire the water from the beaker rushes towards the twig in the horizontal tube along with air bubble. The time spent in the travel of the air bubble from one particular mark to another on the horizontal tube may be noted. The air bubble may be brought back on the first mark in the tube by releasing water from the reservoir. Several observations may be taken in different transpiring conditions and the rate of the transpiration may be calculated. The apparatus must be completely airtight.

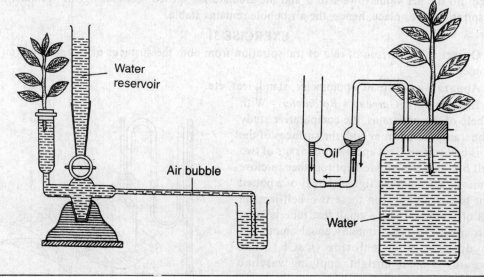

Fig. 1.26. *Rate of Transpiration* : Ganong's Potometer and Bose's Potometer.

(iii) The vacuum develops within the bottle because of the transpiration, and the oil drop gradually rises up in the U-tube towards the twig. As the oil drop reaches the inner bulb, it bursts and goes back again in its original position. The time taken in rising and bursting of the oil drop is being noted. Several such readings may be taken in different conditions. The apparatus must be completely airtight.

Various modifications for transpiring plants : (1) Potometer kept in atmosphere of high humidity. (2) Potometer kept under the fan. (3) Potometer kept in higher temperature. (4) Potometer kept in dark.

(1) Potometer kept in atmosphere of high humidity : Here the air bubble moves with a slow speed. Stomatal transpiration is caused by the diffusion of water vapours from the intercellular spaces of the mesophyll cells into the outer atmosphere through the stomata. This condition is only possible when outer atmosphere possesses less humidity or less vapour contents. Here in the given condition the outer atmosphere is of higher humidity, so the loss of water from the leaves is negligible and consequently the transpiration is lowered. Therefore higher the humidity of air, lower is the transpiration.

(2) Potometer kept under the fan : Here the air bubble will move with a greater speed. The running fan causes to increase the rate of transpiration by sweeping away the water vapours that are present in the vicinity of transpiring plant. Therefore in this area the humidity of air becomes lower and the rate of transpiration is promoted.

(3) Potometer kept in higher temperature : Here the air bubble moves with a faster speed.

Temperature has an indirect influence on the rate of transpiration. Increase in temperature causes the following effects :

(A) Stomata get widened with the increase in temperature. So the loss of water is more, increasing the rate of transpiration.

(B) A rise in temperature decreases the relative humidity of surrounding air. The drier the air, the more rapid is transpiration.

(4) Potometer kept in dark. The air bubble does not move at all. It is due to the fact that the stomata get closed when it is dark. Lowering of pH value (pH - 5) favours in closing of stomata. In dark the reducing osmotically active sugars change into the osmotically inactive starch. So the pH value lowers to 5 and the stomata are closed. On closing the stomata, no transpiration takes place, hence, the air bubble remains stable.

EXERCISE 31

Object : Comparison of rate of transpiration from both the surfaces of leaf by Garreau's Potometer.

Apparatus : Garreau's potometer, stand, leaf, etc.

Experiment : *Garreau's Potometer* - With the help of this apparatus, the comparative study of the transpiration from both the surfaces of the leaf is being done. This apparatus consists of two small bell-jars, which are kept together in close contact as shown in the figure. A leaf of a potted plant is kept in between these two bell-jars. In each of these bell-jars a small test tube is kept. Each small test tube contains equal amount of anhydrous calcium chloride ($CaCl_2$). The apparatus is made airtight, applying vaseline where they press the leaf in between. There are two manometers at the two ends of the bell-jars. They are partially filled with oil. These manometers, however, maintain the vapour of the bell-jars. If the surface of the oil within the manometers changes, then it indicates that the apparatus is not airtight or the vapour released from the leaf surface is not completely absorbed by calcium chloride. The complete apparatus is fitted upon a vertical stand. After few hours, the calcium chloride tubes are taken out and weighed again. This way, the water transpired from both the surfaces of the leaf may be known.

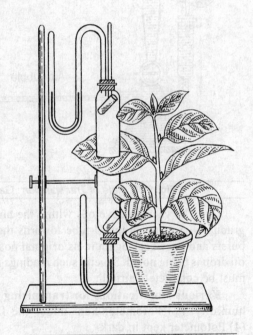

Fig. 1.27. *Garreau's Potometer.*
Measurement of relative transpiration from two surfaces of a leaf.

Observation and Explanation : The amount of water transpired from the lower surface (stomatal surface) of the leaf is always greater, as it bears large number of stomata. The cuticular transpiration takes place from the upper surface of the leaf, which is very much less.

EXERCISE 32

Object : Demonstration of the stomatal opening by Darwin's porometer.

Requirements : Darwin's porometer, water or mercury, a potted plant, stop watch, etc.

Experiment : This apparatus functions on the principle that the stomatal apertures govern the rate of flow of water. Cement the glass cup to the surface of the leaf by an adhesive (durofix, etc.) and immerse the vertical arm of tube in water or mercury. Open the clip and suck the water to a predetermined height in the vertical arm, close the clip.

Observation : Two possibilities occur here :

(A) The water level in arm remains unchanged.

(B) The water column begins to fall.

Explanation : On the closing of the clip, the air inside the porometer undergoes a reduced pressure.

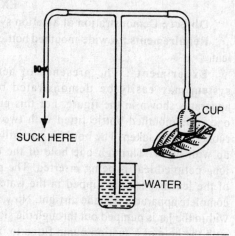

Fig. 1.28. Darwin's porometer.

(A) If the stomata under the cup are closed, the water level in the arm will not change.

(B) If the stomata under the cup are open, the air will find its way through them and water column in the arm will begin to fall.

EXERCISE 33

Object : Demonstration of relation between Transpiration and Absorption.

Requirements : A bottle with a side tube, cork, a plant, oil, balance, etc.

Experiment : Here, the apparatus must be completely filled up with water and airtight. In the side marked tube of the apparatus some oil drops are being added so that the water may not evaporate. The cork is fitted in the wide mouth of the bottle in such a way that the aerial part of a complete plant remains outside of it and the root system or the plant remains within the bottle. Now the apparatus is weighed on a pan balance to note its weight and thereafter it is kept for few hours in such a place where sufficient transpiration from the aerial parts of the plant takes place. In the end the apparatus is weighed once again and the difference from that of the original weight may be calculated.

Observation : This way the quantity of transpired water is known in grams. The oil drops present on the surface of water in the marked side tube travel somewhat downward and we know the actual quantity of absorbed water in c.c. by the

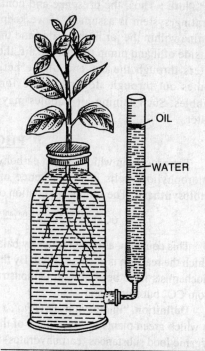

Fig. 1.29. *Relation between Transpiration and Absorption,* demonstration of the phenomenon.

roots. By comparison, it is noted that the quantity of absorbed water is always greater than the transpired water because some of the water is used in other metabolic activities.

EXERCISE 34

Object : Demonstration of aeration system in plants.

Requirements : A wide-mouthed bottle, a cork with two holes, glass tube and a long petioled leaf.

Experiment : The presence of aerating system may easily be demonstrated by the apparatus shown in the figure. For this purpose one wide-mouthed bottle fitted with two holed rubber cork is taken. The bottle is partially filled up with water. Through one hole of the cork a long petioled leaf is being inserted. The petiole of the leaf is partially dipped in the water. The complete apparatus is made airtight. Now, the air within the jar is pumped out through the side tube with the help of a suction pump fitted to it.

Observation and explanation : With the result a negative pressure develops within the jar, and the air from the outer atmosphere enters through the stomata situated on the leaf lamina, and through the cortical region of the petiole, it comes out in the water in the form of air bubbles, which are easily visible.

Note : Thus, the presence and continuity of aerating system is assumed. If we keep the leaf lamina within the jar in the water and the petiole outside of it and pump to oust the air, then the air enters through the cut end of the petiole, and comes out through stomata in the form of air

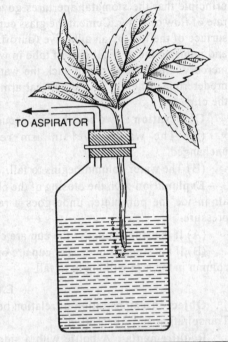

TO ASPIRATOR

Fig. 1.30. *Aeration System in plants, demonstration of the phenomenon.*

bubbles. Such shining air bubbles may easily be seen on the lower surface of the leaf in the water.

PHOTOSYNTHESIS

The process in which certain carbohydrates are synthesized from carbon dioxide and water by chlorophyllous cells in the presence of light, oxygen being a by-product, is generally called **photosynthesis.** The summary equation of photosynthesis is as follows :

$$6CO_2 + 6H_2O \xrightarrow[\text{chlorophyllous cells}]{\text{radiant 673 kg. cal of radiant energy}} C_6H_{12}O_6 + 6O_2$$

This equation, although properly balanced, gives an erroneous impression of the mechanism by which the reaction is accomplished. By the use of H_2O and CO_2 labelled with isotopic oxygen (O^{18}), biochemists have been able to demonstrate that the oxygen released in photosynthesis comes not from CO_2 but from water.

Definition. "Photosynthesis (*Photos* = light; *synthesis* = putting together) is an anabolic process in which green plants or green parts of the plants synthesize or manufacture complex carbonaceous organic food substances (carbohydrates) with carbon dioxide and water (respectively taken from air and water) in the presence of sunlight and evolve oxygen as a by-product. Thus, in this process radiant energy is converted into chemical energy."

However, green plants, apart from taking nutrients from soil, make their own food by utilising carbon dioxide, water and sunlight. This is basis of photosynthesis. During this process, oxygen is evolved and released to the atmosphere.

A simple equation given by C. B. van Niel of Stanford University, U.S.A., is as follows :

$$CO_2 + 2H_2O \xrightarrow[\text{green plants}]{\text{light energy}} (CH_2O)_n + H_2O + O_2$$

During photosynthesis, carbon dioxide CO_2 is chemically reduced to carbohydrate $(CH_2O)_n$. Here, n is an integer.

In glucose, n is 6, *i.e.*, formula of glucose is $C_6H_{12}O_6$.

Water molecule splits in presence of light. This process is called *photolysis* and O_2 is released.

Thus, released O_2 comes from water and not from CO_2.

Importance of photosynthesis. Food is the source of energy needed by animal and plant life. And this food is manufactured by green plants from inorganic substances with the aid of sunlight energy during photosynthesis. Food represents the stored energy of sunrays. Fuel in the form of wood is also the indirect result of photosynthesis activity of plants and it is also thought that coal, petroleum, etc., are also the remote consequences of photosynthesis. A number of other substances are also produced as the by-products, for example, the oxygen needed by animals and human being continues to be supplied by photosynthesis.

TERMS TO REMEMBER

Calvin cycle. Also called C_3 pathway. C_3 type of carbon reactions occur in the stroma of chloroplast.

C_3 Pathway. Where first stable product, 3-carbon molecule, 3-phosphoglycerate (PGA) is formed; reaction is catalysed by an enzyme Rubisco.

C_4 Pathway. C_4 plants possess a CO_2 concentrating mechanism.

Carbon reactions (dark reactions). Take place in the stroma of chloroplast, leading to the photosynthetic reaction of carbon to carbohydrates.

Carboxylation. Fixation of carbon dioxide. For example, formation of 3-carbon compound, 3-phosphoglycerate (PGA).

Carotenoids. Red, orange and yellow coloured pigments.

Chemosynthesis. The process of carbohydrate synthesis, where organisms use chemical reactions to obtain energy from inorganic compounds.

Chemosynthetic autotrophs. When *Nitrosomonas* (bacteria) oxidise ammonia to nitrite, the released energy is used by the bacteria for converting CO_2 to carbohydrate. Such bacteria are chemosynthetic autotrophs.

Crassulacean acid metabolism (CAM). A different mechanism of photosynthesis that occurs in succulent plants.

Electron transport chain. The light driven reactions of photosynthesis.

Jan Ingenhousz (1730-1799). A physician, discovered that release of oxygen by plants was possible only in sunlight and only by the green parts of the plants.

Joseph Priestley (1733-1804). Discovered that plants have the ability to take up CO_2 from the atmosphere and release O_2.

Kranz anatomy. The C_4 plants contain dimorphic chloroplasts, *i.e.*, granal and agranal; granal in mesophyll cells and agranal in bundle-sheath cells.

Photolysis. Light dependent splitting of water molecule.

PEPC. Phosphoenol pyruvate carboxylase, an enzyme, which catalyses formation of a C_4 acid, oxaloacetic acid (OAA).

Photophosphorylation. The process of ATP formation from ADP in the presence of light in chloroplasts.

Photorespiration. Respiration that is initiated in chloroplasts and occurs in light only, also called **photosynthetic carbon oxidation cycle.**

Photosystem. The accessory pigments and the reaction centre together, *i.e.,* PS I and PS II. Here, pigments are anchored in thylakoids in discrete units of organisation.

Photosynthesis. A process by which plants synthesise their own food in the presence of light. It takes place only in the green parts of the plant.

Photosynthetically active radiation (PAR). Portion of the spectrum between 400 nm and 700 nm.

Phytol chain. Side chain of chlorophyll molecule which extends from one of the pyrrole rings.

Pyrrole rings. Chlorophyll molecule composed of four 5-membered rings.

Reaction centre. Chlorophyll *a* molecules which convert light energy into electrical energy by bringing about electrical charge separation.

Rubisco. Ribulose bisphosphate carboxylase oxygenase, an enzyme which catalyses **carboxylation** (*i.e.*, formation of PGA).

Theodore de Saussure. He found that water is an essential requirement for photosynthesis to occur.

Translocation. Long distance transport of photosynthates which occurs through phloem.

PHOTOSYNTHESIS EXERCISES

EXERCISE 35

Object : Demonstration of Starch Test.

Requirements : Green leaves of a plant, burner, water, 70% alcohol, dilute iodine solution.

Experiment and Observation : The green leaves of any healthy plant may be boiled in the day time; thereafter, by keeping the leaves in 70% alcohol, the chlorophyll is extracted from them. Now these chlorophyll-less leaves are kept for some time in dilute iodine solution. The leaves become deep blue or blue black in colour. This is known as 'starch test'. If the plant is kept for a long time, *viz.*, 24 or 48 hours, in darkness, and thereafter the leaves are tested for starch test, it is always negative. The leaves do not become blue black in colour.

Explanation : As the plant was kept in darkness continuously for a long period, there was no photosynthesis, and the starch already prepared was shifted to the lower part of the plant during this period.

EXERCISE 36

Object : Demonstration of release of oxygen during Photosynthesis.

Requirements : Few branches of an aquatic plant, *i.e.,* Hydrilla, etc., beaker, glass funnel, test tube, sodium bicarbonate, etc.

Experiment : The release of oxygen during photosynthetic process may be proved experimentally. A few branches of an aquatic plant, *Hydrilla*, are kept in a big beaker full of the same pond water. Thereafter, the branches are covered with a glass funnel, and a test tube full of water is inverted at the end of the funnel as shown in the figure. If required, a small quantity of sodium bicarbonate may be added in the water, so that the supply of carbon dioxide may become adequate for the photosynthesis. Now, the apparatus is kept in the sunlight.

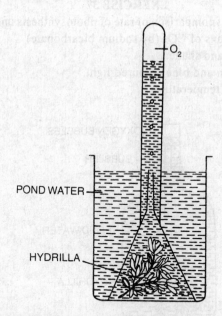

POND WATER

HYDRILLA

O_2

Fig. 1.31. *Liberation of Oxygen in Photosynthesis,* demonstration of the phenomenon.

Observation : The gas bubbles may be observed from the ends of the *Hydrilla* branches kept under the glass funnel in the beaker. These gas bubbles are accumulated in the end of the test tube inverted over the end of the funnel, and the water within the tube goes downward. On test the gas is to be proved oxygen.

Note : To test the gas, the pyrogalol solution is taken in a beaker, and with the help of the thumb the tube partially filled with gas is kept inverted in the pyragalol solution. The solution enters the test tube and the tube again fills up completely because the pyragalol is soluble in oxygen.

Various modifications for this experiment :

(1) When the pond water of beaker is replaced by boiled or distilled water.

(2) When the above experiment is covered by a black cloth.

(3) When the *Hydrilla* twigs are replaced by terrestrial plants.

(1) When the pond water of beaker is replaced by boiled or distilled water : If the pond water in the beaker is replaced by boiled or distilled water, the gas bubbles are not released from the ends of the *Hydrilla* branches kept under the glass funnel in the beaker. Why? The reason is quite clear, that during distillation or boiling of the water, the dissolved carbon dioxide goes out, which is necessary factor for photosynthesis. The photosynthesis does not take place. With the help of this modification of the experiment, the necessity of the carbon dioxide for the photosynthesis of water plants may be proved.

(2) When the above experiment is covered by a black cloth : If this apparatus is covered with black cloth, or kept in darkness, the gas bubbles are not released showing that the light is one of the essential factors for the photosynthesis in the case of water plants.

(3) When the *Hydrilla* twigs are replaced by terrestrial plants : Here the photosynthesis is completely checked. Only hydrophytes may absorb CO_2 from the water, the terrestrial plants, being of different habitat, fail to absorb CO_2 from water, and therefore, the photosynthesis is stopped here.

EXERCISE 37

Object : Demonstration of comparison of rate of photosynthesis under different conditions.

(A) Different concentrations of CO_2 (by sodium bicarbonate)

(B) Reaction of sunlight and shade.

(C) Reaction in red, green and blue coloured light.

(D) Reaction of different temperatures.

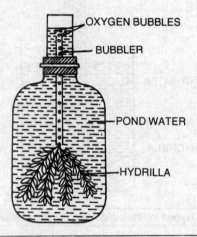

OXYGEN BUBBLES

BUBBLER

POND WATER

HYDRILLA

Fig. 1.32. *Willmott's Bubbler.*

Requirements : Willmott's bubbler, *Hydrilla* plant, sodium bicarbonate, different coloured papers, burner, thermometer, pond water, stop watch, etc.

Experiment : Willmott's Bubbler : It can easily be prepared in the laboratory. Take a wide-mouthed bottle and fix a cork in it. Pass a wide glass tube through this cork. Another narrow glass tube having a jet at its one end is introduced in the former one. Fill this apparatus with pond water and tie the twigs of *Hydrilla* at the lower end of narrow glass tube as shown in the figure.

For different conditions the following factors are provided here :

(A) Add sodium bicarbonate to the water of the bottle and count the bubbles coming out in each case in definite time.

(B) Put the apparatus as such in sun and shade respectively for definite intervals and count the bubbles coming out in each case.

(C) Put the apparatus in double-walled bell-jar providing different coloured papers. Count the bubbles coming out in each case for definite time intervals.

(D) Take another beaker of hot water and put the apparatus in it at definite temperatures. Count the bubbles coming out in each case for definite time intervals.

Explanation : (A) With the increasing concentration of $NaHCO_3$, the rate of photosynthesis increases. This rate of photosynthesis goes on increasing till light or some other factor acts as a limiting factor.

(B) The readings show that the rate of photosynthesis is more in sun.

(C) The readings show that the rate of photosynthesis is the highest in red light and lowest in green.

(D) This experiment shows that photosynthesis occurs at a rapid rate from 10°C to 35°C, provided other factors are not limiting.

Observations :

A.

S.No.	Conc. of NaHCO$_3$	Bubbles coming out in definite time
1.	0.4 gm.	14
2.	0.45 gm.	22
3.	0.5 gm.	23
4.	0.5 gm.	23
5.	0.5 gm.	23
6.	0.5 gm.	25

B.

S.No.	Sun/Shade for definite time-intervals; (5 Seconds in this case)	Bubbles coming out
1.	Sun	9
2.	Shade	5
3.	Sun	9
4.	Shade	4
5.	Sun	10
6.	Shade	4

C.

S.No.	Time	Bubbles coming out in Sunlight	Bubbles coming out in Red light.	Bubbles coming out in Blue light	Bubbles coming out in Green light
1.	10 Minutes	11	13	11	7
2.	-do-	10	12	10	6
3.	-do-	10	12	9	6
4.	-do-	9	13	10	7
5.	-do-	11	13	11	5
6.	-do-	10	12	9	6

D.

S.No.	Different Temperatures	Bubbles cominng out
1.	20ºC	9
2.	30ºC	11
3.	35ºC	14
4.	40ºC	15
5.	45ºC	18
6.	50ºC	21

EXERCISE 38

Object : Demonstration of measurement of photosynthesis by Ganong's photosynthetometer.

Requirements : Ganong's photosynthetometer, green leaf, water, KOH, Kipp's apparatus, etc.

Experiment and Observation : With the help of this apparatus, the quantity of released oxygen and the quantity of utilized carbon dioxide during photosynthesis in a green leaf may easily be detected. This way, the photosynthetic quotient O_2/CO_2 may be known.

This apparatus consists of three parts A, B, and C as shown in the figure. It consists of a bulb C, a measuring graduated tube A and a terminal stop cock B. The photosynthetic material to be utilized in the experiment, *viz.*, about 2 c.c. of green leaves of garden nasturtium, etc., are kept in the bulb. The graduated tube is inverted, the stop-cock is closed and filled up with water up to that mark as much as the carbon dioxide is required. The graduated tube is closed by the hollow stopper. The hollow portion of the stopper is also filled up with water. Now, this end of the tube is to be closed with the help of the hand, and inverted in the trough full of water. Thereafter it is clamped this way that the level of water remains at par to the level of the hole of the stop-cock. Now, the stop-cock of the lower end is opened and the upper end of the graduated tube is connected with the Kipp's apparatus to receive the carbon dioxide. The upper stop-cock is opened carefully, the carbon dioxide enters the tube, this is closed again, when the water of the tube is replaced by carbon dioxide, and its level becomes at par of the level of the outer water. Now, both the stop-cocks are being closed, and the complete tube is attached to the bulb with photosynthetic material. Now, the lower stop-cock is opened, and the carbon dioxide diffuses in the bulb containing

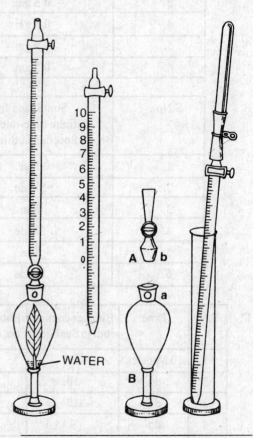

Fig. 1.33. Ganong's Photosynthetometer.

photosynthetic material. This apparatus is kept for 3 or 4 hours in sunlight and after noting the time the lower stop-cock is closed and the tube is pulled out from the bulb. Now, this is placed in the trough filled with water, and by keeping it in the water, the hollow stopper is removed. Now, the zero mark of this measuring graduated tube is kept at par of the water level, and gradually the stop-cock of the upper end is opened and make the water rise up to the zero mark of the tube.

Now a test tube is filled up with 30% caustic potash (KOH) solution and this tube is connected with the graduated tube with the help of rubber tubing. Thereafter, this apparatus is taken out from the water and removed the clamp and let the caustic potash solution enter the graduated tube. The graduated tube is shaken thoroughly and the caustic potash solution is again transferred to the test tube and the rubber tube is clasped. The end of the graduated tube is kept in water by keeping the zero mark at the water level, and the test tube is removed. Now, in the graduated tube that much amount of water rises, as much carbon dioxide is absorbed by caustic potash solution. This way, the volume of carbon dioxide is known which has been used by the leaf in the process of photosynthesis. If this experiment is furnished by filling the test tube with alkaline pyragalol solution the released oxygen is absorbed.

Explanation : The reduction in the volume of carbon dioxide and addition in the volume of oxygen indicate the volume of utilized carbon dioxide and released oxygen during photo- synthesis. Their values are usually identical and this way, the photosynthetic quotient is usually 1.

$$P.Q. = \frac{6O_2}{6CO_2} = \frac{6}{6} = 1$$

EXERCISE 39

Object : Demonstration of necessity of light for photosynthesis.

This may be shown in various ways; some important ones are given here.

(*i*) **Requirements :** A potted plant, 70% alcohol, iodine solution, burner, water, etc.

Experiment and observation:
A potted plant is kept for 48 hours in dark so that it becomes starch free. Now, on testing the leaves for the starch, they give negative test. This shows that in the absence of light there is no photosynthesis.

(*ii*) **Requirements :** A potted plant, a piece of paper, iodine, 70% alcohol, water, burner, etc.

Experiment : A potted plant is kept in dark continuously for 48 hours, to make it free from the starch. Now, again the plant is kept in the light and one of its leaves as in the figure. The photosynthesis

Fig. 1.34. *Ganong's Light Screen*

begins after keeping the plant in light. After some time the partially covered leaf is detached from the plant and tested for starch.

Observation : The exposed portions of the leaf give positive test and the covered portion of the leaf gives negative test. This experiment shows that the photosynthesis takes place only in those portions of the leaf which were exposed to the light and not in covered portions.

(*ii*) **Ganong's Light Screen Test.**

Requirements : A potted plant, a Ganong's Screen, 70% alcohol, burner, iodine, water, etc.

Experiment : A potted plant is kept in darkness for about 48 hours, so that its leaves become starch free. A small Ganong's light screen is attached to a leaf of the plant as shown in the figure. The Ganong's light screen partially covers the leaf. There is proper arrangement in the screen for the aeration of the leaf. Now, the plant along with light screen is kept in the light for photosynthesis. After 3 or 4 hours, the leaf is detached from the plant and tested for starch (see Fig. 1.34).

Observation : The portion of the leaf exposed to light gives positive starch test, *i.e.*, it becomes deep blue in iodine solution, whereas the covered portion of the leaf gives negative starch test and does not become blue-black in iodine solution. This experiment proves the necessity of light for photosynthesis.

EXERCISE 40

Object : Demonstration of necessity of CO_2 for photosynthesis.

Requirements : Two small-sized potted plants, two bell-jars, KOH solution in a petri dish, water, 70% alcohol, iodine, water, burner, etc.

Experiment : Two small-sized potted plants are taken. They are kept in the darkness at least for 48 hours, so that their leaves become starch free. Now, these potted plants are kept under two separate bell-jars. A petri dish partially filled up with KOH solution is kept under bell-jar 'A' and another petri dish partially filled with water is kept under bell-jar B. Now the apparatus is kept in sunlight for photosynthesis. After some time (3 or 4 hours), the leaves from both the potted plants are tested for starch by extracting their chlorophyll and keeping them in iodine solution.

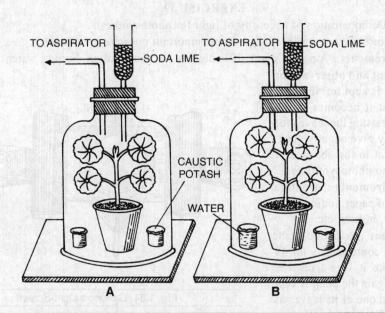

Fig. 1.35. *Necessity of CO_2 for photosynthesis,* demonstration of phenomenon.

Observation : The leaf detached from the plant kept under bell-jar does not give positive test for starch when kept in iodine solution, whereas the leaf detached from the plant kept under bell-jar B gives positive starch test and becomes blue-black in colour in iodine solution.

Explanation : The KOH solution kept under bell-jar 'A' absorbs all the carbon dioxide, ceases the process of photosynthesis and starch formation. This experiment proves the necessity of carbon dioxide for photosynthesis.

EXERCISE 41

Object : Demonstration of Moll's Experiment.

Requirements : A wide-mouthed bottle, a split cork, conc. KOH solution, a leaf, water, beaker, wax, etc.

Experiment : A wide-mouthed bottle with a split cork in two equal halves is taken. The bottle is partially filled up with concentrated caustic potash (KOH) solution. A leaf detached from the plant previously kept in darkness at least fro 48 hours is pressed in between the two halves of the cork of the bottle so that half the leaf remains within the bottle and the other half outside the bottle. The petiole of the leaf remains outside which is kept in water-filled beaker, so that the leaf may not become dry soon. The apparatus is made airtight by applying melted wax so that the atmospheric air may not enter the bottle. Thereafter the apparatus is kept in the sunlight for photosynthesis.

Observation : After few hours the leaf is tested for starch by extracting its chlorophyll and keeping it in iodine solution. The portion of the leaf which remained inside the bottle gives negative test, *i.e.,* this does not become blue-black.

Explanation : The carbon dioxide within the bottle is absorbed by caustic potash (KOH) solution and in the absence of carbon dioxide, the photosynthesis does not take place and the starch is not formed. The portion of the leaf which remained outside the bottle could receive all the necessary factors for photosynthesis and the photosynthesis did take place in this portion forming starch. This portion of the leaf gives positive starch test and becomes blue when comes in contact of iodine solution after extracting the chlorophyll.

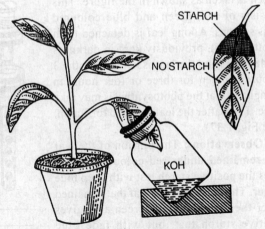

Fig. 1.36. *Moll's Experiment.*

In addition to it, some portion of the leaf remains pressed in between the two halves of the cork. This portion does not get light. With the result there is no photosynthesis and starch formation in this portion of the leaf. This portion also does not give positive starch test. This way this experiment proves the necessity of carbon dioxide and light for photosynthesis at one time.

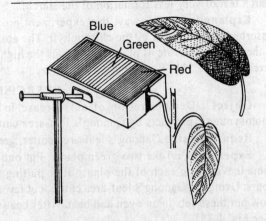

Fig. 1.37. Importance of light's colour for Photosynthesis. (*Ganong's big light screen*)

EXERCISE 42

Object : Demonstration of necessity of chlorophyll for photosynthesis.

Requirements : Some variegated leaves, 70% alcohol, iodine, water, burner, etc.

Experiment : To prove the necessity of chlorophyll for photosynthesis some variegated leaves are taken and tested for starch as usual.

Observation and explanation : The portions of the leaves containing white or yellow spots do not give positive starch test. They do not become blue when brought in contact of iodine solution. This experiment proves that the photosynthesis takes place only in the green coloured portion of the leaves.

EXERCISE 43

Object : Demonstration of importance of light's colour for photosynthesis in land plants by Ganong's big light screen.

Requirements : Ganong's big light screen, a potted plant, 70% alcohol, iodine solution, water, burner, etc.

Experiment : The Ganong's big light screen is taken as shown in the figure. This consists of red, green and blue coloured glass screens. A long leaf is detached from a potted plant, previously kept in darkness for 48 hours and the leaf is kept under the 3 coloured screen for three or four hours in sunlight so that the photosynthesis may take place. Thereafter the leaf is tested for starch. (See Fig. 1.37)

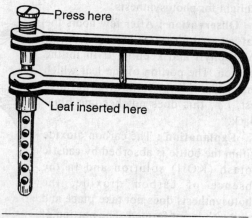

Observation : The portion of the leaf that remained under red-coloured screen gives the positive starch test with deep blue colour. The portion of the leaf that remained under the blue coloured screen also gives positive starch test, but with fade blue

Fig. 1.38. *Ganong's Leaf Punch.*

colour. The part of the leaf that remained under green-coloured screen either gives negative starch test or very less formation of the starch.

Explanation : This way, this experiment proves that the red and blue coloured rays are absorbed to the utmost by the chlorophyll. The absorption of the green rays by the chlorophyll is the lowest. The rate of photosynthesis is the highest under red screen and lowest under green screen. (Fig. 1.37)

EXERCISE 44

Object : Demonstration of an increase in the mass of leaves due to formation of photosynthetic products by Ganong's leaf-area cutter.

Requirements : Ganong's leaf-area cutter, green leaves, an oven, balance, etc.

Experiment : Take two green plants. Put one in the light and another in dark. Now pick some leaves from each of the plants after putting them in their respective conditions for few hours. Using the Ganong's leaf-area cutter, cut few circular discs from respective sets of leaves. Now put these sets in an oven and heat. After heating, they are weighed properly by a balance. (See Fig. 1.38)

Observation : The weight of the set (leaves from the plant kept in light) is found much enough than that of another set (leaves from the plant kept in dark).

Explanation : This simple experiment shows that there is a rise in dry weight of leaves which is due to accumulation of photosynthetic products.

EXERCISE 45

Object : Demonstration of separation of chlorophyll by paper chromatography.

Requirements : *Tecoma* leaves, mortar and pestle, acetone, petroleum ether, beaker, tube, etc.

Experiment : Take about 10 gm. of *Tecoma* leaves in a mortar and crush them by a pestle. Add about 12 to 15 ml. of acetone to it and filter in a beaker. This so obtained filtrate is being concentrated by heating. Take a paper strip and sketch a pencil line 2 cm. above the base of it. Point out the centre of it and pour the acetone filtrate on it drop by drop. The size of spot on the paper strip should be small. Now, add a few drops of petroleum ether in a separate tube and place the above paper strip in a vertical position in this tube. Close the tube tightly.

Observation : Observe the paper strip after some time. The level of solvent, *i.e.*, petroleum ether and different colours should be pointed out by a pencil. Here the pigment may be identified by their different colours.

Colour	Name of pigment
Blue green	Chlorophyll A
Yellow green	Chlorophyll B
Orange	Carotenes
Yellow	Xanthophyll

EXERCISE 46

Object : Demonstration of extraction of chlorophyll by chemical method.

Requirements : Green leaves of spinach, 95% ethyl alcohol, distilled water, benzene, beaker, etc.

Experiment : Boil about 50 gm. green leaves of spinach for some time. Dry these leaves and chop them into small pieces. Now put these pieces in a test tube containing 95% alcohol. Place this tube overnight in a dark place and filter it the following day. Dilute the filtrate with some distilled water and add a few amount of benzene to it. Shake the mixture and stand it for some time.

Observation : Observe the colour of the pigments. The upper layer is of green pigments, these are two, chlorophyll A and chlorophyll B. The lower layer is of yellow pigments, these are also two, xanthophyll and carotene.

RESPIRATION

We know that during photosynthesis, light energy is converted into chemical energy, and is stored in carbohydrate molecules, such as glucose and starch. Organisms make use of such energy for their activities by oxidising these high energy food molecules into simple low energy molecules, *i.e.*, carbon dioxide and water. The reactions involved in the process of oxidation are known as **respiration.** The compounds that are oxidised during the process of respiration are called **respiratory substrates.**

Technically, respiration is defined as follows :

This is a process by which living cells break down complex high energy food molecules into simple low energy molecules, *i.e.*, CO_2 and H_2O, releasing the energy trapped within the chemical bonds.

The energy released during oxidation of energy rich compounds is made available for activities of cells through an intermediate compound called **adenosine triphosphate** (ATP).

During the process of respiration, the whole of energy contained in respiratory substrates is not released all at a time. It is released slowly in several steps of reactions controlled by different enzymes.

Respiration takes place in all types of living cells, and generally called **cellular respiration.** During the process of respiration oxygen is utilised, and CO_2 water and energy are released as products. The released energy is utilised in various energy-requiring activities of the organisms, and the carbon dioxide released during respiration is used for biosynthesis of other molecules in the cell.

As we know, important life processes, such as synthesis of proteins, fats and carbohydrates, require a certain expenditure of energy. Where does this energy come from, how is it stored, and how is it made available to the living cell, are some of the questions, which are to be answered by the process of respiration.

The reaction that occurs in common respiration of glucose may be summed up as follows :

$$C_6H_{12}O_6 + 6O_2 \xrightarrow{\text{enzymes}} 6CO_2 + 6H_2O + \underset{\text{(2870 kJ or 686 kcal)}}{\text{Energy}}$$

Here, 686 kcal or 2870 kJ of energy is liberated per molecule of glucose. Formerly, this calculated value was 673 kcal. One kcal is equal to 1000 calories. This means that one molecule of glucose on complete oxidation yields 686 kcal (kilocalories) of energy, (*i.e.*, 686,000 calories). The main facts associated with respiration are :

1. Consumption of atmospheric oxygen.
2. Oxidation and decomposition of a portion of the stored food resulting in a loss of dry weight as seen in the seeds germinating in dark.
3. Liberation of carbon dioxide and a small quantity of water (the volume of CO_2 liberated is equal to volume of O_2 consumed).
4. Release of energy by breakdown of organic food (such as carbohydrates).

Adenosine Triphosphate (ATP)

This is an **energy intermediate.** As we know, both energy-yielding and energy-consuming reactions occur within the living cell.

The potential or stored energy of one compound, such as glucose, is released and utilised, in a most efficient manner, to drive the synthesis of other compounds, such as proteins.

This energy, now stored in the newly synthesised compound (*e.g.*, protein), can in turn be made available for other synthetic reactions.

However, energy-yielding reactions of the cell occur in many instances in the absence of energy-consuming reactions. The energy released in such situation is in the form of heat and lost to the organism.

However, nature has provided the living cell with a means of temporary energy storage in the form of adenosine triphosphate (ATP).

Thus, energy released in oxidation of compounds, such as carbohydrates, lipids, proteins, etc., is immediately utilised in the synthesis of ATP from adenosine diphosphate (ADP) and inorganic phosphate (i.P.).

The chemical energy transferred to ATP can be used to drive synthetic reactions, while ADP and iP are released during the process. ATP is called **energy currency** of the cell.

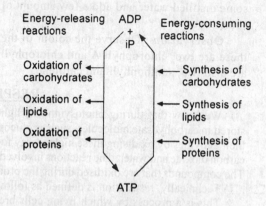

Fig. 1.39. Role of ATP as an intermediate energy transfer compound.

ATP is capable of receiving energy from one reaction and transferring this to drive another reaction. This is of obvious advantage to the living system, as ATP can be formed in the oxidation of a variety of compounds and can be used for synthesis of a variety of compounds.

In other words, oxidation of a compound, such as glucose, can provide the energy, through ATP, for synthesis of several cellular materials.

On the other hand, fuel burned in engines, where a large amount of released energy is lost in the form of heat, the oxidation of substances in the cell occurs with relatively little loss of energy. This is due to reason of the cell's very efficient energy transfer system mediated by ATP.

Here it is notable that the energy locked in a biological compound may be transferred repeatedly. Thus, in the living cell, the stored energy of glucose may be found at one time in ATP and at another time locked in the bonds of a protein molecule.

Respiratory Substrates

Respiratory substrates are those organic substances which are oxidised during respiration. They are high energy compounds and are called **respiratory substrates.** They may be carbohydrates, fats and proteins. Carbohydrates, such as glucose, fructose (hexoses), sucrose (disaccharide) or starch, inulin, hemicellulose (polysaccharide), etc., are main respiratory substrates.

Besides, fats are used as respiratory substrates by a variety of organisms as they contain more energy than carbohydrates.

In rare circumstances, when carbohydrate reserves are exhausted, fats and proteins also serve as respiratory substrates. Blackman termed the respiratory oxidation of protoplasmic protein as **protoplasmic respiration,** while oxidation of carbohydrates as **floating respiration.**

Types of Respiration

There are two main types of respiration, (*i*) **aerobic** and (*ii*) **anaerobic.**

(*i*) **Aerobic respiration.** This type of respiration leads to a complete oxidation of stored food (organic substances) in the presence of oxygen, and releases carbon dioxide, water and a large amount of energy present in respiratory substrate. Such type of respiration is generally found in higher organisms.

The overall equation is :

$$C_6H_{12}O_6 + 6O_2 \xrightarrow[\text{oxidation}]{\text{enzymes}} 6CO_2 + 6H_2O + \text{energy}$$
$$\text{(2870 kJ) or (686 k cal)}$$

(*ii*) **Anaerobic respiration.** This type of respiration occurs in complete absence of oxygen. In the absence of free oxygen, many tissues of higher plants, seeds in storage, fleshy fruits, and succulent plants, such as cacti temporarily take to a kind of respiration, called **anaerobic respiration.** Such respiration generally occurs in lower organisms like bacteria and fungi. This results in incomplete oxidation of stored food and formation of carbon dioxide and ethyl alcohol, and sometimes also various organic acids, such as malic, citric, oxalic, tartaric, etc. Very little energy is released by this process to maintain activity of protoplasm.

The equation is as follows :

$$C_6H_{12}O_6 \longrightarrow 2C_2H_5OH + 2CO_2 + \text{Energy}$$
$$\text{(247 kJ) or (28 k cal)}$$

This process of oxidation in microbes is known as **fermentation.** This is quite similar to that of anaerobic respiration in case of higher plants.

Succulents (RQ is zero). Where incomplete oxidation of carbohydrates takes place RQ is zero. In such cases oxygen absorbed does not oxidise the carbohydrates completely to CO_2 and water but produces intermediate products of partial oxidation. This occurs especially in respiration of succulent plants, such as cacti (*Opuntia*). In such plants respiration of carbohydrates occurs at night when stomata are open which results in production of organic acids that utilise O_2 but do not evolve CO_2. The equation is as follows :

$$2C_6H_{12}O_6 + 3O_2 \longrightarrow 3C_4H_6O_5 + 3H_2O$$
$$\text{Malic acid}$$

$$RQ = \frac{CO_2}{O_2} = \frac{0}{3} = 0$$

Organic acids (RQ more than unity). When substances rich in oxygen are respired, the value of RQ is more than unity. This occurs in respiration of organic acids. Organic acids contain more oxygen than carbohydrates, and therefore, relatively less amount of oxygen is required for their oxidation. The examples are shown by following equations :

(*i*)
$$2(COOH)_2 + O_2 \longrightarrow 4CO_2 + 2H_2O$$
$$\text{Oxalic acid}$$

$$RQ = \frac{CO_2}{O_2} = \frac{4}{1} = 4$$

Here RQ is 4 in case of oxalic acid.

(ii) $$2C_4H_6O_6 + 5O_2 \longrightarrow 8CO_2 + 6H_2O$$
$$\text{Tartaric acid}$$

$$RQ = \frac{CO_2}{O_2} = \frac{8}{5} = 1.6$$

This means, RQ is 1.6 in case of tartaric acid.

(iii) $$C_4H_6O_5 + 3O_2 \longrightarrow 4CO_2 + 3H_2O$$
$$\text{Malic acid}$$

$$RQ = \frac{CO_2}{O_2} = \frac{4}{3} = 1.3$$

In case of malic acid, RQ is 1.3.

Anaerobic respiration (RQ infinity). As we know, in anaerobic respiration CO_2 is evolved but O_2 is not consumed, and therefore RQ is infinite (∞). Equation is as follows :

$$C_6H_{12}O_6 \xrightarrow[\text{enzyme}]{\text{zymase}} 2C_2H_5OH + 2CO_2 + \text{energy}$$

$$RQ = \frac{CO_2}{O_2} = \frac{2}{0} = \text{Infinity} (\infty)$$

Significance of RQ. The RQ value of a respiring tissue may provide valuable information to an investigation. From an RQ value, one can obtain a rough indication of the nature of substrate being oxidised.

It also helps in knowing the type of respiration being performed. It may also provide some information about major transformation of food materials.

If RQ is less than one, then substrate is of low oxygen content, *e.g.*, fats.

In starvation the cell material itself becomes substrate. According to Blackman, in starving conditions, if cellular proteins are the respiratory substrates then it is called **protoplasmic respiration.**

TERMS TO REMEMBER

Aerobic respiration. This process of respiration leads to a complete oxidation of organic substances in the presence of O_2 and release CO_2, water and a large amount of energy present in the substrate.

Anaerobic respiration. This type of respiration takes place in the complete absence of oxygen.

Compensation point. The atmospheric concentration of CO_2 at which photosynthesis just compensates for respiration.

Citric acid cycle (Krebs cycle or tricarboxylic acid cycle TCA). Begins when acetyl-Co-A enters into a reaction to form citric acid.

Electron transport system (ETS). The metabolic pathway through which the electron passes from one carrier to another.

Fermentation. Process of oxidation in microbes.

Glycolysis (EMP pathway). In the process of respiration, the carbohydrates are converted into pyruvic acid through a series of enzymatic reactions, which take place in the cytosol.

Hans Adolf Krebs (1900-1981). He discovered citric acid cycle (Krebs cycle or tricarboxylic acid cycle) for production of energy in the cell in 1937. He was awarded Nobel Prize in 1953.

Hexokinase. An enzyme, which catalyses reaction where glucose and fructose are phosphorylated to give rise to glucose-6-phosphate and fructose-6-phosphate, respectively.

Invertase. An enzyme, by which sucrose is converted into glucose and fructose.

Oxidative decarboxylation. Here, pyruvate is first decarboxylated and then oxidised by the enzyme pyruvate dehydrogenase.

Oxidative phosphorylation. Production of ATP by phosphorylation of ADP.

Pentose phosphate pathway (PPP). Here, glucose-6-phosphate produced during early stages of glycolysis. This reaction takes place in the presence of the enzyme glucose-6-phosphate dehydrogenase.

Phosphofructokinase. An enzyme, which catalyses the reaction where fructose-6-phosphate is phosphorylated and fructose 1, 6-bisphosphate is produced.

Respiration. Phenomenon of release of energy by oxidation of various organic molecules, for cellular use.

Respiratory quotient (RQ) or respiratory ratio. The ratio of the volume of CO_2 evolved to the volume of O_2 consumed in respiration, *i.e.*, $RQ = \dfrac{CO_2}{O_2}$

Respiratory substrate. The compounds that are oxidised during respiration.

RESPIRATION EXERCISES

The Respiratory Ratio (Respiratory Quotient)

The ratio of the volume of carbon dioxide released to the volume of oxygen absorbed in the respiration is termed the *respiratory ratio or respiratory quotient* (R.Q.)

$$R.Q. = \frac{CO_2}{O_2}$$

When a carbohydrate is respired, the R.Q. is equal to one.

$$C_6H_{12}O_6 + 6O_2 \rightarrow 6CO_2 + 6H_2O$$

$$R.Q. = \frac{CO_2}{O_2} = \frac{6}{6} = 1.$$

Proportion of Oxygen to Carbon lower than in Carbohydrates

The proportion of oxygen to carbon is invariably less in fats than in carbohydrates. The respiratory ratio of seeds in which the stored foods are mostly in the form of oils have shown that the respiratory quotient of such seeds is always less than one. The following summary equation represents the complete oxidation :

$$2C_{51}H_{98}O_6 + 145O_2 \rightarrow 102CO_2 + 98H_2O^+$$

$$R.Q. = \frac{CO_2}{O_2} = \frac{102}{145} = 0.7.$$

The fats require comparatively more oxygen for complete oxidation. Actually fats, being insoluble compounds, are not oxidised directly as indicated in the above equation. The fats are oxidised only after hydrolysis to fatty acids and glycerol. Here, the sequence of reactions will require the absorption of oxygen in excess of the quantity of carbon dioxide released. The summation effect of the reactions involved in the respiration of fats will be a respiration quotient (R.Q.) of less than one.

Similarly oxidation of the hydrolytic products of the proteins results in a respiratory ratio of less than one (usually 0.8 — 0.9) since the proportion of oxygen to carbon in such compounds is less than in carbohydrates.

Proportion of Oxygen to Carbon higher than in carbohydrates

When respiratory substrates are rich in oxygen, the value of respiratory quotient is greater than one. This is found in the case of organic acids. The equations for the respiration of malic, tartaric and oxalic acids are :

$$C_4H_6O_5 + 3O_2 \rightarrow 4CO_2 + 3H_2O$$
malic acid

$$R.Q. = \frac{CO_2}{O_2} = \frac{4}{3} = 1.3$$

$$2C_4H_6O_6 + O_2 \rightarrow 8CO_2 + 6H_2O$$
tartaric acid

$$R.Q. = \frac{CO_2}{O_2} = \frac{8}{5} = 1.6$$

$$2(COOH)_2 + O_2 \rightarrow 4CO_2 + 2H_2O$$
Oxalic acid

$$R.Q. = \frac{CO_2}{O_2} = \frac{4}{1} = 4.$$

Oxygen liberation or utilization without consumption of CO_2

When the seeds containing fats attain maturity, simple carbohydrates are converted into fats. Oxygen is eliminated during the process without any corresponding utilization of carbon dioxide, since the molecules of the fats contain much less oxygen in proportion to the carbon and hydrogen present than in the molecules of sugars. The internally freed oxygen is being transferred to other molecules in respiration. The volume of oxygen absorbed by seeds from the outer atmosphere during this period will be less, and the respiratory ratio is greater than one. The R.Q. of maturing flax seeds is about 1.22.

During the germination of fatty seeds essentially the opposite situation prevails in which very low respiratory quotients sometimes prevail after several days. The respiratory ratio of germinating castor bean seeds is as low as about 0.3. Murlin (1934) explained this finding on the assumption that transformation of fat to sugar, i.e., an oxygen consuming process where no carbon dioxide is released is proceeding much more rapidly than oxidation of sugar.

Similar situation is found in many succulent species where incomplete oxidation of sugars to organic acids takes place. For example, in the species of Crassulaceae and Cactaceae, some of the sugar present is often incompletely oxidized to malic acid :

$$.2C_6H_{12}O_6 + 3O_2 \rightarrow 3C_4H_6O_5 + 3H_2O$$
malic acid

$$R.Q. = \frac{CO_2}{O_2} = \frac{0}{3} = 0$$

As a result of similar respiratory process other organic acids are formed in succulent plants. The synthesis of such compounds requires absorption of oxygen for which there is no corresponding evolution of CO_2. In such cases the R.Q. is less than unity.

The leaves of *Bryophyllum* and some other species make direct use of carbon dioxide absorbed in the dark in the synthesis of organic acids. The effect of the occurrence of the process will give such leaves an apparent respiratory quotient of less than unity.

Respiration in the Absence of Oxygen

In anaerobic respiration, the release of carbon dioxide takes place without any corresponding utilization of atmospheric oxygen.

R.Q. values for different respiratory substrates

R.Q.	Respiratory substrate
> 1.0	Carbohydrate with some anaerobic respiration.
	Carbohydrate synthesized from organic acids.
	Organic acids.
1.0	Carbohydrates
0.99	Proteins with NH_3 formation
0.8	Proteins with amide formation
0.7	Fats, *e.g.*, tripalmitin
0.5	Fats with associated carbohydrate synthesis
0.3	Carbohydrates with associated organic acid synthesis

Such anaerobic respiration occurs in higher green plants under certain conditions. Sometimes, when the oxygen supply is deficient, both aerobic and anaerobic respirations occur simultaneously in a plant tissue. In such cases, some cells respire anaerobically while others aerobically. Under these conditions the volume of carbon dioxide evolved may be very large in proportion to the volume of oxygen absorbed, and the respiratory quotient (R.Q.) is much greater than one.

$$\overset{\text{zymase}}{C_6H_{12}O_6 \rightarrow 2C_6H_5OH + 2CO_2}$$

$$R.Q. = \frac{CO_2}{O_2} = \frac{2}{0} = 2$$

EXERCISE 47

Object : Measurement of R.Q. by Ganong's Respirometer.

Requirements : Ganong's Respirometer, respiratory substrate, etc.

Experiment : The respiratory quotient may easily be measured by Ganong's respirometer. In Ganong's respirometer the amount of oxygen absorbed and carbon dioxide released out during respiration are determined simultaneously. The respirometer consists of a bulb with a graduated side tube. The volume of the apparatus is about 102 c.c. The stopper and neck of the bulb are each provided with hole. The stopper may be turned to bring the two holes opposite each other so that the air inside the bulb may communicate with the outer air and is at the atmospheric pressure. The side graduated tube is connected with a levelling tube by a rubber tubing.

For the determination of respiratory quotient the manometer is filled with mercury or a saturated solution of common salt. The water cannot be used since carbon dioxide is dissolved in it. Carbon dioxide is slightly soluble in salt solution and, therefore, best results can be obtained when mercury is used.

Two c.c. of plant material, the R.Q. of which is to be measured, is being placed inside the bulb. In the

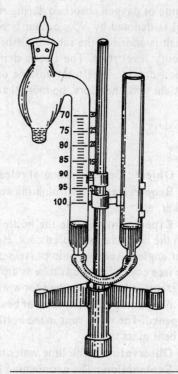

Fig. 1.40. *Ganong's Respirometer.*

beginning the air of the graduated tube is kept in direct communication with the atmospheric air at the atmospheric pressure. The mercury in both the tubes is brought to the same level by raising or lowering the levelling tube. Now the stopper in the neck of the bulb is turned so that the two holes get apart and the air in the apparatus is cut off from the outside air and respiration proceeds in closed chamber.

Observation and Explanation : The initial level of mercury in the graduated tube is noted. The level is again noted after about an hour. If the respiratory substrate kept in the bulb is carbohydrate, the amount of carbon dioxide released during respiration will be equal to the amount of oxygen absorbed, and therefore, there will be neither a rise nor a fall in the mercury level. If caustic potash (KOH) is now added to the apparatus, the accumulated carbon dioxide will be absorbed, and hence a rise in the mercury level, and thus the amount of carbon dioxide can be measured. The volume of oxygen absorbed will be equal to the volume of carbon dioxide measured. Hence the R.Q. is unity.

When the respiratory substrate is a fat, the respiratory quotient is less than one. Here the amount of carbon dioxide released is less than the amount of oxygen absorbed and, therefore, a vacuum is created in the closed chamber. This results in the rise of mercury level. The rise of mercury level is denoted by V_1 c.c. that is equivalent to the excess oxygen. Now the caustic potash (KOH) is added and there is a further rise of mercury level. The second rise in the mercury level is denoted by V_2 c.c. This represents the volume of carbon dioxide liberated. This way, the total amount of oxygen absorbed is equal to $V_1 + V_2$ c.c. The respiratory quotient will, therefore, be less than one.

$$R.Q. = \frac{CO_2}{O_2} = \frac{V_2}{V_1 + V_2}$$

When the respiratory substrate is such that the carbon dioxide released is more than the volume of oxygen absorbed during respiration, the mercury level falls. The fall in the mercury level is denoted by V_1 c.c. that is equivalent to the excess carbon dioxide. Now the caustic potash is added to the tube. It absorbs the total amount of carbon dioxide and, therefore, the mercury level rises. The rise is denoted by V_2 c.c. that is equivalent to the total amount of carbon dioxide. The total volume of oxygen absorbed is then $V_2 - V_1$ c.c. The respiratory quotient will, therefore, be more than one.

$$R.Q. = \frac{CO_2}{O_2} = \frac{V_2}{V_2 - V_1}$$

EXERCISE 48

Object : Demonstration of release of CO_2 during Respiration.

Requirements : Germinating seeds, a bottle, a bent tube, two holed cork, water reservoir, beaker, etc.

Experiment : Inside the bottle some germinating seeds are placed. The bottle is closed with the help of a two-holed cork. Here one of the holes is provided by glass tube bent twice at right angles. Another hole possesses a water reservoir which remains closed by a stop cock. The free end of bent glass tube is dipped in a beaker of water which also acts as a seal. Now this apparatus is left undisturbed for a while.

After some time the water of beaker is replaced by lime water and the stop cock of reservoir is opened. The water runs in the bottle and so it drives out the air of bottle in the beaker through the bent glass tube.

Observation : The lime water turns milky.

Explanation : The germinating seeds undergo the respiration releasing CO_2 in this process. The CO_2 passes through the bent glass tube making the lime water milky.

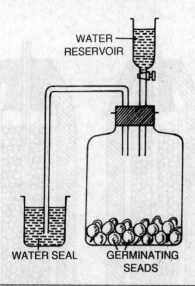

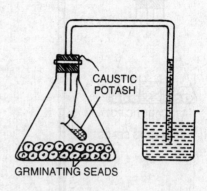

Fig. 1.41. *Release of CO$_2$ during Respiration,* demonstration of the phenomenon.

Fig. 1.42. *Release of CO$_2$ during respiration,* demonstration of the phenomenon.

(*ii*) **Requirements :** Germinating seeds, a conical flask, a single-holed cork, caustic potash in a test tube, a bent glass tube, water beaker, etc.

Experiment : Inside the conical flask some germinating seeds are placed. The bottle is closed with a single-holed cork through which a glass tube bent twice at right angles is inserted. Another free end of this tube is put in a beaker of water. A test tube of caustic potash is hung inside the conical flask. Now this apparatus is put as such for some time.

Observation : Water rises in the far end of glass tube from the beaker.

Explanation : Germinating seeds undergo the anaerobic respiration, releasing CO$_2$ gas which is absorbed by the caustic potash. So a vacuum is created inside the conical flask and consequently water rises in the tube to fulfil it.

Note : The experiment should be performed in dark in case the green leaves are used as the respiratory substrate.

EXERCISE 49

Object : Demonstration of utility of oxygen in Respiration.

Requirements : A conical flask, a bent tube, germinating seeds, caustic potash in a small container, a mercury dish.

Experiment : Germinating seeds are taken in a conical flask in which a container of caustic potash is also put. The mouth of this conical flask is closed by a single-holed cork through which a glass tube bent twice at right angles is inserted. The far end of this tube is put in the mercury dish. Now this apparatus is left undisturbed for some time.

Observation : The mercury in the far end of bent glass tube rises to a height of 15 cm.

Explanation : The germinating seeds undergo aerobic respiration so they use the oxygen available inside the conical flask. As whole of the oxygen is used up by the germinating seeds, the pressure inside the flask is decreased. So consequently the mercury level rises in the far end of the bent glass tube. This level reaches only a height of 15 cm. in the glass tube, as this level is about one-fifth the air. As oxygen constitutes one-fifth of total composition, it is reasonable to infer that the seeds have used this gas of the air in respiration.

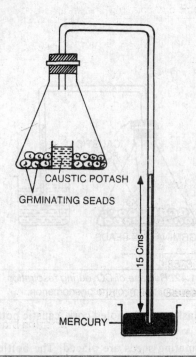

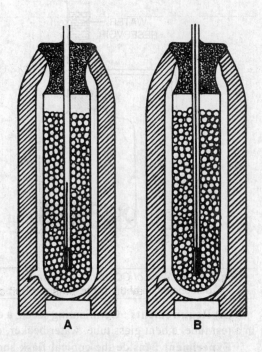

CAUSTIC POTASH

GRMINATING SEADS

15 Cms

MERCURY

Fig. 1.43. *Utility of O$_2$ in Respiration,* demonstration of the phenomenon.

A   B

Fig. 1.44. *Production of Heat in Respiration,* demonstration of the phenomenon.

EXERCISE 50

Object : Demonstration of production of heat in Respiration.

Requirements : Two thermos bottles, germinating seeds, dry seeds, corks with a single hole, two thermometers.

Experiment : Half fill both the thermos bottles with germinating and dry seeds respectively. Now close their mouths with the help of single-holed corks through which a thermometer passes respectively. Put this experiment for about 24 hours.

Observation : There is a rise in temperature in the thermometer which is placed in the thermos bottle of germinating seeds. Another thermos bottle shows no change in previous temperature.

Explanation : The dry seeds or physiologically died seeds do not undergo respiration so there is no change in temperature. But the germinating seeds are going to make respiration where energy also releases alongwith CO$_2$ gas. So this energy causes a higher temperature in another thermos bottle. This release in energy is due to many biological activities going on stepwise with a gradual release of energy.

EXERCISE 51

Object : Demonstration of release of CO$_2$ by Pettenkoffer's gas stream method.

Requirements : Pettenkoffer's tube, soda lime, Ca(OH)$_2$, passing tubes, rubber tubes, respiratory tissue, aspirator, water, Ba(OH)$_2$, plant chambers, etc.

Experiment : The experiment is set as follows :

Firstly, there is a soda lime tower which is open to air by a tube. This tower is connected by passing tubes to the bottles of Ca(OH$_2$) solution. Usually two bottles are used in the experiment. The second bottle is connected to the plant chamber by another passing tube. Pettenkoffer's tube is put between the plant chamber and aspirator by some rubber tubing connections. A two-way tap is also connected to the Pettenkoffer's tube. This tube is filled with $Ba(OH)_2$ solution.

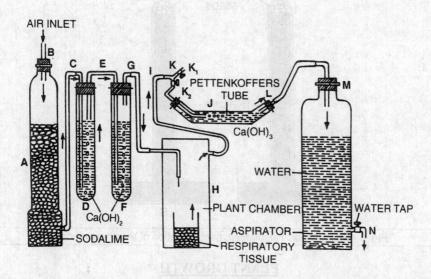

Fig. 1.45. *Pettenkoffer's Tube.*

With the help of two-way tap and aspirator the air is sucked out. Due to a lower pressure, a current of air gets in the soda lime tower. The soda lime and $Ca(OH)_2$ solution remove the whole CO_2 of air. Now the CO_2 free air reaches to plant chamber from which it gets in the Pettenkoffer's tube. Here the $Ba(OH)_2$ solution is turned turbid. The aspirator is set in the way to regulate the slow movement of air in the form of bubbles.

After some time the turbid solution of Pettenkoffer's tube is titrated by using N/10 HCl and phenolpthalin-indicator.

Observation and explanation : The turbidity of the solution of Pettenkoffer's tube is due to formation of $BaCO_3$. The plant tissue respires releasing CO_2 gas. The CO_2 gas reacts with $Ba(OH)_2$ solution forming $BaCO_3$.

EXERCISE 52

Anaerobic Respiration

    Object : Demonstration of anaerobic respiration.

    Requirements : Germinating seeds, a test tube, mercury, KOH crystals, petri dish, etc.

    Experiment : The mercury is filled in the test tube up to the rim. Take a petri dish full of mercury and put the mercury-filled test tube in the inverted condition with the help of thumb. The thumb is removed inside the petridish. Now introduce some seeds (germinating or soaked) in the test tube with the help of a forceps. Let this apparatus be put as such for some time.

    Observation : After some time the mercury level in test tube goes down. Now introduce some KOH crystals in the above test tube. After a little while the mercury level will go up to the former position.

    Explanation : The lowering of mercury level in test tube indicates that some gas has been released by germinating seeds. Only CO_2 gas is it which may be absorbed by KOH crystals. We see that with the introduction of KOH crystals the level of mercury goes high, so the seeds have released CO_2 under the anaerobic conditions.

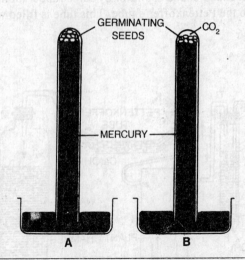

GERMINATING SEEDS

CO₂

MERCURY

A   B

Fig. 1.46. *Anaerobic Respiration,* demonstration of the phenomenon.

PLANT GROWTH

When a seed is sown in soil, it germinates and forms a small seedling which grows over a period of time, and converts into a large and mature plant. This process is termed as **growth.**

Growth is regarded as one of the most fundamental and conspicuous characteristics of a living being. Growth can be defined as an irreversible permanent increase in size of an organ or its parts or even of an individual cell. Generally growth is accompanied by metabolic process (both anabolic and catabolic), that occur at the expense of energy. Therefore, expansion of a leaf is growth but the swelling of wood submerged in water is not.

The most complex of all the physiological processes is growth. The process of growth results from an increase in protoplasm, leading to an irreversible increase in size and weight. The growth involves three stages: **stage of cell division, stage of cell elongation and stage of cell differentiation. Growth** is associated with differentiation of cell which is a change in form and physiological activity. **Development** refers to the sequence of processes in the overall life history of a cell or an organism including growth, differentiation, maturation and senescence.

In unicellular organisms, growth involves increase in their volume and numbers. Cell division serves as a means of reproduction in these organisms, and leads to increase in population. In the multicellular organisms, however, growth is much more complex.

The life of a flowering plant begins with the fertilized egg. Through a series of divisions, an embryo is formed which is enclosed in a seed. Germination then takes place leading to the formation of a seedling. After passing through the juvenile phases, a mature plant is finally formed. After a period of vegetative growth, the plant enters the reproductive stage. With the initiation and development of flowers, fruits and seeds are formed. A new generation of plants starts again. Annual plants like wheat undergo senescence and die after bearing grain. Development associated with each of three steps is controlled by several factors, both internal and external.

In plants, growth is associated with both anabolic and catabolic activities. This is a quantitative phenomenon and can be measured in relation to time. In living organisms, growth is intrinsic, while in non-living objects, it is extrinsic.

In plants, growth is confined only to **meristems.** The extreme apices of root and shoot are occupied by primary meristems, while in their older parts, secondary meristems, *i.e.,* cambia, give rise to additional vascular tissues and to protective layers of cork cells.

The activity of each meristem influences the other meristems which are close to it, giving rise to **growth correlations.** For example, while the main apical shoot meristem is active it retards the activity of more recently initiated lateral bud meristems, a phenomenon called **apical dominance.**

Besides growth, plants also show movements, both at organ-level, as well as whole-plant level. In this chapter, various aspects of growth, such as dormancy and seed germination, characteristics and conditions for growth, its measurement, growth regulators and types of movements have been discussed in detail.

Plant Growth Generally is Indeterminate

Plants are unique in that they retain the capacity for unlimited growth throughout their life. This ability is due to the presence of meristems at certain locations in their body. The cell(s) of such meristems have the capacity to divide and self-perpetuate. The form of growth wherein new cells are always being added to the plant body by the activity of the meristem is called open form of growth.

The root apical meristem (RAM) and the shoot apical meristem (SAM) are responsible for the primary growth of the plant and principally contribute to the elongation of the plant parallel to its axis. In dicotyledonous plants and gymnosperms, the lateral meristems, vascular cambium and cork cambium appear later in life. These meristems cause increase in girth of the organ in which they are active, contributing to what is generally known as **secondary growth** of the plant.

The intercalary meristem, located just above the nodes of grasses and related plants contribute to the elongation growth. Thus, root apical meristem (RAM), shoot apical meristem (SAM), vascular cambium, cork-cambium and intercalary meristem are all called **indeterminate meristem.** However the meristem such as those involved in leaf and flower formation are active only for a short period and are primarily responsible for the formation of an organ. These are called **determinate** meristems. (Also see the chapter : Anatomy of Flowering Plants).

Growth Rates

The expression of increased growth per unit time is termed **growth rate.** Thus, rate of growth can be expressed mathematically. An organism, or a part of the organism can produce more cells in a variety of ways.

The growth rate can be **arithmetic** or **geometrical** increase :

In **arithmetic growth,** following mitotic cell division only one daughter cell continues to divide while the other differentiates and matures. The simplest expression is arithmetic growth, *e.g.*, a root elongating at a constant rate. Mathematically, it is expressed as :

$$L_t = L_o + r_t$$
L_t = length at time 't'
L_o = length at time 'zero'
r = growth rate/elongation per unit time.

Geometrical growth. However, in most systems, the initial growth is slow (lag phase), and it increases rapidly thereafter at an exponential rate (log or exponential phase). Here, both the progeny cells following a mitotic cell division retain the ability to divide and continue to do so. However, with limited nutrient supply, the growth slows down leading to a stationary phase. If we plot the parameter of growth against time, we get a typical **sigmoid or S-curve.** S-curve is characteristic of every living organism growing in a natural environment. It is typical for all cells, tissues and organs of a plant. However, S-curve of the individual cells/tissues/organs/organisms may not be synchronous, *i.e.*, not at the same phase of the curve. For example, one cell may enter stationary phase while other is just entering the lag phase. Individual leaves are initiated, and abscised (each with a S-curve), but the plant/branch on which they occur could be still in exponential (log phase) or other places of growth.

The exponential growth can be expressed as :

$$W_1 = W_{oe}r,$$
$$W_1 = \text{final stage (weight, height, number, etc.)}$$
$$W_0 = \text{initial size at the beginning of the period}$$
$$r = \text{growth rate}$$
$$t = \text{time of growth}$$
$$e = \text{base of natural logarithms}$$

Here, r = is the relative growth rate and is also the measure of the ability of the plant to produce new plant material, referred to as **efficiency index.** Hence, final size of W_1 depends on initial size, W_0.

Quantitative comparisons between the growth of living system can also be made in two ways:

(i) Measurement and the comparison of total growth per unit is called absolute **growth rate.**

(ii) The growth of the given system per unit time expressed on a common basis, *e.g.,* per unit initial parameter is called **relative growth rate.** For example, two leaves A and B of different area sizes show exact absolute increase in area in the given time to give leaves A' and B'. However, one of them has much higher relative growth rate.

Growth is Measurable

Growth is measured by a variety of parameters. Some of such parameters are : (i) increase in fresh weight; (ii) increase in dry weight; (iii) increase in length; (iv) increase in area; (v) increase in volume; and (vi) increase in cell number, etc. For example, one single maize root apical meristem can give rise to more than 17,500 new cells per hour, whereas cells in a watermelon fruit may increase in size by up to 350,000 times. In the former, growth is expressed as increase in cell number; the latter expresses growth as increase in size of the cell. Though every cell, tissue organ and organism exhibit growth, yet all the above parameters are not applicable to all forms of growth at all times. For example, an increase in length is a good parameter for a pollen tube growth, while the growth in a dorsiventral leaf can more easily be measured as an increase in area.

Dormancy and Seed Germination

Seed. *A true seed is defined as a fertilized mature ovule that possesses embryonic plant, stored material, and a protective coat or coats.* Seed is the reproductive structure characteristic of all phanerogams. The structure of seeds may be studied in such common types of pea, gram, bean, almond or sunflower. They are all built on the same plan although there may be differences in the shape or size of the seed, the relative proportion of various parts.

There are hundreds of variations in the seed size, shape, colour and surface. The seeds range in size from tiny dust particles, as found in some orchids, to large double-coconuts. The seed surface may be smooth, wrinkled, striate, ribbed, furrowed, reticulate, tuberculate, alveolate, hairy, pulpy or having patterns like fingerprints.

In the seed, life activities are temporarily suspended in order to enable the plant to successfully pass through unfavourable and injurious climatic conditions. On the approach of favourable conditions, the seed resumes active life and grows into full plant. In the form of seeds, a plant can be carried to long distances without special precautions.

The developed seeds in many plants undergo a period of dormancy before germination and further growth.

Quiescence. Generally, all plants experience a period of suspended growth. This suspension may be due to exogenous control, such as a change in environmental conditions, and is referred to as **quiescence.**

Seed dormancy. Many kinds of seeds, apparently ripe, fail to germinate even if placed under such conditions that all environmental factors are favourable. In such seeds, resumption of growth by the embryo is arrested by the conditions within the seeds themselves. The state of inhibited growth of seeds or other plant organs as a result of internal causes is usually called **dormancy** but is sometimes referred to as the rest period. Seed dormancy is of considerable advantage to the plant. It enables the embryo to safely pass the unfavourable part of the year and germinate when the conditions are suitable for the establishment of the seedlings. In nature, dormancy period coincides with the unfavourable period for the seedling of the species. Dormancy of seeds results from one or a combination of several undermentioned factors.

Impermeability of seed coats to water. The seed coats of many species are completely impermeable to water at the time of their maturity. This condition is very common in the seeds of many legumes, (*e.g.,* clovers, alfalfa, etc.) of the water lotus, and of the morning glory. Germination fails to occur until water penetrates through the seed coats.

Mechanically resistant seed coats. In some seeds as those of mustard (*Brassica*), pigweed (*Amaranthus*), shepherd's purse (*Capsella*), etc., the seed coats are so strong that they do not yield to the pressure of the expanding embryo. The embryos of these seeds have no dormant period and will grow readily if the seed coats are removed.

Seed coats impermeable to oxygen. The two seeds in a fruit of cocklebur (*Xanthium*) are not equally dormant. Under natural conditions, the lower seed usually germinates in the spring following maturity while the upper seed remains dormant until the next year. The dormancy of these seeds has been demonstrated to result from the impermeability of the seed coats to oxygen.

Rudimentary embryos. In plants like ginkgo (*Ginkgo biloba*), European ash (*Fraxinus*), holly (*Ilex*) and many orchids, the embryo is unorganized when the seed is shed and attains full development before it germinates.

Dormant embryos. In many species, although the embryos are completely developed when the seed is ripe, the seed fails to germinate even when environmental conditions are favourable. Dormancy of such seed is a result of the physiological condition of the embryo. The embryos of such seeds will not grow when the seeds first ripen even if the seed coats are removed. During the period of dormancy, some physiological changes called after-ripening occur in the embryo before the seed is capable of germination. The seeds of apple, peach, iris and pine belong to this group. In nature, after-ripening occurs in winter and the seeds formed in autumn germinate in the coming spring.

Germination inhibitors. Germination of seeds is sometimes checked or prevented by the presence of compounds known as **inhibitors.** These are often substances produced in one or more plant organs. For example, the juice of tomato fruits inhibits the germination of tomato seeds and many other seeds as well. Inhibitors may be present in the embryo (*e.g.,* in *Xanthium*), endosperm, (*e.g.,* in *Iris*) or in the seed coat (*e.g.,* in *Cucurbita*). Abscissic acid (ABA) is one of the most commonly detected inhibitors of germination.

Methods of Breaking the Dormancy of Seeds

The dormancy of seeds presents a practical problem of considerable economic importance. Plant growers are often interested in securing seed that will germinate soon after it is harvested. Several methods have been devised for breaking the dormancy of seeds and for shortening the period of dormancy so that they may germinate promptly.

Whenever dormancy results due to any of the causes inherent in the seed coats it can be interrupted by **scarification.** For example, machine thrashed legumes seeds usually show a higher percentage of germination than those that have been harvested by hand. Strong mineral acids have been used successfully to interrupt seed dormancy caused by resistant or impermeable seed coats. Soaking the seeds in certain chemicals like potassium nitrate, ethylene, chlorohydrine, thiourea or in certain plant hormones is known to break dormancy. After-ripening of many seeds occurs more rapidly when they are kept at low temperatures than when stored at higher temperatures. Temperature from 5° to 10°C for two or three months is effective with seeds of conifers. Under natural conditions, seed dormancy is gradually overcome by processes such as weakening of the seed coat by the digestive juices in the alimentary canal of fruit-eating birds and other animals, or in still due to the action of microbes or due to mechanical abrasions. Dormancy of seeds is also broken by subjecting the seeds alternately to relatively low and high temperatures. Light is also considered as means of breaking dormancy of seeds. Seeds of sweet clover (*Melilotus alba*) and alfalfa (*Medicago sativa*) showed greatly improved germination after being subjected to hydraulic pressures of 2000 atm. at 18°C.

GROWTH REGULATORS

Plants produce some specific chemical substances, which are capable of moving from one organ to the other, and provide physiological control on growth. These substances, which are active in very small amounts, are called **plant hormones** or **growth regulators.**

The genetic make-up and **growth regulations** constitute important internal factors that regulate plant growth and development. The main naturally occurring plant growth regulators are **auxins, gibberellins, cytokinins, ethylene** and **abscisic acid.** The first four are called plant hormones. Abscisic acid (ABA) is naturally occurring growth inhibitor. A plant hormone is an organic compound synthesized in one tissue of plant and migrates to another tissue wherein very minute quantity affects the growth.

1. Auxins (*Gk. auxein = to grow*). Auxin is a group of hormones produced by the apical apices of stem and roots which migrate from the apex to the zone of elongation. The role of auxin is essential for the elongation process. Most of the knowledge about auxins comes from the work on oat *(Avena sativa)*. If the growing tip of oat coleoptile is removed, the remaining portion of coleoptile

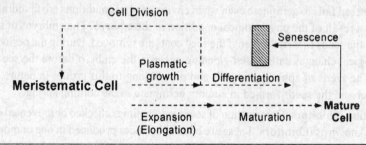

Fig. 1.47. Structures of some common synthetic auxins.

will show a marked decrease in growth which will ultimately stop. This means growth is restricted to or dependent on upper region. If the removed tip is placed on agar block for a period of several hours and then removed and the agar block now transferred to the cut stem, it is observed that block partially substitutes for the tip and the growth is resumed. This may be concluded that substance synthesized in the tip migrates downwards (in agar block) and is responsible for elongation of tip. This substance was denoted as auxin. Went (1928) performed *Avena*-**curvature test.** He placed several freshly cut coleoptile tips on agar block, after few hours which is cut into several pieces. He placed the agar block eccentrically on the coleoptile cut portion for two hours in dark. The growth curvature occurred and the coleoptile bends on one side opposite to the agar block. It occurred due to auxin diffusion from block to coleoptile resulting in elongation and growth on that side, as a result coleoptile bends. The experiments performed by Went showed that auxin is synthesized in the coleoptile tip and is translocated downward.

Auxins are synthesized in the shoot tips, young leaf primordia, developing seeds and from there they migrate to the regions of elongation. The movement of auxin is polar and in stems, it takes place in a basipetal direction whereas in the roots, it is in an acropetal direction. Auxins cause elongation of the stems and roots.

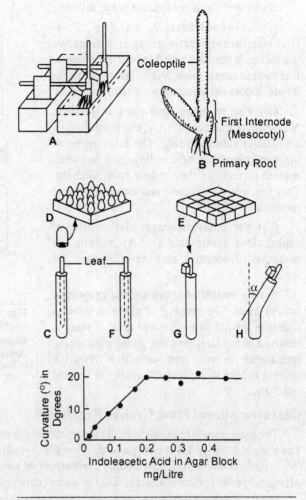

Fig. 1.48. Diagrammatic representation of the *Avena* curvature test.

Extensive work has been done on auxin and several related compounds have been isolated in pure forms. Among them the most common one is Indole 3-acetic acid (IAA) which is derivative of amino acid tryptophan.

The primary physiological effect of auxin is to promote the elongation of the cells which may be due to increasing osmotic pressure and permeability of cytoplasm to water and decreasing wall pressure. Some work done by Coartney *et al* (1967), Masuda *et al* (1967) and Nooden (1968) indicates that auxin is associated with nucleic acid metabolism. It affects the site of DNA responsible for increasing plasticity of walls and its extension.

The compounds which can be converted into auxins are called **auxin precursors.**

The compounds which inhibit the actions of auxins are called **anti-auxins.**

The auxins which are hard to extract and need the use of organic solvents are referred to as **bound auxins.** The free form of auxin is active, whereas the bound auxin is inactive in growth. A dynamic equilibrium exists in between these two forms.

The functions of auxins are generally tested with the help of bioassays. **Bioassay** means the testing of substance for its activity in causing a growth response in a living plant or its organ. This test is quantitative in nature, which measures the concentration required to produce the effect.

For example, *Avena* curvature test and root growth inhibition test are bioassays for examining auxin activity.

Uses of auxins. There are several horticultural and agricultural uses of auxins. They are as follows

The applications of auxins have a wide range, such as (*i*) enhancing the formation of roots, (*ii*) development of parthenocarpic fruits, (*iii*) thinning of flowers and fruits for healthy growth of remaining ones, (*iv*) control of preharvest fruit drop, (*v*) enhancement of flowering, (*vi*) improving quality during storage, (*vii*) weed control by herbicidal action, (*viii*) control of apical dominance.

Some specific uses of auxins are as follows :

(*i*) **As weedicides.** 2, 4-D (*i.e.,* 2, 4-Dichlorophenoxyacetic acid) is a selective weedicide. It destroys broad-leaved dicot weeds. It is used in cereal crops and in lawns to kill the weeds. It does not affect the growth of monocots.

(*ii*) **For fruiting and root initiation.** Naphthalene acetic acid (NAA) and indole butyric acid (IBA) induce fruiting. The foliar spray on litchi and pineapple induces flowering and when applied to cuttings they induce root initiation. They also retard abscission, and therefore prevent premature fruit fall.

(*iii*) **For potato storage.** Methyl ester of naphthalene acetic acid (NAA) inhibits the sprouting of potatoes, and therefore used for storage.

(*iv*) **To inhibit or stimulate the growth of lateral buds.** The pruning of plants is done to stimulate growth in the desired area. If apex is removed lateral buds develop, giving a branching appearance. In roses and many fruit trees, the pruning is done to improve the quality of flowers and fruits.

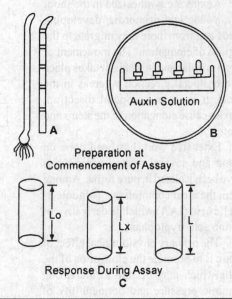

Fig. 1.49. Avena Section Test. LO = length of freshly cut segment. LX = Length of untreated segment after floating in water for length of test period; L = length of treated segment after floating in test solution for length of test period.

Characteristics of Plant Growth Regulators

The plant growth regulators (PGR) are small, simple molecules of diverse chemical composition. They could be indole compounds (indole-3-acetic acid IAA); adenine derivatives (N^6 – furfurylamino purine, Kinetin); derivatives of carotenoids and fatty acids (abscisic acid, ABA); terpenes (gibberellic acid, GA_3) or gases (ethylene, C_2H_4).

Plant growth regulators are variously described as **plant growth substances, plant hormones or phytohormones.**

The plant growth regulators (PGR) can be broadly divided into two groups based on their functions in a living plant body.

One group of PGRs are involved in growth promoting activities, such as cell division, cell enlargement, pattern formation, tropic growth, flowering, fruiting and seed formation. These are also called **plant growth promoters,** *e.g.,* Auxins, gibberellins and cytokinins.

The PGRs of other group play an important role in plant responses to wounding and stress of biotic and abiotic origin. They also are involved in various growth inhibiting activities such as promotion of dormancy and abscission. The PGR abscisic acid (ABA) belongs to this group.

The gaseous PGR, ethylene (C_2H_4), could fit either of the groups, but it largely inhibits growth activities.

Functions of PGRs. Each of these PGRs belonging to any group brings about a variety of growth and developmental responses, and not all responses are similar and simultaneous at any given time, *e.g.,* a given concentration of auxin which promotes shoot growth may inhibit root growth.

Secondly, similar responses are affected by different PGRs, *e.g.,* both auxins and gibberellins can result in cell enlargement, while cell division could be promoted by auxins, gibberellins and cytokinins.

The PGRs are active at very low concentrations, usually in 10^{-6} M range. However, site of production and sites of action (target cells) of PGRs could be same or different. Also they are synthesised at several sites and in different tissues within a plant body and not in any specialised gland or tissue, as in animals.

Moreover, each of the major classes of PGR brings about a variety of growth and differentiation responses.

PHYSIOLOGICAL EFFECTS OF PLANT GROWTH REGULATORS

Auxins

Auxins (GK *Auxein* = to grow), isolated initially from human urine, were the first plant PGR to be discovered.

However, IAA also occurs in human urine, especially in persons suffering from pellagra (niacin or nicotinic acid deficiency)

The term **auxin** is applied to the indole-3-acetic acid (IAA), and to other natural and synthetic compounds having certain growth regulating properties. They are generally produced by the growing apices of the stems and roots, from where they migrate to the regions of their action.

Auxins, like IAA and indole butyric acid, IBA, have been isolated from plants.

2, 4-D (2, 4 dichlorophenoxyacetic), NAA (naphthalene acetic acid) are the synthetic auxins.

All abovementioned auxins have been used extensively, particularly in agricultural practices.

Applications of auxins have a wide range. They have been used for more than 50 years in horticulture and agriculture. They help to initiate rooting in stem cuttings, an application widely used for plant propagation. Auxins promote flowering, *e.g.*, in pineapples. They help to prevent fruit and leaf drops at early stages but promote the abscission of older/mature leaves and fruits.

In most higher plants, the growing apical bud inhibits the growth of lateral (axillary) buds, a phenomenon called **apical dominance.**

Removal of shoot tips (decapitation) usually results in the growth of lateral buds. It is widely applied in tea plucking, hedge-making.

Auxins also induce parthenocarpy, *e.g.*, in tomatoes. They are widely used as herbicides. Auxin 2, 4-D, does not affect mature monocotyledonous plants. It is also spread to kill dandelions/daisies in lawns by gardeners. Auxins also control xylem differentiation and help cell-division.

Gibberellins

This is another kind of promotery PGR. There are more than 100 gibberellins reported from different organisms such as fungi and higher plants, and the number is still increasing.

They are denoted as GA_1, GA_2, GA_3 and so on. However, GA_3 was one of the first gibberellins to be discovered and remains the most intensively studied form.

All GA_s are acidic. They produce a wide range of physiological responses in the plants. They specifically make genetic dwarfs, *e.g.*, in peas, grow tall. Their ability to cause increase in length of axis is used to make the stalks of graphs lengthy, thereby allowing the grapes to grow larger.

Gibberellins GA_4 and GA_7 cause apple fruits to elongate and improve shape. They also delay senescence, thus the fruits can be left on the tree longer to extend market period.

GA_3 is used to speed up malting process in brewing industry.

Spraying sugarcane crop with gibberellins increases the length of the stem. It helps increase yield as much as by 20 tons per acre.

Spraying juvenile conifers with GA_4 and GA_7 hastens the maturity period, thus leading to early seed production. Gibberellins also promote bolting (*i.e.*, internode elongation prior to flowering) in beet, cabbages and many plants with rosette habit.

Cytokinins

These PGRs have specific effects on cytokinesis, and were discovered as **kinetin** (a modified form of adenine, a purine) from the herring sperm DNA. Kinetin does not occur naturally in plants. The searches for natural substances with cytokinin like activities led to the isolation of **Zeatin** from corn-kernels and coconut milk, etc. Since the discovery of zeatin, several naturally occurring cytokinins, and some synthetic compounds, with cell division promoting activity, have been identified from plants.

Natural cytokinins are synthesised in regions where rapid cell division is occurring, *e.g.*, root apices, developing shoot buds, young fruits, etc.

They help in production of new leaves, chloroplasts in leaves, lateral shoot growth as well as adventitious shoot formation. Cytokinins overcome apical dominance. They promote nutrient mobilization that helps in delay of leaf senescence.

Ethylene

This is a simple gaseous PGR. It is synthesised in large amounts by tissues undergoing senescence and ripening of fruits. Ethylent influences of plants include horizontal growth of seedlings, swelling of the axis, tighter apical look formation in dicot seedlings.

Ethylene promotes senescence and abscission of plant organs (especially leaves, flowers etc.)

Ethylene is highly effective in fruit ripening. It enhances the respiration rate during ripening of fruit. This rise in rate of respiration is called **respiratory climacteric.**

Exposure of plants to ethylene causes drooping of leaves and flowers, a phenomenon known as **epinasty.**

Ethylene is a natural PGR and product of metabolism in plants.

Ethylene breaks seed and bud dormancy, initiates germination in peanut seeds, sprouting of potato tubers.

Ethylene promotes rapid internode/petiole elongation in deep water rice plants. It also helps leaves/upper parts of shoot to remain above water.

This also promotes root growth and root hair formation, thus helping plant to have more absorption surface.

Ethylene promotes in pineapple family (Bromeliaceae), and is used for synchronizing fruit set.

Ethylene also induces flowering in mango. Ethylene regulates so many physiological processes.

It is one of the most widely used PGRs in agriculture. The most widely used compound is **ethepon, 2-chloroethyl phosphonic acid (Ether).** Ethepon in aqueous solution is readily absorbed and transported within the plant and releases ethylene slowly. Ethepon hastens fruit ripening in tomatoes and apples. It accelerates abscission in flowers and fruits (thinning of cotton, cherry, walnut, etc.). It promotes female flowers in cucumbers, and therefore, increases the yield.

Abscissic Acid

Abscissic acid regulates abscission and dormancy. However, like other PGRs it also has wide range of effects on plant growth and development. It acts as general plant growth inhibitor and also inhibits plant metabolism. Abscissic acid (ABA) inhibits closure of stomata in epidermis, and increases tolerance of plant to various kinds of stresses, and therefore, it is also called **stress hormone.**

ABA plays an important role in seed development, maturation and dormancy. By inducing dormancy, ABA helps seeds to withstand desiccation and other factors unfavourable for growth. In most situations ABA acts as an antagonist to gibberellins.

However, for any and every phase of growth, differentiation and development of plants, one or the other PGR has to play some role. Such roles may be complimentary or antagonistic. They could be individualistic or synergistic.

Abscission. The shedding of leaves, flowers and fruits from the living plant is known as abscission. These parts abscise in a region called the **abscission zone,** which is located near the base of petioles of leaves. In most plants leaf abscission is preceded by the differentiation of a distinct layer of cells, the **abscission layer.** During abscission the walls of the cells in the abscission layers are digested, which causes them to become soft and weak.

Auxins delay the onset of early stages of leaf abscission but promote the later stages.

Auxin level within leaves is very high in young leaves and progressively decreases in maturing leaves and is very low in senescent old leaves.

When applied externally to young leaves, IAA (indole acetic acid) inhibits leaf drop. However in later stages of leaf growth, if applied externally, it hastens the process.

It is also known that high levels of auxin triggers biosynthesis of ethylene within cells. Ethylene strongly hastens the formation of abscission zone.

There is an interaction between auxin and ethylene for an event, *i.e.*, the abscission zone formation.

In the similar way, there are so many events in the life of a plant where more than one PGR interact to affect that event, *e.g.,* dormancy in seeds/buds, senescence, apical dominance, etc.

Practicals

Two experiments on gibberellins and cytokinins are given here :

Experiment 1.

Object : Demonstration of effect of gibberellic acid GA_3 on elongation.

Requirements : Prepared aqueous (1000.0) solutions of GA_3 having 0.01, 0.1, 1.0, 10.0 and 1000.0 mg/ml, young plants of dwarf and tall varieties of peas, distilled water.

Experiment : Take ten dwarf variety plants and ten tall variety plants. Apply 1 ml. of a GA_3 solution to a young leaf of each of the plants. Do this application again after one week. Distilled water is applied as a control in separate plants. Measure the height of each daily for fifteen days.

Observation and Explanation : Each time there is a clear elongation in the plant height. The growth response in dwarf variety increases with the increase of concentration of GA_3.

Experiment 2.

Object : Demonstration of effect of kinetin of senescence.

Requirements : Solutions of kinetin containing 0, 0.001, 0.01 and 100.0 mg./litre of hormone, mature fresh leaves of radish, sterile distilled water, petri dish, filter paper, etc.

Experiment : Take mature fresh leaves of radish plant and wash them with sterile distilled water. Keep them in petri dishes on moist filter paper. Apply 0.5 ml of one of the kinetin solutions per leaf. Examine the leaves daily for a week.

Observation and Explanation : The leaves turn yellow after a week. This is due to disappearance of chlorophyll and degradation of proteins.

TERMS TO REMEMBER

Abscission. The phenomenon of breaking of leaves and fruits from the plant.

Apical dominance. When the growth of apical bud at the apex of shoot inhibits the growth of lateral buds into branches, it is called apical dominance.

Aleurone layer. The outer layer of endosperm in cereal grains, (*e.g.*, maize, wheat, etc.) which produces hydrolysing enzymes, such as amylase and protease.

Autonomic movement. The self-controlled growth movements of the plants.

Catabolism. The breaking down phase of metabolism, such as digestion and respiration.

Cytokinin. A growth regulator concerned with stimulation of cell division and nucleic acid metabolism.

Day-neutral plants. The plants that flower after a period of vegetative growth indifferent to day length or the photoperiod.

Emergence. The appearance of root and shoot from seed.

Epigeal germination. During germination, the cotyledons are pushed above the ground level due to rapid elongation of hypocotyl.

Germination. The awakening of dormant embryo in the seed.

Growth. The phenomenon of growth represents an increase in mass or volume of an organism accompanied by an irreversible change in form and structure.

Hypogeal germination. In this type of germination, the cotyledons and endosperm remain below the soil and epicotyl elongates.

Imbibition. Initial intake of water by the seed.

Indole acetic acid (IAA). A type of auxin (a growth promoter).

Long-day plants. Such plants flower when the day length exceeds critical length.

Nastic movement. Non-directional growth movements.

NAA. Naphthalene acetic acid.

Paratonic movements. The growth movements induced by external stimuli.

Photoperiodism. Response of a plant to the changing relative lengths of the day and night.

Phototropism. Growth movements of plants induced by stimulus of light.

Phytochrome. A light sensitive protein pigment involved in several plant activities.

Response. The reaction of a plant to a stimulus.

Senescence. Gradual decline in the smooth functioning of the organisms ultimately leading to death.

Short-day plant. When the flowering of a plant is induced by uninterrupted dark period, longer than the critical length.

Vernalization. Low temperature treatment required by plants for flowering.

PLANT GROWTH EXERCISES

EXERCISE 53

Object : Measurement of growth in plants.

Requirements : Auxanometers : (*i*) Arc auxano-meter (*ii*) Pfeffer's automatic auxanometer.

(*i*) **Arc auxanometer :** It consists of a vertical stand with a pulley to which is attached a long thread and a needle or pointer movable over a graduated arc. One end of the thread is tied with the growing point of the plant and another is stretched with a suitable weight.

(*ii*) **Pfeffer's automatic auxanometer :** It consists of a vertical stand with two pulleys. One of these two pulleys possesses a thread carrying two weights at either ends to keep it stretched. This thread on one side is also attached with a fine scratching pointer which touches a smoked drum. Another pulley is also provided with a thread of which one end is tied with the growing point of plant and another is stretched with a suitable weight.

Observation and Explanation : (*i*) With the growth of plant, the weight moves the thread down and the movement of needle can be read easily on the scale.

There exists a notable ratio between the size of pulley and the needle. If pulley is 4 inches with the needle 20 inches from the centre of the disc of pulley, growth will be magnified ten times on the scale. It can easily be illustrated by an example :

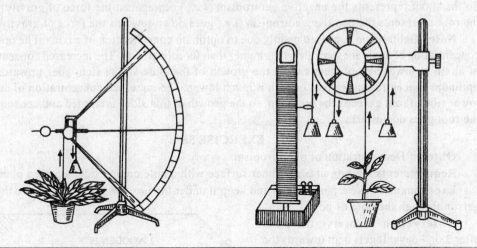

| Fig. 1.50. *Arc Auxanometer.* | Fig. 1.51. *Pfeffer's Auxanometer* |

If indicator moves 4 cm. in 8 hours and the magnification is 10 times, then the actual growth is :

$\because$ Growth in 8 hours $= 4/10$ cm.
$= 0.4$ cm. or 4 mm.
$\therefore$ Growth in one hour $= 4/8$
$= 0.5$ mm./hour

(*ii*) With the growth of plant first pulley makes moving the another which in turn moves the pointer. This pointer moves downwards and traces a spiral on the rotating smoked drum. Thus the growth for a certain period is recorded.

PLANT MOVEMENTS EXERCISES

EXERCISE 54

Object : Demonstration of geotropism by clinostat.

Requirements : Clinostat apparatus and a potted plant.

Experiment : The potted plant is fitted in the clinostat apparatus in a horizontal position.

(*i*) The clinostat is rotated with an even and slow speed.

(*ii*) The clinostat is stopped in a particular direction after some definite intervals.

Observation : (*i*) The shoot and root do not represent any curvature.

(*ii*) Here the stem goes high or against the gravity while the root moves down or towards the gravity.

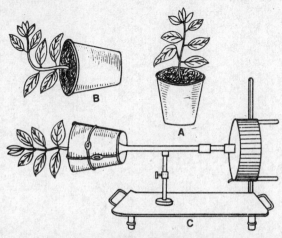

Fig. 1.52. *Clinostat Apparatus.*

Explanation : Here in first case the plant possesses a simultaneous and equal effect of gravity so no curvature is seen here.

In second case the definite intervals possess some special effects of gravity on the plants. So the shoot represents the negative geotropism (*i.e.*, goes against the force of gravity) while the root represents the positive geotropism (*i.e.*, goes down towards the force of gravity).

Note : Geotropism is caused mainly due to optimum concentration of auxins. The optimum concentration of auxin for stem growth is higher than for root growth. The increased concentration of auxin at lower part of stem causes the growth of that side so the stem goes upwards. The optimum concentration for root growth is much lower. The increased concentration of auxin at lower side of root exceeds the optimum, so the growth of that side is retarded and consequently the root goes downwards.

EXERCISE 55

Object : Demonstration of phototropism.

Requirements : A box of black inner surface with a hole on one side, a potted plant.

Experiment : Take a potted plant and keep it under the box for 3 or 4 days. Here the light gets in through the hole of box.

Observation : Observe the plant after 3 or 4 days. It gets bent towards the hole of the box from which light is getting in. So the stem curves towards the source of light.

Explanation : The growth-curvature of plants caused due to stimulation by unilateral light source is known as phototropism. This phototropism occurs due to unequal distribution of auxin on the two sides of the stimulated stem. The concentration of auxin is more on the side which is away from the light so this far off area of stem shows the maximum growth. Consequently, the whole process results in a curvature towards the source of light.

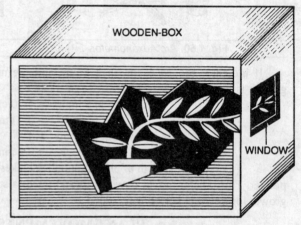

Fig. 1.53. *Phototropism,* demonstration of the phenomenon.

2

CHAPTER

Mineral Nutrition

The basic needs of all living organisms are similar and they require macromolecules, such as carbohydrates, proteins and fats, for their growth and development. They also require minerals for their development.

However, green plants prepare their food from simple substances, such as water and carbon dioxide, through process of photosynthesis. This type of green organisms, which prepare their food through photosynthesis, are called **autotrophs.**

While other organisms and non-green plants cannot prepare their own food as autotrophs do, they obtain their nutrition from autotrophs, and are called **heterotrophs.**

In the formation of carbohydrates, proteins and fats, carbon (C), hydrogen (H) and oxygen (O) are required. In addition to these elements (*i.e.*, C, H and O), plants need several other important elements, called **mineral elements.**

The mineral elements that are essential in the life of a plant, with the exception of carbon and oxygen, are obtained through the root system from the soil. Carbon and oxygen are obtained from the atmosphere. The utilization for various absorbed ions by a plant for growth and development is called the **mineral nutrition** of the plant. It has been demonstrated by water and sand culture experiments that carbon, hydrogen, oxygen, nitrogen, sulphur, phosphorus, calcium, magnesium and iron are essential for the healthy growth and development of plants. These elements are referred to as the **macronutrients or major elements** because of the relatively large quantities in which they are needed for plant life. Plants also require some elements in minute or trace quantities which are called the **micronutrients or trace or minor elements.** Some important micronutrients are manganese, zinc, boron,' copper and molybdenum.

ESSENTIAL MINERAL ELEMENTS

An **essential element** is known, without which the plant cannot complete its life cycle. It has clear physiological role to play. The important criteria for an essential element are as follows:

(*i*) This element is absolutely necessary for supporting normal growth and reproduction of plant.

(*ii*) This element is always specific, and cannot be replaced by any other element.

(*iii*) This element is directly involved in the metabolism of the plant.

However, among the mineral elements absorbed by the plants, not all are essential.

Out of 105 or more elements discovered so far, only 20 elements have been found to be essential for growth and development of the plant.

These essential elements are classified into two broad categories called (*i*) **macronutrients** and (*ii*) **micronutrients.**

The **macronutrients** are: carbon, hydrogen, oxygen, nitrogen, phosphorus, sulphur, potassium, calcium, magnesium and silicon.

The macronutrients are generally present in plant tissues in concentrations of 1 to 10 mg per gram of dry matter.

The **micronutrients** or **trace elements** are: iron, manganese, copper, molybdenum, zinc, boron and chlorine. Recently some other such elements have also been discovered, *e.g.*, cobalt, vanadium and nickel.

The microelements are required in very low amounts, *i.e.*, about 0.1 mg per gram of dry matter.

SOURCES OF ESSENTIAL ELEMENTS FOR PLANTS

All elements incorporated into plants are ultimately derived from the atmosphere, water and soil.

Carbon (C). It is derived from atmosphere as CO_2.

Hydrogen (H). It is mainly obtained from water.

Oxygen (O). It is either derived from the air or from the water in the form of inorganic ions.

Nitrogen (N). The plants are unable to use atmospheric nitrogen. It is inert and plants cannot make use of it directly. However, by means of atmospheric activities nitrogen combines with oxygen and is brought down by rain to the soil. Besides, there are certain highly specialised organisms called **nitrogen fixers,** such as bacteria and cyanobacteria. They fix atmospheric nitrogen into the soil in the form of nitrites (NO_2) and nitrates (NO_3). These heterotrophic organisms, occurring in the soil, convert nitrogen gas (N_2) to anionic forms such as nitrates (NO_3) or nitrite (NO_2^-), or a reduced cationic form such as NH_4^+ (ammonium). These nitrogenous compounds enter plants as nutrients through the roots and are assimilated as organic nitrogen. The plants, in turn, provide organic nitrogen to heterotrophic organisms.

The other elements are absorbed from the soil, such as phosphorus (P) as phosphate (PO_4), and sulphur (S) mainly as sulphate (SO_4).

ROLE OF ESSENTIAL ELEMENTS

The essential elements perform several important roles. They may be as follows:

The most important role of the elements is to participate in various metabolic activities, such as regulation of permeability of cell membranes; some elements are required for maintenance of osmotic pressure of cell sap, while others take part in an electron transport system. Some elements are responsible for buffer action, and some for electrical neutrality.

Macronutrients

Mineral elements include N, P, K, Ca, Mg, S and Fe. They are absorbed from soil.

Nitrogen (N). About 78% of nitrogen is found in atmospheric air, but this is of no use to plants, in its free state. This enters in the plants through stomata along with other gases, and comes out in the same state, unused. The plants can take nitrogen found in the soil in the form of NO_2^-, NO_3^- or NH_4^+. This is required by all parts of a plant, particularly the meristematic tissues. Nitrogen is found in the constituents of proteins, chlorophyll, protoplasm, nucleic acids, vitamins and hormones. For proper and normal growth of leaves of plants, it is one of the most essential elements.

Phosphorus (P). It is usually found in nucleoproteins and protoplasm It also helps in the division of nucleus and the cell. It also helps in the decomposition of carbohydrates during respiration. Phosphorus is a constituent of cell membranes, nucleic acids and nucleotides. This is needed for all phosphorylation reactions. It plays a very important role in the ripening of the grains and fruits. This also helps a lot in the development of root system. For the development of underground parts of

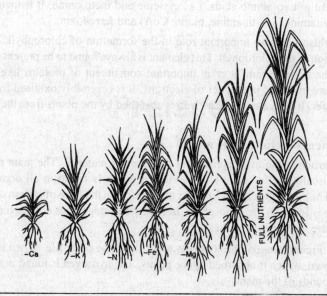

Fig. 2.1. Barley plants grown in water culture showing deficiency of certain nutrients.

radish, beet root, and potato, etc., this element is required. Phosphorus is absorbed from the soil in the form of phosphate $H_2PO_4^-$ ions.

Potassium (K). This element is usually found in the growing regions of the plant. It is one of the constituents of the protoplasm. It is related to metabolic activities. This helps in the synthesis of carbohydrates and proteins. The plant grows normally in its presence, and the fruits and seeds remain quite healthy. On the scarcity of potassium, the normal growth of the leaves become yellowish, and the stem becomes somewhat thin. The plants take potassium from the soil in the form of potassium nitrate and potassium chloride, etc.

Potassium helps to determine anion-cation balance in cells, and is involved in protein synthesis, opening and closing of stomata, activation of enzymes, and maintenance of turgidity of cells. It is absorbed as K^+ ion by plants from the soil.

Calcium (Ca). This element is always found in green plants. The middle lamella of the cell wall consists of calcium pectate. Only because of this element, the permeability of the protoplasm is maintained. Usually for the growth and development of the fruits, calcium is very essential. In its deficiency the cells of the plant become disorganized, and the growth of the plant is also checked. But, usually the leaves become chlorotic, when its overdose is present in the soil. Calcium is required by meristematic and differentiating tissues. It is also used in the mitotic spindle in cell division. It activates certain enzymes and plays an important role in regulating metabolic activities. Calcium accumulates in older leaves. Calcium is absorbed by the plants from the soil in the form of Ca^+ ions.

Magnesium (Mg). It is found in the chlorophyll. The chlorophyll does not form in its absence, the leaves become chlorotic, and the growth of the plant is retarded. In the seeds of pulses and cereals, this element is found in sufficient quantity. Magnesium activates enzymes in respiration and photosynthesis. It helps in synthesis of DNA and RNA. This also maintains ribosome structure. Magnesium is absorbed by the plants from the soil in the form of divalent Mg^{2+}.

Sulphur (S). It is usually found in the complex proteins of the plants. It is found in sufficient quantity in the mustard oil. It is also found in the protoplasm. In its deficiency, the leaves become chlorotic, and the stem becomes thin. The plants take this element from the soil in the form of calcium and potassium sulphate (SO_4^{2-}).

Sulphur is present in two amino acids, *i.e.*, cysteine and methionine. It is main constituent of several coenzymes, vitamins (*i.e.*, thiamine, biotin, CoA) and ferredoxin.

Iron (Fe). This also plays an important role in the formation of chlorophyll, though it is not found in the constitution of the chlorophyll. This element is always found to be present in the chromatin material of nucleus and protoplasm. It is an important constituent of proteins like ferredoxin and cytochromes which are involved in transfer of electrons. It is reversibly oxidised from Fe^{2+} to Fe^{3+} during electron transfer. It activates catalase. Iron is absorbed by the plants from the soil in the form of ferric (Fe^{3+}) ions.

Non-mineral elements include C, H and O

Carbon (C). Carbon is the main constituent of the plant material. The main part of the plant consists of it. It is usually half of plant's dry weight. Carbon is found in all organic compounds present in the plant. The plants get carbon from the atmosphere in the form of carbon dioxide. Usually, .03% carbon dioxide is found in the atmosphere, but this percentage goes down even to .01% in day time, because of its use in the photosynthesis.

Hydrogen (H). Free hydrogen does not play any role in the plant life. When it combines with oxygen, water is formed, which is absorbed by the plants. The hydrogen is found in so many organic and inorganic compounds of the plant.

Oxygen (O). Free oxygen is taken from the atmosphere by the plants, which helps in the respiration of the living cells. Besides this, the oxygen is found in many organic compounds of the plant.

Micronutrients

Boron (B). This is also an essential element for the growth of nearly all the plants. The plants of tomato, tobacco, lemon, root, mustard, cotton and others are sufficiently benefited by these elements. Boron also helps in the formation of the nodules of the leguminous plants. It also adds to the quantity of the sugar of beet root. The beet root becomes susceptible to various diseases, because of its deficiency. In its deficiency, the normal growth of the plant is obstructed and various leaf spots are developed. In its absence, the apices of roots and stems become brittle, and gradually they die.

Boron is also required for uptake and utilisation of Ca^{2+}, membrane function, pollen germination, cell elongation, cell differentiation and carbohydrate translocation.

Manganese (Mn). Manganese activates many enzymes which are involved in photosynthesis, respiration and nitrogen metabolism. Manganese helps in splitting of water to liberate oxygen during photosynthesis. Various vitamins are formed in the fruits, only because of its presence. The cabbage plants, pine trees and the leguminous plants require its optimum doses. Manganese is absorbed by plants in the form of manganous cation (Mn^{2+}).

Zinc (Zn). Zinc helps in the formation of chloroplasts. It activates various enzymes, especially carboxylases. Zinc is required in synthesis of auxin. It is absorbed by plants from soil in the form of (Zn^{2+}) ions.

Copper (Cu). Copper helps in formation of starch. It is required for the overall metabolism in plants. It is associated with certain enzymes involved in redox reactions and is reversibly oxidised from Cu^+ to Cu^{2+}. Copper is absorbed by plants as cupric ion (Cu^{2+}).

Molybdenum (Mo). This helps in formation of proteins. It also helps in fixation of nitrogen in soil by *Azotobacter* and *Rhizobium*. This is a constituent of several enzymes, including nitrogenase and nitrate reductase which take part in nitrogen metabolism. This is absorbed by plants from soil in the form of molybdate ion (MoO_2^{2+}).

Chlorine (Cl). With Na^+ and K^+, chlorine helps in determining solute concentration and anion-cation balance in cells. It is required for cell division in roots and leaves. It is needed to perform water-splitting reaction in photosynthesis, which evolves oxygen.

DEFICIENCY SYMPTOMS

Deficiency Symptoms (Macronutrients)

Nitrogen (N). Nitrogen deficiency causes yellowing of older leaves (chlorosis). The plant growth is stunted as protein content, cell division and cell enlargement are decreased. It also causes dormancy of lateral buds, late flowering, purple colouration and shoot axis surface and wrinkling of cereal grains.

Phosphorus (P). Phosphorus deficiency causes premature leaf fall. Dead necrotic areas develop on leaves or fruits, and leaves turn dark to blue-green in colour. It also causes delay in seed germination.

Potassium (K). Mottled chlorosis of leaves occurs. Necrotic areas are developed at the tips and margins of leaves, and they curve downward. Internodes become short, and plants adopt bushy habit. It also causes loss of cambial activity, disintegration of plastids and increase in rate of respiration.

Calcium (Ca). Calcium deficiency causes disintegration of growing meristematic regions of the root, stem and leaves. Chlorosis occurs along the margins of the younger leaves, and malformation occurs. This also leads to stunted growth of the plant.

Magnesium (Mg). Magnesium deficiency causes interveinal chlorosis of the leaves. The older leaves are affected first, and dead necrotic patches appear on the leaves. This also causes premature leaf abscission.

Sulphur (S). Sulphur deficiency causes yellowing (*i.e.*, chlorosis) of leaves, younger leaves are affected first, tips and margins of leaves roll inward, and stem becomes hard due to development of sclerenchyma. These symptoms are similar to those of nitrogen deficiency symptoms, as sulphur and nitrogen are constituents of proteins.

Iron (Fe). Iron deficiency causes rapid chlorosis of the leaves which is generally interveinal.

Deficiency Symptoms (Micronutrients)

Manganese (Mn). Manganese deficiency causes chlorotic and necrotic spots in the interveinal areas of leaves.

Zinc (Zn). Zinc deficiency causes chlorosis of older leaves which starts from tips and margins. Malformation of leaves takes place, and stunted growth of plant occurs. Its deficiency causes **mottle leaf** disease in apple, citrus, walnut, etc., and **khaira** disease in rice.

Copper (Cu). Copper deficiency causes necrosis of the tips of young leaves. It causes **die-back** of citrus and other fruit trees where leaves wither and fall, bark becomes rough and splits exuding gummy substances. **Reclamation disease** of cereals and leguminous plants is also caused due to its deficiency.

Boron (B). Boron deficiency causes death of the shoot tip. Flower formation is suppressed, root growth is stunted and shoot apices die. Fruits become of small size and root nodules in leguminous plants are not formed, and leaves become coppery in texture.

Molybdenum (Mo). Molybdenum deficiency causes chlorotic interveinal mottling of the older leaves. This may cause nitrogen deficiency, as it is component of enzymes involved in nitrogen metabolism. Flower formation is inhibited, and also causes **whip tail** disease in cauliflower plants.

Chlorine (Cl). The deficiency of chlorine in plants causes wilting of leaves, stunted root growth and reduced fruiting.

Table 2.1. Roles of Mineral Elements in Plants

Element	Obtained as	Regions of plant in which required	Functions	Deficiency symptoms
Nitrogen N	NO_2, NO_3 or NH_4^+	In all tissues, particularly in meristematic tissues.	Constituent of proteins, nucleic acids, vitamins, hormones, coenzymes, ATP, chlorophyll.	Stunted growth, chlorosis.
Phosphorus P	H_2PO_4	Young tissues, withdrawn from the older metabolically less active cells.	Constituent of cell membrane. Required for the synthesis of nucleic acids, nucleotides, ATP, NAD and NADP.	Poor growth of plant, leaves dull green.
Potassium K	K^+	Meristematic tissues, buds, leaves, root tips.	Involved in protein synthesis; involved in formation of cell membrane and in opening and closing of stomata; increases hardness; helps in determination of anion-cation balance in cells; activates enzymes and helps in maintenance of turgidity of cells.	Stunted growth; yellow edges to leaves; premature death and mottled appearance of leaves.
Calcium Ca	Ca^{++}	Meristematic and differentiating tissues, accumulates in older leaves.	Involved in selective permeability of cell membranes; activates certain enzymes; required for development of stem and root apices, and as calcium pectate in the middle lamella of the cell wall.	Stunted growth; chlorosis of young leaves; die back of shoots.
Magnesium Mg	Mg^{++}	All the leaves of plants; withdrawn from ageing leaves and directed to developing seeds.	Activates enzymes in phosphate metabolism; constituent of chlorophyll; maintains ribosome structure.	Chlorosis
Sulphur S	SO_4^{++}	Young leaves; stem and root tips; remobilized during senescence.	Constituent of amino acids, cysteine, methionine and proteins, coenzyme A, and ferredoxin.	Chlorosis

Element	Obtained as	Regions of plant in which required	Functions	Deficiency symptoms
Iron Fe	Fe^{+++}	Everywhere in leaves, along leaf veins.	Constituent of ferredoxin and cytochromes; required for synthesis of chlorophyll.	Chlorosis
Manganese (trace) Mn	Mn^{++}	Leaves and seeds	Activates certain enzymes (carboxylases).	Chlorosis; grey spots on leaves
Molybdenum (trace) Mo	Mo^{+++}	All parts; particularly in roots.	Activates certain enzymes in nitrogen metabolism.	Retardation of growth to some extent.
Boron (trace) B	B	Leaves and seeds	Increases the uptake of water and Ca; essential for meristematic activity and growth of pollen tube; involved in translocation of carbohydrates.	Death of stem and root apices; leaves become curled and brittle; reduces flowering; causes brown heart disease.
Copper (trace) Cu	Cu^{++}	All parts of plant	Activates certain enzymes	
Zinc (trace) Zn	Zn^{++}	All parts of plant	Activates various enzymes especially carboxylases, carbonic anhydrate and various dehydrogenases; required for auxin synthesis.	Malformation of leaves Dieback of shoots.
Chlorine Cl	Cl^-	All parts of plant	With Na^+ and K^+ helps in determining solute concentration and anion-cation balance in cells; essential for oxygen evolution in photosynthesis.	

TERMS TO REMEMBER

Active absorption. Ions accumulated in cells may move against concentration or ecp gradients.

Ammonification. The dead remains of animals and plants are decomposed through microbial activities to produce ammonia.

Autotrophs. The organisms which can prepare their own food through photosynthesis.

Bacteroids. Some of the bacteria that enlarge to become membrane bound structures.

Denitrification. Where nitrates convert to nitrogen gas.

Donnan equilibrium. Theory, explains the passive accumulation of ions that are fixed or non-diffusible, against an ecp gradient.

Essential element. An element without which the plant cannot complete its life cycle.

Flux. Movement of ions. The movement into the cell is **influx** and the outward movement is **efflux.**

Heterotrophs. Organisms, including non-green plants, which cannot make their own food and obtain their nutrition from autotrophs.

Hydroponics. Soil-less culture of plants, where roots are immersed in nutrient solution without soil.

Ion exchange. The process of exchange between adsorbed tons and ions in solution.

Leghaemoglobin. Pink-coloured substance, similar to haemoglobin of vertebrates.

Macronutrients. Generally present in plant tissues in concentration of 1 to 10 mg per gm of dry matter.

Mass flow hypothesis. Mass flow of ions through root tissue occurs as a result of transpirational pull in the absence of metabolic energy.

Micronutrients. Also known as trace elements, generally present in plant tissues in very small amounts, *i.e.*, equal to or less than 0.1 mg per gm of dry matter.

Mineral nutrition. The study of how plants obtain mineral elements, either through water, air or soil and utilise them for their growth and development.

Nitrification. Ammonia, first converts to nitrites and then to nitrates.

Passive absorption. Absorption of minerals by physical processes not involving direct expenditure of metabolic energy.

Reductive amination. In this process ammonia reacts with α-ketoglutaric acid and forms glutamic acid.

Transamination. Transfer of amino group from one amino acid to the keto group of keto acid. The enzyme responsible for such reaction is transaminase.

UNIT–2

BIOCHEMISTRY

Biochemistry. *The study of the chemistry of living organisms, especially the structure and function of their chemical components (principally proteins, carbohydrates, lipids, and nucleic acids). Biochemistry has advanced rapidly with the development, from the mid-20th century, of such techniques as chromatography, X-ray diffraction, radioisotopic labelling, and electron microscopy. Using these techniques to separate and analyse biologically important molecules, the steps of the metabolic pathways in which they are involved (e.g. glycolysis and the Krebs cycle) have been determined. This has provided some knowledge of how organisms obtain and store energy, how they manufacture and degrade their biomolecules, how they sense and respond to their environment, and how all this information is carried and expressed by their genetic material. Biochemistry forms an important part of many other disciplines, especially physiology, nutrition, and genetics, and its discoveries have made a profound impact in medicine, agriculture, industry, and many other areas of human activity.*

CHAPTER 3

Methods of Biochemical Analysis

1. Chromatography

The name chromatography was given by a Russian Botanist, *Michael Tswett*, in 1906 to a process in which the solution of green pigments was allowed to percolate down in a packed column of alumina or chalk inside a glass cylinder to give coloured bands, representing the different pigments present. By this method Tswett showed that the chlorophyll is made up of two pigments and it became more clear when petroleum ether was poured in the packed column. It was known as the *chromatogram*.

The concept of chromatography as given by *Tswett* was revised with advancement in technique. Now not only the solids, but liquids and the gases are also used to separate the pigments and other colourless compounds. A.F.P. Martin has described chromatography as the uniform percolation of a fluid through a column of more or less uniformly divided substance which selectively retards, by whatever means, certain components of a fluid. This may be defined as a technique in which the components of a mixture are caused to migrate at different rates through an apparatus which involves equilibration of compounds between a stationary and a mobile phase.

It, thus, involves separation of components in a fluid by causing the fluid, which is either a liquid solution or a mixture of vapours, to flow over a stationary phase which may be a pure solid powder as in adsorption chromatography, a porous gel or resin as in partition and ion-exchange chromatography, or may be a solid coated with a liquid as in gas chromatography.

Although the procedure is called chromatography as it was initially used to separate coloured substances, it is also applied to colourless substances that absorb ultraviolet light or fluorescein. They give a colour when treated chemically.

2. Kinds of Chromatography

In all the chromatographic techniques the phenomenon of adsorption or partition is involved. In adsorption, the binding of a compound to the surface of the solid phase (stationary phase) takes place, whereas in partition the relative solubility of a compound in two phases results in the partition of the compound in two phases. Thus, all types of chromatography known so far have been grouped in either of the two categories.

I.	Partition Chromatography.	1.	Partition column chromatography.	Liquid as mobile phase & solid as stationary phase.
		2.	Paper chromatography	
		3.	Thin layer chromatography.	
		4.	Gel filtration	
		5.	Gas liquid chromatography or vapour phase chromatography.	Gas as mobile & liquid as stationary phase.
II.	Adsorption Chromatography	1.	Adsorption column chromatography.	Organic solvent as mobile phase and some ionic polymer as stationary phase.
		2.	Thin layer chromatography.	
		3.	Ion-exchange chromatography.	

Flow chart of classification

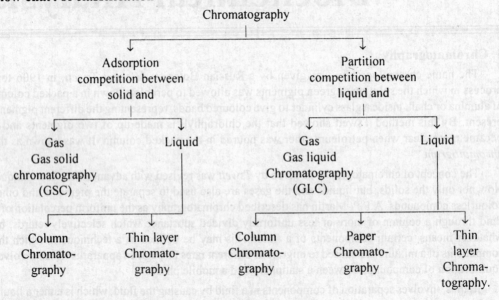

3. Outline steps in different kinds of chromatography

1. *Partition column Chromatography*

The column is packed with a porous solid of high surface area, *e.g.*, silica gel and cellulose which is coated with water (stationary phase). The components of a mixture are separated by passing an organic solvent (mobile phase) through the column.

2. *Paper Chromatography*

The dissolved substances are applied as a small spot on a cellulose bound filter paper which is then kept in a container dipped in an organic solvent. The mixtures are partitioned between paper (stationary) and organic solvent (mobile phase).

3. *Thin layer Chromatography*

The adsorbent (stationary phase) is spread over a glass plate in a thin film of even thickness. The solvent (mobile phase) moves up the plate by capillary action and thus affects separation.

4. *Ion-exchange Chromatography*

Ionized compounds are separated in aqueous solution (mobile phase) by virtue of their differences in affinity for ionized compounds which are an integral part of the insoluble solid phase (stationary phase).

5. *Gas liquid Chromatography*

A column is packed with a porous inert solid coated with a thin layer of an involatile liquid as the stationary phase. Components of a mixture are separated by being partitioned between this phase and a gaseous (mobile) phase.

6. *Adsorption Column Chromatography*

The separation of a mixture is determined by the differential adsorption of the components on an active solid like alumina, silica gel (stationary phase) when an organic solvent (mobile phase) containing them passes over and affects separation.

4. Chromatographic Methods of Popular Use

1. *Adsorption Column Chromatography*

It was the earliest method used in the history of chromatography where the phenomenon of adsorption was used in separating and identifying the unknown substances. The name column chromatography was given to it because column of materials were used for adsorption of different substances. By column chromatography the different coloured components of a mixture are separated and the separated components travel down the column at different rates. By changing receivers the different fractions are collected separately as they leave the bottom of the column. Colourless substances are frequently separated by collecting many small fractions in succession from the column, testing each fraction chemically or by other means, and combining all fractions containing single component.

The essential apparatus for a column chromatography consists of a tube with means for supporting the packed adsorbent and openings for the admission and collection of the mobile phase. The tube can be made up of any chemically resistant material. Usually it is made up of glass.

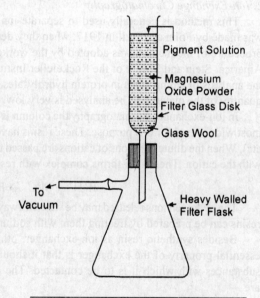

Fig. 3.1. Apparatus for the separation of pigments by column chromatography

The criteria for selecting an adsorbent are : (*a*) The adsorbent should be insoluble in the solvent used, and (*b*) It should not react chemically either with the solute or with the solvent. Deutz (1951) has described the physical properties of more than 100 compounds which can be used as adsorbents. Sometimes, inert solid diluents are mixed to improve the adsorbing capacity of the substance used. The purified diatomous earth is frequently used as a filter and is commonly known as celite or supercell under trade name.

Various adsorbents which are in common use are usually inert compounds like charcoal, alumina, calcium carbonate, calcium phosphate, cellulose, glass kaolin (clay material), magnesium oxide, magnesium silicate, sucrose etc. Silicagel and kiesulguhr are most commonly used now-a-days. The individual adsorbent particles should be of uniform size and sufficiently hard for adsorption during the packing of the column. For these purposes, the adsorbents are finely divided before they are packed in the column.

During the selection of solvent, two things are kept in mind : (a) the solvent should be pure and stable, (b) the recovery of dissolved substance from it should be easy. The most common method of recovery is distillation. However, electrolytic and ion-exchange mechanisms have also been employed for this purpose. Petroleum ether, butanol, acetic acid, water, acetone, chloroform, benzene, phenol, ammonia and many other organic and inorganic solvents are used. Sometimes a mixture of two or more solvents are used in definite proportion in resolving a particular substance. In separating the photosynthetic products of *Scenedesmus*, for example, *Calvin* and *Benson* used the solvents phenol saturated with water and butanol, propionic acid and water. Similarly, in resolving gibberellin-like substances, a mixture of isopropanol: 7N ammonium hydroxide : Water (8 : 1 : 1 by volume) is usually employed. Acetone or organic compounds of this type are frequently used in the chromatography of plant pigments.

Adsorption chromatography is widely used in the separation of aminoacids, lipids, steroids, sugars and similar other compounds of relatively low molecular weight. Purines, pyrimidines and nucleic acids have also been resolved by this method.

2. Ion-Exchange Chromatography

This method is generally used to separate ionic substances. The first biochemical application was made by Folin and Bell in 1917, when they determined ammonia in urine. However, the actual procedure of the method was adopted by the workers in Plutonium projects in the United States of America. Stein and Moore of the Rockefeller Institute in New York have applied this technique for the analysis of amino acids in protein hydrolysates. Ion-exchange chromatography is used when the quantity of the material to be analysed is very low.

In ion-exchange chromatography the column is filled with any ion exchanger. A synthetic resin is most widely used for this purpose. These resins have one type of acidic ions (sulphonic or carboxylic etc). When the dilute solutions of cations are passed through this, the acidic group of resin is exchanged with the cation. The cation forms complex with resin and it can be recovered.

$$R'H^+ + MX^+ \rightarrow R'X^+ + H^+ + M.$$

The hydrogen ions released may be washed away with the distilled water. Similarly, anion exchange resins can be prepared by treating them with sodium hydroxide.

Besides synthetic resin as ion-exchanger, other chemicals are also used for this purpose. An essential property of the exchanger is that it should be an acid or base practically insoluble in the substances with which it is to be contacted. The other important categories of the ion-exchanger are —

1. Natural or artificial siliceous matter,
2. Sulphonated carbonaceous materials,
3. Synthetic polymers, and
4. Derivatives of cellulose.

Of these categories only (3) and (4) are of importance in the biochemical field. The synthetic polymers were first discovered by Adams and Halms of Chemicals Research Laboratory in England in 1934. These were prepared by the condensation or polymerisation of polyhydric phenols with formaldehyde, and their cation exchange properties are due to the presence of free phenolic groups.

Some other commercially used ion-exchangers are : Phenols with active-SO_3H, polystyrene with SO_3H, and polymethocrylic acid with-$COOH$.

The apparatus used for ion exchange chromatography is slightly different from column. A wider column is used for it. When cellulose paper is used as ion-exchanger, the apparatus is the same as in paper chromatography. When resin or other chemicals are used as ion-exchanger, the apparatus is similar to column chromatography.

The method of ion-exchange chromatography has been applied to a wide variety of compounds of biochemical importance, both synthetic as well as of natural importance. Certain ionic complexes have been discovered by Gabrielson and Samuelson (1953) for the separation of carbonyl compounds. Certain biologically important proteins were separated by *Heinrich, Dewey* and *Kidder* (1953) by this method. Separation of folic acid and its derivatives was accomplished by *Usdin* and *Porath* (1957). Vitamin thiamine and its esters were separated by *Siliprandi* and *Siliprandi* (1959).

Amino acids bearing an appropriate charge can be deposited on the column of the proper type of resin by an exchange reaction with the functional groups of resin, while other amino acids pass through the column. The deposited amino acids can then be displaced from the column by using strong solutions of the proper acids or bases.

3. *Partition Chromatography*

For this chromatography, credit goes to two British scientists *Martin* and *Synge*, who in the year 1941 originally described their method as liquid-liquid chromatography. They considered that basic mechanism of separation of solutes is their separation between two immiscible liquids. The term 'partition chromatography' was suggested later by *Lester Smith*. In actual procedure the material to be analysed or separated is distributed between two immiscible liquids.

In partition chromatography, the stationary phase consists of a gel which can be penetrated by diffusion. In partition chromatography the gel is saturated with water or another solvent, so acting as a stationary water phase and the separation of components put on the column is mainly due to a partition between the flowing solvent and the stationary solvent.

Theory : Every compound capable of being analysed chromatographically possesses a definite speed of migration in a definite solvent. Thus, long chain amino acids migrate more rapidly than glycols, monosaccharides quicker than disaccharides, aglycons faster than glycosides. A substance, thus, can be characterized by the speed at which it migrates.

Rf Value : Position of a substance on a chromatograph is characterized by its Rf value (flow ratio) which is the measure of the velocity of migration of the substance. Rf value is defined as the quotient or ratio of the distance of the solute divided by the distance of the solvent from the starting point.

$$Rf = \frac{\text{Distance of the solute from starting point}}{\text{Distance of the solvent from starting point}}$$

It is important to note that the Rf value of a solute is always less than one.

4. *Paper Chromatography*

In paper chromatography separation is carried out on strips of paper which correspond to the chromatographic column of Tswett. Many grades of filter papers are used in paper chromatography, but the most widely used have been those manufactured by Whatman, Schleicher and Shull, and D. Arches. Papers woven from glass fibres or from synthetic materials such as nylon, orlon or teflon have also been manufactured for special purposes. Paper impregnated with inorganic adsorbents such as alumina or silicic acid was at one time advocated for the separation of some substances like vitamins, steroids and derivatives of ketones.

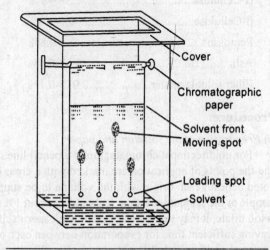

Fig. 3.2. Demonstration of ascending paper chromatography.

Whatman No. 1 is the standard slow running paper. The apparatus used is a cylindrical jar or cubical specimen jar.

Solvents used are mostly immiscible with water or partially miscible. It should be preferably of low vapour pressure. As a rule, previous purification of solvents is more necessary. Phenol, butanol, butanol mixture or a wide variety of organic acids and alcohols are used as solvent. Alcohols, pyridines, carboxylic acids, acetone and tetrahydrofuran are the solvents which are miscible with water. These compounds when employed for the purpose must contain small quantities of water, otherwise they do not migrate at all. Rf values of these substances depend on high degree of the water content. The paper chromatography may be :

1. Vertical (a) Ascending,
              (b) Descending
2. Horizontal
3. Circular

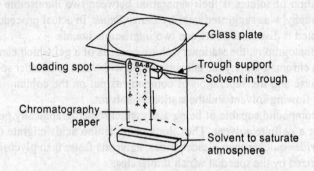

Fig. 3.3. Demonstration of descending chromatography.

For good separation of components of a mixture, now-a-days *bidimensional* (or bidirectional) paper chromatography is most widely used. In this technique, after development of the chromatogram with a solvent in one direction the paper is dried, turned right angles (90°) and the process of development is repeated with another solvent.

Chemical composition of *Whatman filter paper no. 1*

α-Cellulose...............................98-99%

β-Cellulose................................ 0.3-1.0%

Pentosans.................................... 0.4-0.8%

Ash... 0.07-0.1%

Ether soluble matter...................0.015-0.1%

Procedure:

(i) Preparation of the solution and paper

For unidirectional chromatography a pencil line is drawn about 2.5 cm up from the lower edge and the points of application are marked with a cross or dot. The name and code of each solution is noted beneath each origin with the volume to be supplied. Spotting solution is either the unknown sample or the standard solution. It should be about 1% with respect to each component. If the solution is too dilute, it may be concentrated on the paper itself by applying several spots at regular intervals leaving sufficient time for evaporation between each application. In water soluble compounds some preservative like alcohol is mixed with the aqueous solution.

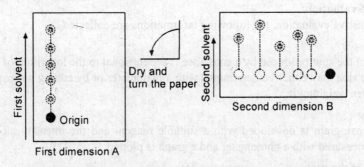

Fig. 3.4. Representation of two-dimensional chromatographs.

(ii) Spotting

Spotting is done either by a platinum loop or by a micropipette. In spotting the aqueous solutions, a platinum loop of about 2-3 mm in diameter is used. The advantage of this method is that the wire can be cleaned by placing it over the flame for a few seconds. For volatile substances graduated micropipettes are used. The pipettes used for taking blood samples are well suited for this purpose. Melting point tubes with their ends cut off are also of limited use. After some little practice drops may also be applied with a glass-rod. However, there is always a danger of applying too much of solution.

(iii) Running of the Chromatogram

After applying the spot it is dried and then the paper is suspended in the chromatographic chamber for several hours, so that the solvent may travel up to maximum distance. When the solvent front has reached the end of the paper strip, this is cautiously raised up out of the trough and the front is marked.

(iv) Drying of the paper

The chromatogram is hung up on a washing line or clamped in an adjusting drying frame. According to the nature of the solvent, it is either dried in the air at room temperature or placed horizontally in a drying oven. Drying may also be accomplished with a drier which is the best method for preventing damage to the paper.

(v) Developing

If the spots on the chromatogram are not visible, it is necessary to develop them by treating with some suitable reagent. The reagent is either sprayed over or the chromatogram is dipped in that. A few spots are rendered visible by exposing them to gases or vapours. For example, the spots of the fats are seen when the chromatographic paper is exposed to iodine vapours. Amino acids are visible after treating with ninhydrin solution and sugars with $KMnO_4$ or benzidine solution.

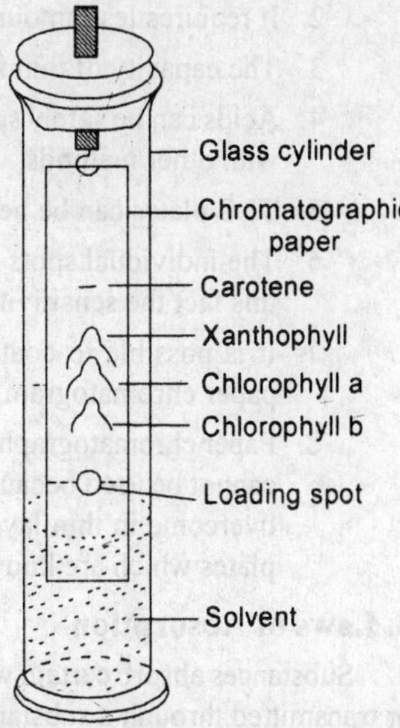

(vi) Evaluation of Results

Qualitative Evaluation:

Fig. 3.5. Demonstration of separation of plant pigments by paper chromatography.

Pencil circles are drawn around the spots on the completed chromatogram. The centres of the spots are marked and distances from centre point to starting point are measured off. Division of these lengths by the distance of starting point to solvent front gives Rf values.

Quantitative Evaluation:

For quantitative evaluation, the following informations are collected :

(*a*) *Size of the spot*

The area of the spot produced by a substance is proportional to the logarithm of the quantity of the solute. The area may either be determined with a planimeter or by cutting out paper covered by the spot and then weighing it.

(*b*) *Photometry*

The chromatogram is developed with a suitable reagent and the intensity along the strip is subsequently measured with a photometer and a graph is plotted.

(*c*) *Extraction of the spots*

After locating the spots on the chromatogram, the respective portions are cut off and the solute to be estimated is eluted. It is then estimated by a suitable micromethod.

5. *Thin layer chromatography*

Thin layer chromatography (TLC) was introduced recently by *Izmailov* and *Williams*. They achieved some success with adsorbents plated out on a glass surface, rather than packed in the column. In this chromatography a glass plate coated with an adsorbent is used as a substitute of paper. A slurry of adsorbent and a binder (usually silicagel and plaster of Paris) is spread evenly on a glass plate and is dried in a hot air oven at about 105°C for 30 minutes to activate the silicagel.

Spotting, running, drying, developing and evaluation of the results are done in the same way as in paper chromatography.

TLC is considered far superior to paper chromatography and column chromatography because of the following specific reasons :

1. In TLC the separation is sharpest as compared to other two methods.

2. It requires less amount of the substances (0.4 mg) and less time (15-50 minutes).

3. The capacity of thin layer of an adsorbent is higher than that of paper.

4. Acids can be safely sprayed on TLC plates for identification purpose which is not possible with other methods.

5. TLC plates can be heated to higher temperatures without causing any damage.

6. The individual spots are less diffused as compared to paper chromatography. Because of this fact the sensitivity of detection is increased several times.

7. It is possible to coat the plates with a variety of corrosive reagents that would destroy paper chromatogram.

8. Paper chromatography is limited only to cellulose and other media, as alumina and silicagel cannot be used because they cannot be made into suitable sheets. But this difficulty can be overcome in thin layer chromatography where thin layers of these substances are put on plates which are known as **chromatoplates.**

5. Laws of Absorption

Substances absorb certain wavelengths of visible light and emit the rest. The light that is reflected or transmitted through a substance imparts colour to that substance. The intensity of the transmitted light may be compared with that of a standard. The amount of light absorbed differs with the concentration of the substance. The mathematical relationship between absorption of light and concentration of the substance is provided by the following fundamental laws :

Beer's law

Beer's law states that **the amount of light absorbed is directly proportional to the concentration of the solute in solution.**

Suppose, the solution of 'C' concentration is filled in a vessel and I_0 and I_t are the initial and transmitted light intensities respectively (Fig. 3.6).

The fraction of light transmitted will be I_t/I_0. In general it will be less than I_0, whenever the concentration of the absorber is greater than zero. The amount of light transmitted (I_t/I_0) is related to the concentration and length of the substance. According to the general equation -

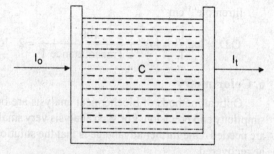

Fig. 3.6. Transmittance of light through the solution.

$$I_t/I_0 = a\ b\ c$$

where, **a** is the absorptivity or absorbance of the sample,

b is the length of the light through the solution *i.e.*, the thickness of sample, and

c is the concentration of the sample.

Or

$A = a\ b\ c$ (where 'A' is the absorbance of the solution).

Mostly, '**a**' '**b**' are constant *i.e.*, '**A**' is directly proportional to the concentration of the substance. This is simply Beer's law. If we plot a graph between '**A**' and '**c**', we get a linear line but if the concentrations are very high, linear relationship is not obtained. Some of the solutions do not obey Beer's law due to following reasons :

1. In concentrated solutions, physical and chemical changes in the solute particles may occur which may further cause interaction between solute and solvent molecules.

2. The temperature of the absorbing substances may change the absorbance.

3. Extraneous materials may affect the absorbance of the solution. For example, large molecules may cause an excessive amount of light scattering.

4. Instrumental difficulties may also lead to change in Beer's law.

The abovementioned reasons may be invalidated to some extent if the following precautions are taken :

a. Monochromatic light is used,

b. The system is made up of randomly oriented molecular or atomic alcohols.

2. Lambert's law

This law states that **when a monochromatic light passes through a solution of constant concentration, the light absorbed is directly proportional to the thickness of the solution.**

The combined *Lambert-Beer's* law can be expressed as :

$$\log I_0/I_t = K.\ C\ b$$

where, I_0 = Intensity of incident light

I_t = Intensity of emergent light

C = Concentration of solute in moles per litre

b = Length of light path in centimetres

K = molar extinction coefficient.

or $\text{Log } I_0/I_t = A$ or OD where A = absorbance of the medium

OD = optical density.

The constant K is referred to as the *molar extinction coefficient* only when the concentration is expressed in moles per litre and light path in centimetres. The constant has the dimensions :

litremole^{-1} cm^{-1}

$$O.D. = \log \frac{I_o}{I_t} = \log \frac{100}{\% \text{ Transmittance T}} = 2^{-} \log T.$$

6. Colorimetry

Optical methods of biochemical analysis are better than other methods because of their speed, simplicity and precision. For such analysis very small amount of reagents and the biological materials are needed. One further advantage is that the solution listed often remains unchanged and thus it may he recovered.

Of the various optical methods of analysis, the colorimetric and spectrophotometric methods are most widely used in biological laboratories. In colorimetric analysis a comparison is made between the light transmitted through an unknown and a standard solution.

The term colorimeter refers either to an instrument which compares the light transmitted by an unknown and a standard solution or to an instrument capable of measuring directly the amount of light energy absorbed by a solution. The first type is known as a 'colour comparator' and the second type as a 'photometer'. Now, in practice colorimeters with a photocell galvanometer system are employed to measure the intensity of transmitted light. Such photometers are commonly called as 'photoelectric colorimeters'. Colorimeters with photoelectric cell are more sensitive than visual colorimeters.

Photoelectric colorimeters are designated in such a way that the length of the substance remains constant. For this purpose, there is an absorption cell with a fixed holder. Definite indicators are prescribed and transmittance (I_t/I_o) or percentage transmission $(I_t/I_o \times 100)$ is calculated. I_o is the initial intensity of light at the time of entering in the solution and I_t is the intensity of light after coming out of the solution or after transmittance. Optical density of the substance is log I_o/I_t. These values are calculated according to the colorimeter used. Absolute values of I_o and I_t are not calculated because first the apparatus is set with the solvent for 100% transmittance. On replacing the blank with the coloured sample, the fraction of the light absorbed or transmitted by the latter is obtained.

By colorimetric analysis only coloured substances or those colourless substances which are capable of producing colour after reacting with suitable reagents, are analysed. The solutions to be analysed should have the following characteristics:

1. The colour of the solution should be sufficiently intense and should not fade rapidly.
2. There should be no effect of temperature and pH on the colour of the solution.
3. The reacting reagent with colourless solution should not itself be coloured to show light absorption.

7. Spectrophotometry

The basic principles of spectrophotometry are the same as for colorimetry. In spectrophotometer the spectrum of the coloured substance is analysed. Sometimes, the substances are not coloured but their spectrum differs from that of pure water or pure sample. The spectrophotometry shows the following advantages:

   a. Increased sensitivity,
   b. Increased spectral range,
   c. The presence of monochromatic light source,
   d. Narrowness of the spectral region,
   e. Determination of absorbancy even in very dilute solutions,
   f. Measuring absorption at ultraviolet and infrared regions, and
   g. In the determination of the absorption spectrum of the substance.

1. *Spectrophotometer*

Spectrophotometer (spectrometer and photometer) is an instrument which is used for measuring the distribution of energy in the different wavelengths of spectra. It is employed principally to supply a discrete narrow wavelength band of radiation from any portion of the spectrum. The range of spectrophotometer is from ultraviolet to infrared. It is equipped with phototubes, with some indicators to measure intensity of radiation emerging from the slit of the monochromator segment of the instrument.

In general, a spectrophotometer is made up of following essential parts :

1. A source of radiant energy, *e.g.*,
    a. Incandescent lamps,
    b. Hydrogen and Mercury discharge lamps,
    c. Globars, and
    d. Nernst glowers.

2. A monochromator, *i.e.*, a device for isolating monochromatic (homogeneous) or, more generally, narrow bands of radiant energy from the source.

3. Cell or holders for substances under investigation.

4. A device to receive and measure the radiant flux passing through or reflected from the substances under investigation. The different devices used are — (*a*) Photoemissive cells, (*b*) Gas-filled photoemissive cells, (*c*) Photomultipliers, (*d*) Barrier layer cells, (*e*) Thermocouples etc.

A typical instrument, the Beckman's Spectrophotometer, is outlined in Fig. 3.7.

Different types of spectrophotometers are available in the market. Some of them have additional absorption vessel compartments for maintaining a constant temperature, and devices that automatically record the optical density of a sample over the whole or part of the spectrum. This operation is referred to as "scanning". Some of these scanning devices can be set to repeat the operation at definite intervals of time. The degree to which the instrument can separate out individual wavelengths is called *resolution*.

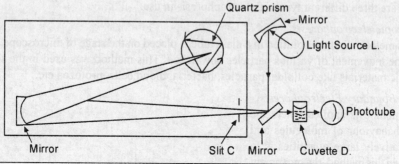

Fig. 3.7. Beckman's Spectrophotometer.

2. *Quantitative estimation*

Quantitative estimation of any solution by Spectrophotometer is done in the same way as by colorimeter. It can deliver radiation of a particular wavelength and then the optical density of a layer of solution containing an unknown concentration of a substance which absorbs this wavelength is compared with optical density of a layer of the same thickness of a solution containing a known concentration of the same substance (standard).

$$\text{Conc. of unknown substance} = \frac{\text{Conc. of standard}}{\text{Optical density of standard}} \times \text{Optical density of unknown substance}$$

This equation applies only when the system meets the requirements of Beer's law.

3. *Applications*

1. Spectrophotometer is used in determining the concentration of the absorbing substances.
2. pH of any solution can be determined.
3. It is used in the determination of ionization constant of weak acids and bases.
4. The dissociation of complex ions may be obtained.
5. Ultraviolet spectrophotometry is most widely used in the detection of nucleic acids and proteins. Both have characteristic absorption bands in the ultraviolet region (2000Å—3300Å).
6. Infrared spectroscopy was used in the determination of α-helical structure of proteins (*Ambrose* and *Elliott*, 1950).
7. Various chemical bonds in complex molecules can be determined. This has led to the finding that the ⟩NH and C = O bonds in folded protein molecules lie along the axis of the folded molecule from which followed the elucidation of the α-helical structure of proteins.
8. The progress of many metabolic reactions, particularly those of an oxidative nature, is frequently determined. This utilizes the fact that the most cofactors of biological oxidation have different absorption spectra in the reduced and oxidized state.
9. With the help of spectrophotometer gases, liquids and solids can be measured.
10. Reaction rates of reactions involving at least one component are determined by spectrophotometer.

8. Electrophoresis

This is an important method for the separation of proteins and amino acids. It was developed by *Tiselius* in 1937. The principle of this method is based on the fact that the separation takes place only of charged particles at a given pH in an electric field towards cathode and anode. The electric potential here is the driving force.

There are three different types of electrophoresis in use.

1. *Microscopic electrophoresis.*

In this method, first the solution in a glass tube is placed on the stage of microscope horizontally and then the movement of various particles is watched. This method was used in the separation of microscopic materials like colloidal particles, bacteria, blood cells, protozoa etc.

2. *Moving Boundary Electrophoresis*

This method is applied where the electrical behaviour of molecules and ions in relatively large quantities is to be studied. In this method, the movement of the boundary of a mass of particles is measured. The apparatus is simply made up of U-tube. It is first filled with the substance which is to be studied and then the rest is filled with a buffer solution. Lastly, a positive and a negative electrode is introduced into the two different arms of the U-tube and the current is passed. As a result of passing of the current, the boundary moves towards the positive or negative electrode depending upon the particles of the material in study.

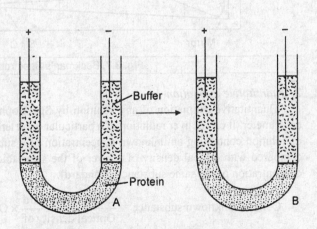

Fig. 3.8. Demonstration of moving boundary electrophoresis.

3. *Zone Electrophoresis*

This method is similar to that of paper chromatography and column chromatography. Here, the movement of the particle takes place on a solid medium or paper. After electrophoresis, the individual constituents occupy definite bands or zones as in chromatography. Zone electrophoresis is also known as *paper electrophoresis or ionography.*

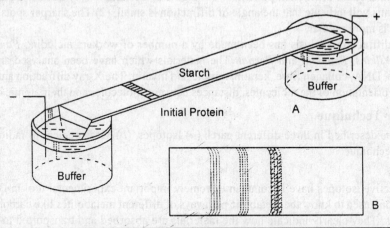

Fig. 3.9. Demonstration of zone electrophoresis.

The whole process consists of different steps. At first, a narrow strip of about 3-4 cm in width of Whatman paper No. 1 is cut and in the middle of it a drop or a narrow zone of the sample mixture is applied with the help of an applicator and hair drier. Now, it is moistened in the electrolyte and is kept in the electrophoretic chamber containing the buffer solution in such a manner that both the ends are dipped in it. An electric current is now passed through the electrodes for the separation of different constituents of the sample mixture. After some time the chromatogram is developed by the same technique as in paper chromatography. The chamber is covered so as to check evaporation of the solvent.

9. Centrifugation and Ultracentrifugation

Centrifugation is the process employed for the separation of the different cell organelles to a high degree of purity. The centrifuge is an instrument to produce high gravitational field. Here, the samples are rotated horizontally around the central axis to produce centrifugal force. In recent years ordinary centrifuges have been replaced by ultracentrifuges which have very high revolutions per minute. The development of the ultracentrifuge was the work of Swede *Svedberg,* after whom the unit of sedimentation (S = Svedberg) is named. The Svedberg unit is defined as the velocity of the sedimenting molecule per unit of gravitational field or 1×10^{-13}cm/sec/dyne/g. Typical S values calculated for cytochrome-C and Tobacco mosaic virus are 183 and 185 respectively.

Ultracentrifuge equipped with an optical device to observe exactly how fast the molecules sediment is extremely valuable in obtaining data on the molecular weight of protein and establishing the concept that proteins are of discrete molecular weights and shapes. This work has revealed that sizes of proteins vary greatly, with a continuous range in weights between the extremes of approximately 10,000 and 1,000,000. Ultracentrifuge also facilitates in isolation, localization and characterization of enzymes. Ultracentrifuges are used further in the isolation of viruses, ribosomes, nucleic acids and in the determination of molecular weight of nucleic acids.

10. X-Ray diffraction

This technique is based on the diffraction of radiations when they counter small obstacles. If a ray of white light impinges upon a diffraction grating that has 1000 lines per millimeter, it will be diffracted and will show the various bands of spectrum.

To record the diffraction pattern of the material to be analysed, a beam of collimated X-rays is passed through the material and a photographic plate is placed beyond this. On the plate a series of concentric spots or bands appear due to interference between the different diffracted rays. The distance between these spots and the centre of the pattern depends upon the spaces between the regularly repeating units. From diffraction pattern, two things may be clear — (1) Greater distance between repeating units will indicate that the angle of diffraction is small, (2) The sharper spots indicate that the spacing is more regular.

X-ray diffraction analysis has been made by a number of workers including *Pauling*, *Perutz*, *Kendrew*, *Wilkins*, *Franklin* and *Bernal*. The materials which have been analysed are crystals of hemoglobin, DNA, collagen fibre, keratin, muscle and myelin. The X-ray diffraction analysis throws light on the orientation of the molecules, distances between molecules and their atomic organization.

11. Tracer Technique

It can be described in three different parts: (*a*) Isotopes, (*b*) Measurement of radioactivity, and (*c*) Tracer technique.

(*a*) *Isotopes*

Radioactive isotopes have become an extremely important experimental tool in Biochemistry. They are being used to know the metabolic pathways of different metabolites like carbohydrates, fats and proteins. They clearly indicate how the materials are absorbed and transported to the different parts in living beings.

An atom consists of a dense nucleus which contains two types of particles : *Protons* and *neutrons*. Protons are positively charged, while the neutrons have no charge (neutral). Around the nucleus, revolve small negatively charged bodies known as *electrons*. The protons are very large in comparison to electrons, about 1836 times more in weight. Both are equal in number, and thereby create a condition of neutrality, *e.g.*, hydrogen has one of each. Neutrons have the weight about equal to that of protons, thus adding weight to the atom without altering its charge. Besides, they also play an important role in the stability of atom.

The atom contains a high amount of bond energy and when alteration in its neutron number takes place, an unstable condition arises in which the atom tends to split or give off particles or energy, thereby achieving stability. Such unstable atoms are known as *radioactive isotopes* or *radioisotopes*. The radioisotopes are defined as "the atoms of same element having different atomic weights, but the same atomic number," *e.g.*, the carbon atom usually has six protons and six neutrons in its nucleus and six electrons in the orbit around the nucleus. The carbon atom is called ^{12}C. Thus, it has its atomic number 6 and atomic weight 12. There is another form of carbon atom (radioisotopic form) which has 8 neutrons in place of normal 6 and has a weight of 14 rather than 12. Other known isotopes of carbon are ^{11}C (6P + 5n) and ^{13}C (6P + 7n).

Radioisotopes usually emit radiations (energy) in the form of X-rays, (β- or γ-rays. The movement of energy in either particles or wave form through the space is considered as *radiation*. The radiations are of many types. The radiations in the form of high energy atomic particles, which can transfer their kinetic energy to any matter through which they pass, is known as *particulate* or *Corpuscular radiation*. The radiations in the form of high energy short waves, which cause electric and magnetic disturbances affecting the internal structure of matter, is known as *electromagnetic radiation*. The treatment of plants or animals with radiations is called *irradiation*.

The common biologically important radioactive isotopes are ^{14}C, ^{11}C, ^{32}P, ^{35}S, which emit β-, γ- or X-rays. The radioactive isotopes move in transpiration stream as ions of these elements, but being unstable, transmutate to other elements (^{32}P to S; ^{35}S to Cl; ^{11}C to B etc.) when β-particles are emitted. This process is called *transmutation* and it is due to the fact that on emission conversion of a proton to a neutron takes place.

The complete life span of many isotopes is not definite, but half life is definite. Within a certain time period half of the atoms of the unstable isotope will disintegrate. This time period is known as the half-life of an isotope. The half lives vary from a few seconds to several thousand years. Table 3.1 shows the properties of some biologically important radioactive isotopes.

TABLE 3.1

S.No.	Name of isotope	Atomic number	Atomic weight	Half-life	Nature of radiation
1.	Carbon	6	^{11}C	20.35 minutes	β-rays
2.	Carbon	6	^{14}C	5568 years	β-rays
3.	Chlorine	17	^{36}Cl	308,000 years	β-rays
4.	Cobalt	27	^{60}Co	5.27 years	β-, γ-rays
5.	Hydrogen	1	^{3}H	12.46 years	β-rays
6.	Iron	26	^{55}Fe	2-7 years	β-rays
7.	Magnesium	12	^{28}Mg	21.4 hours	β-, γ-rays
8.	Molybdenum	42	^{93}Mo	67 hours	β-rays
9.	Phosphorus	15	^{32}P & ^{33}P	14.5 & 25.4 days	β-rays
10.	Potassium	19	^{42}K	12.4 hours	β-rays
11.	Sodium	11	^{22}Na	2.6 years	β-, γ-rays
12.	Sulphur	16	^{35}S	87.1 days	β-rays
13.	Zinc	30	^{66}Zn	250 days	β-rays

(b) Measurement of radioactivity

There are many methods for the measurement of radioactivity, but some of the important ones are described here.

1. *Geiger-Muller Counter (G-M tube)*

This is one of the most popular devices for measuring radioisotopes. The instrument is made up of two main parts — a *Geiger-Muller Tube* and a *recording device* (Scaler). The G-M tube is simple and is filled up with helium and ethanol. It contains two electrodes. One electrode is the tube itself, while the other electrode is a large, round and fine wire stretched in the centre. The fine wire electrode is maintained at a high potential (1000-2500 V) with respect to the second tube electrode. The open end of the tube is covered with a thin window of mica or plastic, which is filled up with helium and ethanol. The radioactive material, which is to be measured, is kept beneath this mica window. The radioactive material emits radiations into the tube and the radioactive particles then ionise the gas molecules of helium with the release of free electrons. These free electrons are attracted towards the positive electrode and thus a mild current is established, which can be measured by suitable electric counter (scaler). The result is referred as ionizations or counts per minute.

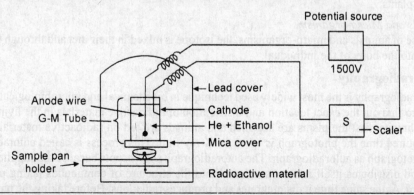

Fig. 3.10. Schematic diagram of Geiger-Muller tube & scaler (Geiger-Muller counter).

2. *Mass spectroscope*

This instrument is applied to determine isotopic contents of electromagnetic field. In this method, the substances to be measured are first changed into gases and then the separation of different isotopes is done by means of an ion collector present in the spectroscope, in which the quantity of any particular ion can be estimated by an amount of electric current generated in the collector. The results obtained are calculated in either of the two ways :

   (a) It is calculated as the ratio of one isotope to the other. For example, C^{12}/C^{11} in air is 0.011%.

   (b) It is calculated on the basis of percentage composition as the oxygen in air.

C. *Tracer Technique*

Any element which is a constituent of plant or animal body can be used as a tracer-atom Usually radioactive isotopes (^{18}O ^{11}C ^{13}C ^{14}C ^{33}S ^{34}S ^{35}S, ^{32}P) are used as tracers in biochemistry. The compounds containing these radioactive isotopes in their molecular structure are said to be labelled. The different tracer atoms, which have been used in finding out the biochemical reactions, are Deuterium, Tritium, ^{14}C, ^{15}N, ^{18}O, ^{32}P. Deuterium and tritium isotopes of hydrogen are given as water. ^{15}N isotope of nitrogen has been used as $^{15}NO_3$ or $^{15}NH_4$ in nitrogen metabolism. Similarly, ^{14}C has been used as $^{14}CO_2$ gas to trace its role in photosynthesis and fat metabolism.

The isotopes are applied to the plants or fed to the animals for a required time. The material (plant or animal) is then killed to stop further biochemical reactions. The labelled compounds are then isolated from the tissues and identified by chromatographic or other chemical methods. Their radioactivity is measured by any of the above methods. The ultimate result can be represented by one of the following three ways :

   (a) Total isotopic content.

   (b) Specific isotopic content (cpm/mg of the substance).

   (c) Distribution of the isotope within the molecule of the compound itself.

Application of radioactive materials

There are different methods of application of radioactive materials in plants and animals.

In Plants. In plants, various parts like roots, leaves, flowers and seeds are treated with the solution of required concentration containing the radioisotopes or stable isotopes. In case of root-application, they are dipped directly into the solution, from where the solution ascends through the roots to the various other organs. In case of foliar application, a drop of the isotope is applied to the lower or upper surface of the leaf and is allowed to be absorbed for a specific period of time. In case of flower treatment, the cotton moistened with isotopic solution is used. It is directly put at the tip of inflorescence. In seed treatment, they are first soaked in the solution and then grown in the laboratory conditions: All these treatments indicate that the isotope should be present in the solution or liquid form. Sometimes gaseous forms of the isotopes are also applied as in case of photosynthesis where labelled $^{14}CO_2$ is fed to the plants.

In Animals and Micro-organisms

In case of animals and micro-organisms, the isotope is mixed in their diet and through the mouth it enters into the body of the individual.

12. Autoradiography

Autoradiography is the most widely used technique in biochemical and microbiological research. It is used to find out the exact location and distribution of radioactive materials in the living tissues. In this technique, first the plants are supplied and animals are fed on radioactive material and then after a required time the photograph is taken on X-ray film. This process is called autoradiography and the photograph as autoradiograph. The autoradiograph shows spots because the supplied isotope reaches and distributes itself in the tissues and into the structure of compounds taking part in the metabolism. At the same time it disintegrates and produces radiations. Before taking the photograph, the tissue is killed and dried between two hot copper plates.

CHAPTER 4

Biochemistry: Laboratory Exercises

FERMENTATION

EXERCISE 1

Object : Demonstration of "Alcoholic Fermentation" by yeast cells.

Requirements : Kuhne's fermentation tube, glucose or sucrose solution (10% aqueous solution), yeast power (Baker's yeast), beaker, etc.

Experiment : Take some glucose solution in beaker and add 1 gm. yeast powder to it. Now fill the Kuhne's fermentation tube with this solution. The half of the bulb and complete vertical tube is filled with the solution. The open end of the bulb is plugged with some cotton.

Observation : There is a consequent fall in the level of solution in vertical tube.

Explanation : The gas produced in vertical tube is proved to be CO_2 with the help of caustic potash. At the same time ethyl alcohol is also liberated :

$$C_{12}H_{22}O_{12} \xrightarrow{\text{yeast Invertase}} \underset{\text{Glucose}}{C_6H_{12}O_6} + \underset{\text{Fructose}}{C_6H_{12}O_6}$$

$$C_6H_{12}O_6 \xrightarrow{\text{Fermentation}} 2C_2H_5OH + 2CO_2$$

Alcohol may also be tested 'by Iodoform test'.

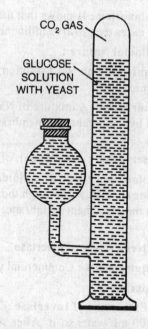

Fig. 4.1. *Kuhne's Fermentation tube*

ENZYMES

EXERCISE 2

Object : Demonstration of properties of enzyme : (*i*) specificity; (*ii*) thermolability and (*iii*) colloidal nature.

(i) Specific Nature (Specificity) :

Requirements : Test tubes, 1% starch solution, castor oil, diastase enzyme solution, Iodine, Sudan III, etc.

Experiment : Take 1 ml. of 1% starch solution in a test tube and in other tube 1 ml. of castor oil. Add 2 ml. of diastase enzyme solution to each test tube. After about 5 minutes add few drops of iodine solution to the starch solution and few drops of Sudan III to castor oil.

Observation : The former tube shows no test of starch while in the latter castor oil is turned red.

Explanation : In the test tube of starchy solution the diastase enzyme has hydrolysed this solution indicating that the diastase enzyme is specific for starch in action.

(ii) Sensitivity to heat (Thermolability) :

Requirements : Four test tubes, diastase enzyme solution, beaker, water, starch solution, Iodine, etc.

Experiment : Take four test tubes and pour diastase enzyme solution in each of it. The temperature for these four test tubes is quite different, i.e., 0°, 20°, 40° and 50°C respectively. Four beakers with water of 0°, 20°, 40° and 50°C temperature are used here to obtain the required condition. Add 10 c.c. of starch solution after some time. Now take few drops from each test tube and treat it with iodine solution.

Observation : Solution gives no colour at about 40°C.

Explanation : It shows that the rate of enzymatic reaction is optimum at this temperature. In other cases the positive iodine test is obtained.

(iii) Colloidal Nature :

Requirements : NaCl solution, enzyme solution, thistle funnel, beaker, $AgNO_3$, parchment membrane.

Experiment : A mixture of NaCl solution and enzyme solution is taken in a thistle funnel covered by the parchment membrane. Immerse it in a solution of starch. Test the filtrate with $AgNO_3$.

Observation : A white ppt. of AgCl is obtained here.

Explanation : Due to colloidal nature the enzyme molecules are large. Here only NaCl molecules are diffused through the parchment membrane, while the colloidal particles are held back on the parchment membrane.

EXERCISE 3

Object : Assay of invertase.

Requirements : Commercial yeast, distilled water, 3% sugar solution, Fehling's solution.

Experiment :

(i) Extraction of Invertase : Take 5 gm. of commercial yeast in a dish. Powder it and add about 100 ml. water to it. After some time filter the yeast in a beaker. The filtrate contains invertase in solution form.

(ii) Test : Take 3% sugar solution. Add 10 c.c. of each of the solutions in a test tube. Pour some Fehling's solution in this test tube.

Observation : No colour develops here. Put the enzyme sugar (sucrose) solution for an hour and test it again with Fehling's solution. Here red colour appears.

Explanation : Sucrose (sugar solution) is not a reducing agent so no change appears in the beginning. After some time (about an hour) it has broken down into reducing hexoses which give the test.

$$C_{12}H_{22}O_{12} \xrightarrow[\text{Enzyme}]{H_2O} C_6H_{12}O_6 + C_6H_{12}O_6$$

Sugar solution   Hexoses

Note : Assay is a test of biologically active substance which is done by a living material.

EXERCISE 4

Object : To prepare the enzymes from wheat or rice seeds.

Requirements : Rice or wheat seeds, water, mortar and pestle, centrifuge, phosphate buffer at pH 6.9, ice bucket, etc.

Method : Take rice or wheat seeds soaked and germinated for 0, 24 and 48 hours. Place 50 seeds in a mortar and pestle with a little bit of 10 ml. phosphate buffer at pH 6.9. Now grind seeds adding more fluid to extract thoroughly until 35 ml. has been added. Now this process may be repeated with each set of seeds (for 0, 24 and 48 hours). Allow the homogenate to stand approximately for 10 minutes in the ice bucket. After doing so, centrifuge the debris, starch grains and other major organelles at 15,000 g for 10 minutes. Use the supernatant as enzyme source.

ENZYMES

An **enzyme** is a specialized protein produced within an organism or cell which is capable of catalysing a specific chemical reaction. Since the enzyme acts as a catalyst, it is sometimes referred to as **biocatalyst.** A catalyst influences the rate of a chemical reaction, usually without undergoing any change itself. Thus, an enzyme differs from a normal catalyst. The enzyme may participate in a reaction by combining with the substrate. Ultimately, however, it is set free. The DNA in each cell has the necessary message (blueprint) for the production of all the enzymes required by it. The cell uses this information as and when necessary to produce the enzymes required to catalyse specific reactions at any point of time.

Enzymes are synthesised by living cells. But they retain their catalytic action even when extracted from cells. For example, Rennet tablets containing the enzyme rennin from the calf's stomach have long been used for coagulating milk protein to obtain casein (cheese from milk), for various uses, including the preparation of eatables.

Discovery of enzymes. The term enzyme was coined by **Kuhne** (1878) for catalytically active substances previously called **ferments.** Enzymes were discovered by accident. In 1897 a German chemist Edward Buchner was preparing yeast extract for medicinal purposes. The extracts he prepared invariably turned bad. He added some sugar to prevent spoilage. To his surprise the sugar fermented into alcohol. Pasteur had already demonstrated that living yeast cells promoted fermentation. Buchner discovered that living cells were not necessary but that yeast extract could bring about fermentation. The word **enzyme** was coined. It literally means '**in yeast**' but is now used as a general name for biocatalysts.

Definition. Mayrback (1952) defined 'enzymes are simple or compound proteins acting a specific catalysts'. They may also be defined as 'organic substances capable of catalysing chemical reactions in the living systems.'

However, enzymes speed up the rate of reaction without affecting the equilibrium. They exhibit a striking specificity to manifest themselves in their catalytic reactions, enhancing and controlling the course of these processes.

In **1878, Freidrich W. Kuhne** coined the word **enzyme** (Gk. *en + zyme* = in yeast), and replaced the older word 'ferment' by it.

NOMENCLATURE AND CLASSIFICATION OF ENZYMES

Enzymes were variously named in the past. Enzymes, such as ptyalin (salivary amylase). pepsin and trypsin give no indication of their action, while other enzymes such as amylase, sucrase, protease and lipase were named after the substrates on which they acted — amylose (starch), sucrose, protein and lipids respectively. Still others were named according to the source from which they were obtained — papain from papaya, bromelain from pineapple (of family Bromeliaceae). Some like DNA polymerase indicate its specific action, polymerisation. To facilitate scientific communication and to maintain uniformity, enzymes are now categorised and named by an **international code of enzyme nomenclature.**

The name of each enzyme ends with an **ase** and consists of two parts. The first part indicates its **substrates** and the second the reaction catalysed. For example, glutamate pyruvate transaminase transfers an amino group from the substrate glutamate to another substrate pyruvate.

Enzymes are grouped into *six* major classes :

Class 1. Oxireductases. These catalyse oxidation or reduction of their substrates and act by removing or adding electrons from or to substrates, *e.g.*, cytochrome oxidase oxidises cytochrome.

Class 2. Transferases. These transfer specific groups from one substrate to another. The chemical group transferred in the process is not in a free state, *e.g.*, glutamate pyruvate transaminase.

Class 3. Hydrolases. These break down large molecules into smaller ones by the introduction of water (hydrolysis) and breaking of specific covalent bonds. Most digestive enzymes belong to this category, *e.g.*, amylase which hydrolyses starch.

Class 4. Lyases. These catalyse the cleavage of specific covalent bonds and removal of groups without hydrolysis, *e.g.*, histidine decarboxylase cleaves C-C bond in histidine to form carbon dioxide and histamine.

Class 5. Isomerases. These catalyse the rearrangement of molecular structure to form isomeres, *e.g.*, phosphohexose isomerase changes glucose-6-phosphate to fructose-6-phosphate (both are hexose phosphates).

Class 6. Ligases. These catalyse covalent bonding of two substrates to form a large molecule. The energy for reaction is derived from the hydrolysis of ATP. Pyruvate carboxylase combines pyruvate and carbon dioxide to form oxaloacetate at the expense of ATP.

TERMS TO REMEMBER

Activation energy. An initial input of energy to start the reaction.

Active site. All enzymes have specific three-dimensional structure, a part of which is known as **active site** which serves as a 'lock' into which the reactant (substrate) fits in like a 'key'.

Allosteric enzymes. Where a modulator substance binds with a specific site of the enzyme different from its substrate binding site. This binding increases or decreases the enzyme action. Such enzymes are called allosteric enzymes.

Catalyst. A small amount of a substance that influences significantly the rate of a chemical reaction. The substance itself is not used up or changed at the end of reaction.

Catalysis. The phenomenon is called catalysis.

Coenzymes or Co-factors. Certain organic compounds and inorganic ions are required for enzyme activity ; they are loosely bound to the enzyme, such as NAD and FAD *(i.e.,* nucleotides of the vitamin nicotinamide and riboflavin).

Enzymes. Molecules synthesized by the cells; they are biological catalysts.

Feedback inhibition. Decline in enzyme activity by the allosteric effect of the product, *e.g.*, allosteric inhibition of hexokinase by glucose-6-phosphate.

Michaelis constant (K_m). Substrate concentration at which the reaction attains half its maximum velocity.

PLANT HORMONES

EXERCISE 5

Object : Demonstration of effect of auxin by *Avena* section test.

Requirements : Coleoptiles, distilled water, auxin solution, Petri dishes.

Experiment : Take some germinating *Avena* seedlings. Cut the coleoptiles, 25-30 mm. in length. Remove the tip of coleoptile and sections 3-5 mm. in length of each coleoptile. Put all the sections for an hour in distilled water and then transfer them into other petri dishes containing auxin solution. Remain the experiment as such for a day or two.

Observation : The length of each section, measured after some time, is found more than the previous one.

Explanation : This experiment explains the growth response of the solution which is found to be directly proportional to the logarithm of the concentration of auxin used.

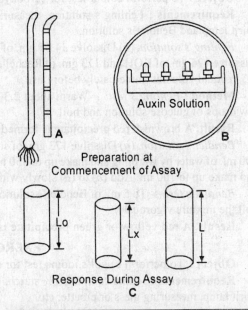

Auxin Solution

A   B

Preparation at
Commencement of Assay

Lo   Lx   L

Response During Assay
C

Fig. 4.2. *Avena Section Test.* LO = length of freshly cut segment. LX = Length of untreated segment after floating in water for length of test period ; L = length of treated segment after floating in test solution far length of test period.

EXERCISE 6

Object : Demonstration of effect of gibberellic acid GA_3 on elongation.

Requirements : Prepared aqueous solutions of GA_3 having 0.01, 0.1, 1.0, 10.0 and 1000.0 mg/ml, young plants of dwarf and tall varieties of peas, distilled water.

Experiment : Take ten dwarf variety plants and ten tall variety plants. Apply 1 ml. of a GA_3 solution to a young leaf of each of the plants. Do this application again after one week. Distilled water is applied as a control in separate plants. Measure the height of each daily for fifteen days.

Observation and Explanation : Each time there is a clear elongation in the plant height. The growth response in dwarf variety increases with the increase of concentration of GA_3.

EXERCISE 7

Object : Demonstration of effect of kinetin on senescence.

Requirements : Solutions of kinetin containing 0, 0.001, 0.01 and 100.0 mg./litre of hormone, mature fresh leaves of radish, sterile distilled water, petri dish, filter paper, etc.

Experiment : Take mature fresh leaves of radish plant and wash them with sterile distilled water. Keep them in petri dishes on moist filter paper. Apply 0.5 ml. of one of the kinetin solutions per leaf. Examine the leaves daily for a week.

Observation and Explanation : The leaves turn yellow after a week. This is due to disappearance of chlorophyll and degradation of proteins.

BIOCHEMISTRY : COLOUR TESTS

EXERCISE 8

Object : To perform colour test for carbohydrates (reducing sugars).

Requirements : Fehling's solution, measuring glass or pipette, test tubes, glucose solution, spirit lamp and Bendict's solution.

Fehling's solution. (a) Dissolve 34.65 gm. of $CuSO_4.5H_2O$ in water and make up to 500 ml. (b) Dissolve 125 gm. of KOH and 173 gm. of Rechelle salt in water and make up to 500 ml. Mix (a) and (b) in equal volumes immediately before use.

Method : *Fehling's test* — Warm about 2.3 ml. of Fehling's solution in a test tube and add a few drops of glucose solution and boil.

Result. A brownish red precipitate is formed on boiling.

Bendict's solution. (a) Dissolve 173 gm. of sodium citrate and 100 gm. of sodium carbonate in 800 ml. of water by warming and make up to 850 ml. (b) Dissolve 17.3 gm. of $CuSO_4.5H_2O$ in water and make up to 100 ml. Add (b) to (a) slowly with constant stirring.

Bendict's test — To 5 ml. of Bendict's solution add about 1—2 ml. of the glucose solution, and boil the mixture vigorously.

Result. A red yellow or green precipitate is formed.

EXERCISE 9

Object : To perform Lugol's iodine test for carbohydrates (non-reducing sugars).

Requirements : Iodine solution, 1% starch, conc. HCl, Na_2CO_3 or $NaHCO_3$, distilled water, spirit lamp, measuring glass or pipette, etc.

Iodine solution. Prepare a 2% solution of potassium iodide and add sufficient iodine to colour it a deep yellow.

1% Starch solution. Dissolve 1 gm. of soluble starch in 10 ml. of boiling distilled water and make up to 100 ml.

Method : Starch, sucrose and other non-reducing sugars can be tested by first of all hydrolysing them to yield the non-reducing sugars. The hydrolysis may be carried out by adding an equal volume of conc. HCl to the sugar solution and boiling the mixture for 5 minutes. The resulting solution after neutralisation with Na_2CO_3 or $NaHCO_3$ is then subjected to the test for reducing sugars.

Result : Starch or sucrose gives a blue-violet colour with iodine.

EXERCISE 10

Object : To perform colour test for lipids.

Requirements : Castor oil, Sudan III, test tube, measuring cylinder or pipette.

Sudan III. Dissolve 0.1 gm. (100 mg.) Sudan III in 50 ml of 95% ethyl alcohol and then stir 50 ml. of glycerol into the solution.

Method : To few ml. of castor oil add few drops of Sudan III.

Result : A red colouration is produced which shows the presence of lipids in castor oil.

EXERCISE 11

Object : To perform colour test for proteins.

Requirements : Protein solution, conc. HNO_3, spirit lamp, test tubes, alkali (NaOH, KOH, etc.), Biuret reagent, Millon's reagent, measuring flask or pipette, etc.

Proteins. Egg albumin solution - Egg albumin solution may be prepared by either of the following two methods :

(i) 1% solution of egg albumin crystals in water, or

(ii) beat egg white with 6-10 volumes of water, filter as the egg albumin solution.

Biuret reagent. (Welker's) (a) 1% $CuSO_4$ solution. (b) 40% NaOH solution.

Add few drops of (*a*) to (*b*) till a deep blue colour is obtained. The blue solution is the Biuret reagent.

Millon's reagent. (*a*) Digest 1 part by weight of mercury (Hg) with 2 parts by weight of conc. HNO_3. Dilute the digest with two volumes of water.

(*b*) 10% $HgSO_4$ in 10% H_2SO_4.

Method : The procedure for colour test is as follows :

1. *Biuret test.* To 2-3 ml. of protein solution add an equal volume of Biuret reagent. In a few minutes a violet colour is produced.

2. *Millon's test.* Take 5 ml. of the protein solution in a test tube. Add 2-3 drops of Millon's reagent in the test tube. Mix and boil the solution over a flame of spirit lamp. On doing so a precipitate forms which dissolves on further heating to yield a red solution.

3. *Xanthoproteic test.* To 2-3 ml. of protein solution add 1 ml. of conc. HNO_3. A white precipitate forms, which on heating turns yellow and dissolves to give a yellow solution. On addition of excess of alkali the colour deepens into orange.

CHLOROPHYLL : CHROMATOGRAPHY

EXERCISE 12

Object : Demonstration of separation of chlorophyll by paper chromatography.

Requirements : *Tecoma* leaves, mortar and pestle, acetone, petroleum ether, beaker, tube, etc.

Experiment : Take about 10 gm. of *Tecoma* leaves in a mortar and crush them by a pestle. Add about 12 to 15 ml. of acetone to it and filter in a beaker. This so obtained filtrate is being concentrated by heating. Take a paper strip and sketch a pencil line 2 cm. above the base of it. Point out the centre of it and pour the acetone filtrate on it drop by drop. The size of spot on the paper strip should be small. Now, add a few drops of petroleum ether in a separate tube and place the above paper strip in a vertical position in this tube. Close the tube tightly.

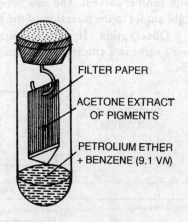

FILTER PAPER

ACETONE EXTRACT OF PIGMENTS

PETROLIUM ETHER + BENZENE (9.1 V/V)

Fig. 4.3. Paper chromatography, strip filter paper method

EXERCISE 13

Object : To separate the amino acids by means of paper chromatography.

Requirements : Paper strip (Whatman No. 1 filter paper), aqueous or alcoholic solution of amino acid, organic solvent, *i.e.*, alcohol, oven, ninhydrin, chromatography jar, etc.

Experiment : One-dimensional paper chromatography : Take a paper strip (Whatman No. 1 filter paper) and mark a pencil dot near the bottom of it. Now put a small drop of alc. or aqu. solution of amino acid on it. (The amino acid is obtained by grinding imbibed germinating seeds in 80% ethyl alcohol. It is filtered and the filtrate is dried. The dried solid is dissolved in few drops of distilled water.) Place this strip of filter paper in the chromatography jar so that the bottom of strip is being dipped into any one of following solvents.

Solvent	Ratio by Volume
(*i*) Alcohol : Water Ammonium hydroxide	80 : 20 : 1
Or	
(*ii*) Butanol : Acetic acid : water	4 : 1 : 1

(Mostly the (*i*) solvent is preferred for this experiment).

The solvent flows through the paper strip by capillary action passing over the amino acid drop. The amino acid having more solubility in the solvent than that of in water goes along with the solvent. Each amino acid travels a specified distance under the similar conditions. After a sufficient amount of time the paper strip is taken out and put in the oven. Spray this dried strip with ninhydrin that will produce a certain colour for a certain amino acid. Up to now the paper strip has attained some coloured spots and it is called as the Chromatograph.

Two-dimensional paper chromatography : It is done with two different solvents in order to separate the substances having the same Rf value. Turn the filter paper at 90° to the first plant and another rechromatograph is obtained with another solvent. The new solvent travels at right angles to the direction of the first one.

Observation : Here the partition coefficient or Rf value in a chromatograph may be obtained as :

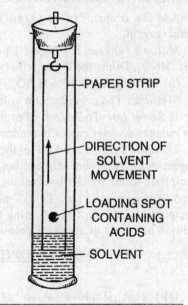

Fig. 4.4. Apparatus for one dimensional paper chromatography.

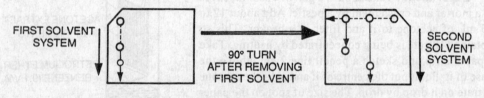

Fig. 4.5. Two-dimensional paper chromatography.

$$Rf = \frac{\text{Distance travelled by the compound from the origin}}{\text{Distance travelled by the solvent from the origin}}$$

EXERCISE 14

Object : To separate the amino acids by TLC (thin layer chromatography) method.

Requirements : Silica gel (Kieselgel G or H), distilled water, slides, oven, amino acids (glycine and aspartic acid), 80% phenol solvent, beakers, 0.1 per cent ninhydrin, capillarity pipette, atomiser, etc.

Method : Weigh 2 gm. of silica gel and put it in a test tube, filled with 10 ml. of distilled water. Stir the suspension. Now pour the suspension over 3 to 4 slides and allow the gel to set at least for 15 minutes. Activate the slides by heating them in an oven at 120°C for about 30 minutes. Thereafter take out the slides and allow them to cool. After this, repeat the procedure as mentioned in exercise 52. Make a scratch on the margin of slide, and dip the slide in beaker filled with 80 per cent phenol solvent.

This method is supposed to be better than the method given in exercise 52 (*i.e.*, of paper chromatography).

SAPONIFICATION NUMBER

Saponification : When fats are mixed intimately and heated with an alcoholic solution of strong alkali, such as sodium or potassium hydroxide, the glyceride molecules are split and the ultimate products are glycerol and sodium or potassium salts of the fatty acids. This process is known as soap producing or **saponification.**

Saponification Number : It is a number of milligrams of KOH required to saponify completely 1 gm. of fat.

EXERCISE 15

Object : To determine 'Saponification Number' of the given oil.

Requirements : Pipettes (2 of 5 ml. and one each of 25 and 50 ml.), burette (1), flasks (3), water bath (1), oil or fat, hydrochloric or sulphuric acid of known strength and 0.1% phenolphthalein and 0.5 N KOH (alcoholic).

Procedure : (*i*) Take two flasks.

(*ii*) In one flask take 50 ml. of alcoholic KOH and in the other pre-weighed flask take one ml. of the oil and add 51 ml. of alcoholic KOH of known strength.

(*iii*) Label both the flasks (*The first one will function as control*).

(*iv*) Boil for about half an hour on a water bath. After removing the flasks from water bath, let them be cool.

(*v*) To each flask add one ml. of 0.1% phenolphthalein. The colour of the solution becomes pink.

(*vi*) Titrate the solution of both the flasks with sulphuric or hydrochloric acid of known strength and note the reading.

(*vii*) Calculate the saponification number with the help of following formula :

$$Y = \frac{28(A-B)}{X}$$

where Y = Saponification number

A = Reading of control (volume of acid required for titration of KOH).

B = Reading of KOH and oil (volume of acid required for titration of KOH and oil)

X = Weight of oil

28 gm. KNH = 1 ml. 0.5N acid.

IODINE NUMBER

The iodine number is defined as the number of grams of iodine absorbed by 100 gm. of fat.

EXERCISE 16

Object : To determine the iodine number of the given oil.

Requirements : Burette (1), pipettes 25 ml. and 10 ml., conical flasks (4), fat or oil, pyridine sulphate dibromide reagent, 7.5% potassium iodide, 0.1N sodium thiosulphate, 0.5% starch suspension and chloroform.

Preparation of Stock Solution : A given amount of fat or oil is dissolved in a given amount of solvent, *e.g.* take 2 gms of oil or fat and dissolve it in 100 ml of chloroform. This will serve as stock solution for the determination of iodine number.

Preparation of Pyridine Sulphate Dibromide Reagent : This reagent is prepared by mixing 5.4 ml. of conc. H_2SO_4 with 20 ml. of glacial acetic acid (*Note that this is an exothermic reaction and will evolve heat. So be careful in pouring H_2SO_4 into acetic acid*). To this is added 8.1 ml. of pyridine dissolved in 20 ml. of glacial acetic acid. This solution is added very carefully to a solution of bromine (2.5 ml. of bromine in 20 c.c. of glacial acetic acid). The whole mixture is diluted with acetic acid to make 1 litre of reagent. This is then kept in well-stoppered bottle in a warm place where it will keep fit for a fortnight or so.

Preparation of 0.5% Starch Suspension : Dissolve 0.5 gm. of starch in 100 c.c. of distilled water. Boil it, and use when it is cool.

Procedure :

(*i*) Take 10 ml. of stock solution of fat or oil.

(*ii*) Add to this 25 ml. of pyridine sulphate dibromide reagent and wait for five minutes.

(*iii*) Determine the residual bromine by adding 10 ml. of pot. iodide solution. The equal amount of iodine will be liberated by residual bromine and can be determined by titration with 0.1N sod. thiosulphate.

(*iv*) 2 ml. of starch suspension is also added before titration. The starch will act as an indicator and a blue colour is obtained.

(*v*) On the other hand, a total amount of bromine is determined by titrating 25 ml. of pyridine sulphate dibromide reagent against 0.1N sodium thiosulphate solution.

(*vi*) Complete disappearance of blue colour will indicate the end point.

Calculations :

Suppose the volume of sodium thiosulphate required for total bromine added is 'O' ml.

The volume (sodium thiosulphate) required for residual bromine is 'P' ml.

So the volume of thiosulphate required = (O – P) ml.

Because 1 ml. of 0.1N sodium thiosulphate = 0.0127 gm. of iodine,

so (O – P) ml 0.1N sodium thiosulphate (= 0.0127 × (O – P) gm. of iodine.

Because 10 ml. of chloroform solution of fat requires = 0.0127 x (O-P) gm. of iodine,

so, 100 ml. chloroform solution of fat requires =0.0127 x (O-P) 10 gms. of iodine.

It indicates that 2 gm. of fat requires

= 0.0127 × (O – P) gm. of iodine.

So 100 gm. of fat requires

$$= \frac{0.127 \times (O - P) \times 100}{2}$$

So Iodine Number = 6.35 × (O – P).

If the reading of control = 13.2 c.c. and reading with fat = 3 c.c.,

so O – P =13.2 – 3 = 10.2 c.c.

Iodine Number = 6.35 × 10.2

= 65.405.

DETECTION OF Ca & P IN MILK

EXERCISE 17

Object : To detect Ca and P in milk and to determine the specific gravity of milk.

Requirements : Boiling tubes, small test tubes, beakers, spirit lamp, filter paper, funnel, lactometer, pH paper, acetic acid, nitric acid, ammonia, milk, ammonium molybdate and ammonium oxalate.

Principle : If the milk is treated with 1% acetic acid, Ca and P are filtered, and fat and casein remain on the filter paper.

So the first part of the experiment is the preparation of fat and protein-free filtrate which can be prepared in the following manner :

Take 10-15 ml. of milk in a boiling tube and add 1% acetic acid till a white precipitate appears. This white precipitate is due to casein and fat. Its pH can be tested by pH paper which comes to 4.6. Filter it with the help of filter paper and funnel. This filtrate contains Ca and P.

Test for Phosphate :

Procedure : Take about 5 ml. of casein and fat-free filtrate in a test tube and add about 1 ml. of HNO_3 (conc.) and 3 ml. of ammonium molybdate.

Result : Appearance of yellow colour or precipitate is due to phosphate.

Test for Calcium :

Procedure : (*i*) Take about 5 ml. of casein and fat-free filtrate.

(*ii*) Add little amount of ammonia to make it alkaline.

(*iii*) Now add ammonium oxalate.

Result : Appearance of white precipitate shows the presence of calcium in the milk.

Observations : Tabulate your observations and results in the form of following table :

S.No.	Experiment	Observations	Inference
(*i*)	In 10-15 ml. of milk add 1% acetic acid.	White ppt. is formed	
(*ii*)	Filter it and take this filtrate		
(*iii*)	In filtrate (5 ml.) add 1 ml. of HNO_3 (conc.) and 3 ml. of ammonium molybdate.	Yellow colour or ppt. is formed	Phosphate confirmed
(*iv*)	Take 5 ml. of filtrate and add few drops of ammonia and ammonium oxalate.	White ppt.	Calcium confirmed

Results: Milk contains Ca and P.

Specific Gravity : It can be determined by a simple apparatus of glass called lactometer. Lower conical part of this apparatus is filled with mercury. Due to the presence of mercury in the lower part, it floats in the liquids in a straight position. Upper part of lactometer consists of a straight tube containing a sort of scale.

ENZYMES

These are macromolecules of biological origin consisting largely of amino acids condensed via peptide bond, and are specific in altering the rates of reaction. In brief, enzymes can be defined as proteins with catalytic activities. So in their chemical and physical properties, enzymes resemble with proteins except their catalytic function.

Enzymes are very specific to their actions. There are enzymes which help in hydrolysis and are known as hydrolytic enzymes, like proteases, esterases, lipases, carbohydrases, phosphatases, etc. Oxidation reduction enzymes like oxydases, dehydrogenases; Transferring enzymes such as transphosphorylases, transaminases etc.; Carboxylation enzymes like decarboxylases, carboxylases; Isomerizing enzymes etc. Enzymes placed in one category does not directly affect the reactions catalyzed by enzymes from any other category, and thus showing their great specificity.

Any change in temperature characteristically changes the rates of all reactions, including those involving enzymes. Molecules of enzymes are large and colloidal in nature. Change in pH of enzyme systems also alter the rates of reactions.

EXERCISE 18

Object : To observe the specificity, thermolability and colloidal nature of enzymes.

Preparation of Amylase Enzyme Solution : Take one tablet of Taka diastase and dissolve it in 50 ml. of distilled water. The resulted solution is known as enzyme solution, and can be used for observing these properties.

Specificity

Requirements : Test tubes, starch, castor oil, enzyme solution, Sudan III, iodine.

Procedure : (*i*) Take two test tubes.

(*ii*) In one take 1 ml. of 1% starch solution and in the other 1 ml. of castor oil.

(*iii*) Add 2 ml. of enzyme solution in both the test tubes.

(*iv*) Keep both the test tubes for 5 minutes in test tube stand.

(*v*) In the test tube containing starch add few drops of iodine. But there is no test for starch, showing the fact that starch has been hydrolysed by the enzyme.

(*vi*) In the test tube containing castor oil add Sudan III. There is no change in the oil. It is because of the fact that the enzyme used is specific for starch.

Thermolability

Requirements : Test tubes, starch, spirit lamp and enzyme solution.

Procedure : (*i*) Take two test tubes.

(*ii*) Add 2 ml. of enzyme solution in both. To one test tube heat for few minutes.

(*iii*) Adding 1 ml. of starch solution to both (heated as well as unheated) test tubes will show the clear effect of temperature on the enzymes.

Colloidal Nature

Requirements : Enzyme solution, NaCl, thistle funnel, parchment membrane, starch.

Principle : Large colloidal particles of enzyme will settle on the parchment membrane and the NaCl will diffuse out.

Procedure : (*i*) Take a thistle funnel covered with parchment paper and put in it the enzyme solution containing NaCl.

(*ii*) Immerse it in a solution of starch. Observe after some time.

Large enzyme particles remain unable to diffuse through parchment membrane showing its colloidal nature.

UNIT-3

ECOLOGY

'Ecology is a study of the interactions among different kinds of organisms and between organisms and their physical environment.' The term ecology comes from the Greek word for house, **oikos.** Our planet Earth is the house in which all organisms reside. It is the house that contains all of the materials necessary to sustain life. Ecology is the study of related interactions of living organisms with one another and with nonliving aspects of their surroundings. The environment is the living and nonliving components surrounding an organism. Ecology includes the influence this environment has on the living things and how living things can, in turn, influence their environment. It is also the study of the flow of energy from the sun through the plants and the animals on Earth.

An understanding of ecology is important to us in two major ways. First, ecology provides the knowledge people must have to deal effectively with environmental considerations. Second, as living organisms, human beings affect and are affected by the environment. Whenever human beings make changes in the environment, they influence the relationships of all the living organisms within the environment. Changes can also affect the physical setting of the environment, such as air and water quality and the shape of the land.

Sometimes it is said that the knowledge of ecology comes from the study of **ecosystems.** The organization of an ecosystem starts with the **organism.** A group of the organisms of the same species living in a particular place at the same time is a **population.**

All populations of organisms that live together in a specific area and depend upon one another for food and shelter make up a **community.** Different types of environments support different populations. A desert community consists of populations of plants and animals different from those in a tropical rainforest.

Populations also interact with the nonliving components of the environment, such as water, heat, light, soil, air and the landforms of the area. The interactions of a community with the nonliving parts of its environment make up an **ecosystem.** Around the Earth similar ecosystems can be found where the environmental conditions are similar. Ecosystems can be grouped according to similarities in their most common plants. These groups of major ecosystems are called **biomes,** e.g., deserts, grasslands and rainforests.

When all of the biomes of the Earth are considered together, they make up the nonliving surface of the earth and the living organisms that inhabit it. These biomes, together with soil, minerals, water and atmosphere, are called the **biosphere.**

Density. The number of individuals of a species living in a particular area is the **density** of that population. Density is dependent upon many factors, such as the availability of food, water, light, heat, etc. You can find one thousand or more grass plants in a square metre of well-maintained lawn. In a semi-desert where water is limited, less than ten grass plants may be found per square metre. The study of population density and factors that limit it are important in ecology.

CHAPTER 5

Plant Ecology Exercises

EXERCISE 1

Object : To study the communities by 'Quadrat Method' by working out frequency, density and abundance.

The structure of a plant community can be studied in quantitative terms through vegetational analysis of small sample units dispersed widely. This may be done in small sample area by quadrat method. **Frequency, abundance** and **density** for different species can be worked out by the formulae given below :

Frequency. This is described as the % of Quadrats occupied by a given species.

$$\%F = \frac{\text{No of Quadrats in which it occurred}}{\text{Total No. of Quadrats studied}} \times 100$$

Density. This is described as the number of individuals per unit area.

$$D = \frac{\text{Total No. of individuals}}{\text{Total No. of Quadrats studied}}$$

Abundance. No. of individuals per quadrat of occurrence.

$$A = \frac{\text{Total No. of individuals}}{\text{No. of quadrats of occurrence}}$$

Plant species	No. of individuals Quadrat Number 1 2 3 4 5 6 7 8 9 10	Total No. of segments occurrence	Total No. of segments studied	Total No. of individuals	F	D	Abundance
A							
B							
C							
D							
E							
F							
G							
H							

(Size of the Quadrant = 50 cm. × 50 cm.)

Requirements : Quadrat (or four nails), metre scale, string, field notebook or data sheet.

Method. Lay a quadrat in the study area and record the name and number of individuals of a species occurring there. Lay another quadrat at random anywhere else and record the same data for it and so on. Minimum 10 quadrats should be taken for frequency, density and abundance. The data should be tabulated as given in the table on next page.

   Calculations. Calculate Frequency, Density and Abundance from the data by the above given formulae.

EXERCISE 2

Object : To study communities by quadrat method and to determine % Frequency, Density and Abundance.

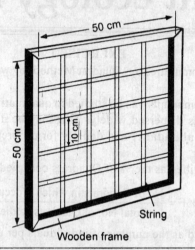

Fig. 5.1. A wooden quadrat of 50 × 50 cm.

Requirements : Metre scale, string, four nails or quadrat, notebook.

Principle : (*i*) *Frequency* : It is the number of sampling units or quadrats in which a given species occurs. Percentage frequency (%F) can be estimated by the following formula :

$$\% \text{ Frequency (F)} = \frac{\text{Number of quadrats in which the species occurred}}{\text{Total number of quadrats studied}} \times 100$$

(*ii*) *Density* : It is a number of individuals per unit area and can be calculated by the following formula :

$$\text{Density (D)} = \frac{\text{Total number of individuals}}{\text{Total number of quadrats studied}}$$

(*iii*) *Abundance* : It is described as number of individuals per quadrat of occurrence. Abundance for each species can be calculated by the following formula :

$$\text{Abundance (A)} = \frac{\text{Total number of individuals}}{\text{Number of quadrats of occurrence}}$$

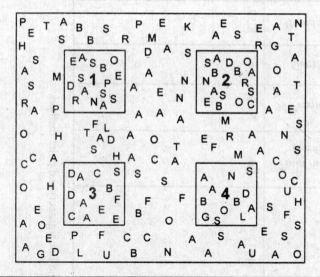

Fig. 5.2. Sketch of an artificial field showing four quadrats

Method : Lay a quadrat (Fig. 5.1) in the field or specific area to be studied. Note carefully the plants occurring there. Write the names and number of individuals of plant species in the notebook, which are present in the limits of your quadrat. Lay at random at least 10 quadrats (Fig. 5.2) in the same way and record your data in the form of Table 5.1.

In Table 5.1 % frequency, density and abundance of *Cyperus* have been determined. Readings of the other six plants, occurred in the quadrats studied, are also filled in the table. Calculate the frequency, density and abundance of these six plants for practice.

Results : Calculate the frequency, density and abundance of all the plant species with the help of the formulae given earlier and note the following results :

(1) In terms of % Frequency (F), the field is being dominated by.....

(2) In terms of Density (D), the field is being dominated by ......

(3) In terms of Abundance (A), the field is being dominated by ...

BIOMASS STUDY

What is Biomass ?

It is usually expressed as dry weight of all the living materials (plants as well as animals) in an area. Under biomass we include plants (their aboveground and underground parts) as well as animals.

Fallen leaves and twigs of the plants are also taken in consideration at the time of studying biomass. In the forests, the *humus* is in different stages of decomposition. The floor of the forest remains covered by organic matter which is slightly or not at all decomposed. This is called *litter*. A partially decomposed matter is present below this layer. It is called *duff*. Further decomposed matter, which has lost its original form, is present below duff and called *leaf mould.*

EXERCISE 3

Object : To determine the biomass of a particular area.

Requirements : Nails (4), metre scale, string, *khurpa* (a weeding instrument), polythene bags, oven.

Observations :

TABLE 5.1. Size of quadrat [+] [*] : 50 cm × 50 cm = 2500 cm^2

S.No.	Name of plant species	Number of individuals in quadrat number										Total number of quadrats of occurrence	Total number of quadrats studied	Total number of individuals	% Frequency (F)	Density (D)	Abundance (A)
		1	2	3	4	5	6	7	8	9	10						
1.	Cyperus	10	9	7	0	0	3	8	15	0	7	7	10	60	70%	6	8.57
2.	Cassia	0	0	2	0	3	0	5	0	6	10						
3.	Cynodon	50	0	7	41	6	0	0	8	0	5						
4.	Eclipta	0	0	4	0	3	0	0	0	0	2						
5.	A	0	0	0	0	2	0	0	1	3	0						
6.	B	5	10	0	0	0	1	3	0	0	2						
7.	C	3	5	0	0	2	8	8	0	2	0						

* The community structure can be studied by quadrat method, transect method (belt transect and line transect) and point method.
+ Various kinds of quadrats are list, count, chart, clip and permanent quadrats.

Method : 1. Make a quadrat in the field of the size of 50 cm × 50 cm by digging the nails and connecting them with the string. Weed out all the aboveground parts of the plants growing in that limit with the help of weeding instrument. Collect all of them in a polythene bag.

2. Collect the fallen leaves and other parts of the plants in the second polythene bag.

3. Collect all the animals such as ants, larvae, earthworms, insects, *etc.* in the third polythene bag.

4. By digging the soil to about 20 to 25 cm., take out all the underground parts of the plants and collect them in a separate bag after washing.

In the same way lay some more quadrats in the area under study and collect all the materials in polythene bags.

Calculations :

Suppose -

Dry weight of aboveground parts = 15 gm

Dry weight of underground parts = 4 gm

Dry weight of animals = 1 gm

∴ Total dry weight = 20 gm

50 × 50 cm field area contains = 20 gm total dry biomass.

∴ 100 × 100 cm field area will contain $= \dfrac{20 \times 100 \times 100}{50 \times 50} = 80$ gm

Result : 80 gm is the biomass of 100 × 100 cm. field area.

Results of Different Parts :

(i) 50 × 50 cm. field area contains 15 gm of aboveground parts.

∴ 100 × 100 cm. field area will contain $= \dfrac{15 \times 100 \times 100}{50 \times 50}$ gm = *60 gm biomass.*

(ii) 50 × 50 cm. field area contains 4 gm. of underground parts.

∴ 100 × 100 cm. field area will contain $= \dfrac{4 \times 100 \times 100}{50 \times 50}$ gm = *16 gm biomass.*

(iii) 50 × 50 cm. field area contains 1 gm of animals.

∴ 100 × 100 cm field area will contain $= \dfrac{1 \times 100 \times 100}{50 \times 50}$ gm = *4 gm biomass.*

Result : One square metre (100 × 100 cm.) field area contains 80 gm biomass in terms of dry weight of the total plant and animal parts.

CHAPTER 6

Ecological Anatomy

ECOLOGICAL ANATOMY

According to their habitat generally the plants are subdivided into three main groups, *i.e.*, (1) Mesophytes (2) Hydrophytes and (3) Xerophytes.

MESOPHYTES

The plants with thin leaf blades, having no special structures to protect them against excessive transpiration, and develop in regions of average water supply, are termed **mesophytes**.

HYDROPHYTES

The number of species of flowering plants, known as **hydrophytes**, live under extremes of water supply. The plants which are entirely submerged grow comparatively in deeper water. In submerged plants, the conducting and mechanical tissues are very poorly developed. As they float in the water, they do not need mechanical tissue to strengthen their body, and as they do not transpire, there is no need of water conducting tissue. The plants with floating leaves possess conspicuous air spaces. These air spaces serve as an aerating system of the plant and also give them buoyancy to float. The characteristic anatomical features of the hydrophytes are as follows.

Epidermis. In aquatic plants, the epidermis does not serve the purpose of protection but it absorbs nutrients and gases directly from the water. Usually the chloroplasts are found in epidermal cells of the leaves, especially when the leaves are very thin they enable the photosynthesis. The epidermis of typical hydrophytes possess an extremely thin cuticle and thin cellulose walls. In submerged plants, stomata are also not found, and exchange of gases takes places directly through the cells. The plants with floating leaves possess abundance of stomata on the upper surface of leaf.

Air spaces. Usually the aquatic plants are provided with well developed air spaces, which serve as an aerating system for the diffusion of the oxygen from the leaves to the roots. On the other hand, the air spaces make the plants buoyant to float. The air spaces are quite big in size. The tissue with many large air spaces may be termed as 'aerenchyma'. Usually the intervening walls of air spaces are constituted of thin walled cells. Sometimes sclereids or idioblasts are also seen on the uniseriate rows of thin walled cells which strengthen the plant body. Suitable examples of this type of structure are *Hippuris*; *Potamogeton*; *Nymphaea*; *Victoria regia*; *Limnanthemum*; *Hydrilla*, etc.

Absence of mechanical tissue (Sclerenchyma). The submerged plants usually do not possess sclerenchymatous tissue. Instead of sclerenchyma a few star-shaped sclereids or idioblasts may be formed to strengthen the general body of the plant, *e.g., Nymphaea* leaf ; *Limnanthemum*, etc.

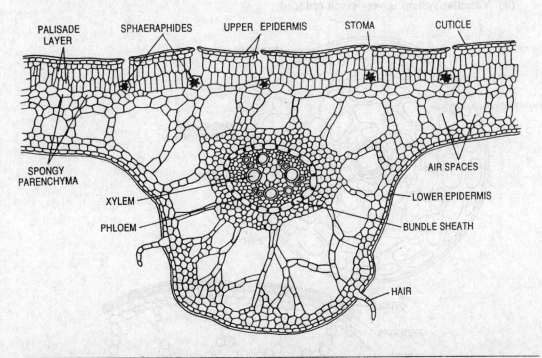

Fig. 6.1. Hydrophytic leaf. T.S. of floating leaf of *Trapa bispinosa*, showing big air spaces, the stomata confined to upper epidermis only.

Reduced vascular system. In aquatic plants the vascular system is very much reduced. The root system is also greatly reduced. The absorption of nutrients and water takes place through the leaves and stems. In the vascular tissues, the xylem is greatly reduced and sometimes in many species it is fairly developed as compared with the xylem. The endodermis is usually present around the stele but in undeveloped condition.

1. T.S. of Stem of *Hippuris* (dicot)

Epidermis. The epidermis consists of a single row of cells usually provided with a thin cuticle. The cells are radially elongated. The outer and inner tangential walls of the cells are considerably thickened whereas radial ones less.

Cortex. The region is sufficiently wide and consists of thin parenchymatous cells and big air spaces. The two subepidermal layers of cells have no big intercellular spaces, whereas rest of the cortex is permeated by large intercellular or air spaces. The air spaces or cavities are separated from one another by single layered multicellular plates. The innermost layer of the cortex is endodermis which is well defined.

Vascular system. The vascular system is very much reduced due to hydrophytic nature of the plant. The outer part consists of a narrow zone of phloem and the inner part of xylem. The vessels are small in diameter, with spiral or reticulate thickenings.

Pith. Though there is no true pith in young stems, yet according to Solereder in old stems due to obliteration of certain central vessels a pseudopith is developed.

Hydrophytic Features :
  (1) The big intercellular spaces or air spaces are very much developed.
  (2) No mechanical tissues are present.
  (3) Very thin walled parenchymatous tissues are present.
  (4) Vascular system is very much reduced.

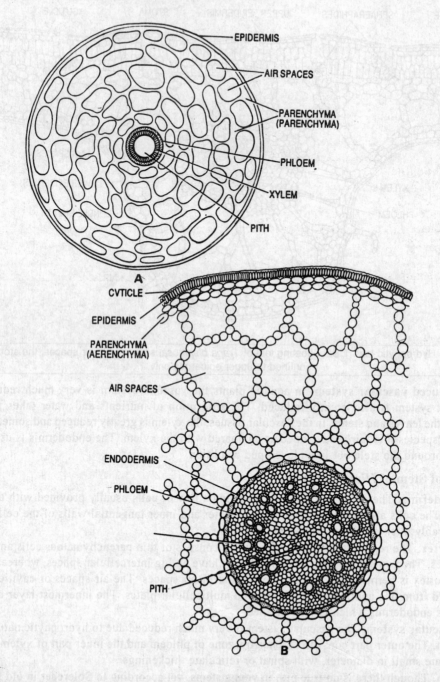

Fig. 6.2. Anatomy of hydrophytic stem. T.S. *Hippuris* (dicot) stem. A, diagrammatic; B, detail of a sector and stele.

2. T.S. Stem of *Trapa* (dicot)

Epidermis. It consists of a single row of thin walled cells.

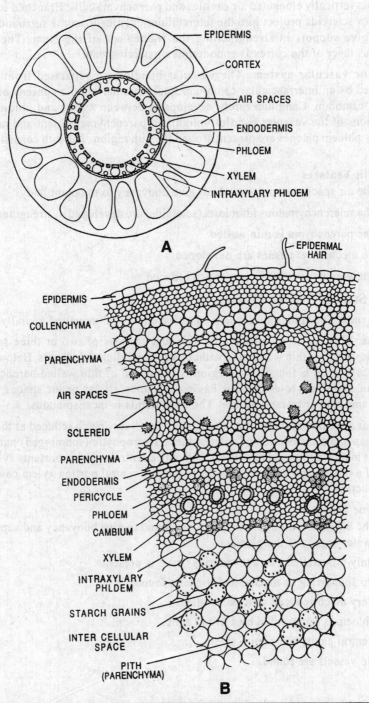

Fig. 6.3. Anatomy of hydrophytic stem of *Trapa* (dicot) A, T.S. of stem, diagrammatic; B, T.S. of stem, detail of a sector.

Cortex. The cortex is broad and consists of multilayered subepidermal region of collenchymatous cells having no intercellular or air spaces, rest of the cortical region consists of numerous vertically elongated air cavities and parenchyma cells. Branched sclerenchymatous idioblasts or sclereids project into the intercellular cavities from the surrounding cells. These sclereids give support in strengthening the framework of the stem. The innermost and conspicuous layer of the cortex is endodermis or starch sheath.

Stele or vascular system. The vascular bundles are separated from each other and unconnected by an interfascicular cambium. Each vascular bundle consists of phloem, xylem and rarely cambium. Cambium rarely develops in between xylary and phloic regions. In the inner portions of the vascular bundles unlignified parenchyma present and no sclerenchyma, Intraxylary phloem patches are present around the pith region. The pith consists of parenchyma cells.

Hydrophytic Features

(1) The air spaces are present which give buoyancy to the plant body.

(2) The sclerenchymatous idioblasts (sclereids) are developed to strengthen the framework.

(3) The parenchyma is thin walled.

(4) No mechanical tissues are developed.

(5) The vascular system is very much reduced.

3. T.S. of Stem of *Hydrilla* (Monocot)

Epidermis. The epidermis consists of a single row of thin walled, radially elongated cells.

Cortex. This region is sufficiently wide and consists of two or three layers of cells of hypodermis which are thin walled and without big intercellular air spaces. Below the hypodermis main cortical region is found. This region is composed of thin walled parenchymatous tissue arranged in uniseriate rows of cells having big intercellular or air spaces, bigger towards periphery and smaller towards centre. The endodermis is inconspicuous.

Stele or vascular system. The vascular system is very much reduced as there is no need of ascent of sap and translocation of solutes due to hydrophytic (submerged) nature of the plant. The stele is mainly composed of phloem, and only a central cavity represents xylem. The phloem consists of a broad zone towards outside, and in the central portion xylem cavity is developed due to reduction.

Hydrophytic Features

(1) The big intercellular or air spaces are found to give buoyancy and supply of oxygen to the underwater organs of the plants.

(2) Only thin walled parenchymatous tissue is present.

(3) No supporting or mechanical tissue is found.

(4) Very much reduced vascular system.

(a) Phloem is represented by a broad zone.

(b) Central cavity represents xylem.

(c) No vessels are found.

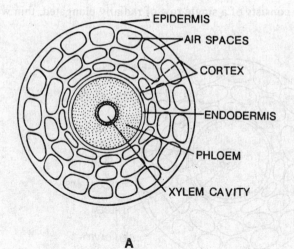

EPIDERMIS
AIR SPACES
CORTEX
ENDODERMIS
PHLOEM
XYLEM CAVITY

A

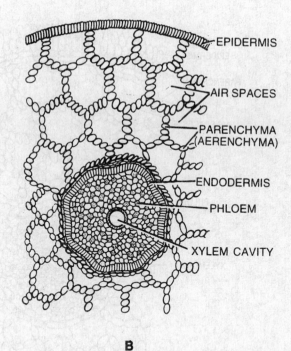

EPIDERMIS
AIR SPACES
PARENCHYMA
(AERENCHYMA)
ENDODERMIS
PHLOEM
XYLEM CAVITY

B

Fig. 6.4. Anatomy of hydrophytic stem of *Hydrilla* (submerged - monocot T.S. of stem). A, diagrammatic; B, detail of a sector and central stele.

4. T.S. of Stem of *Potamogeton* (Monocot)

Epidermis. It consists of a single row of radially elongated, thin walled cells.

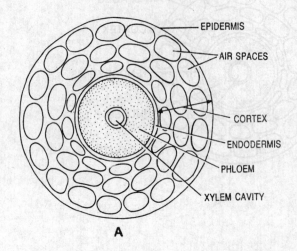

A

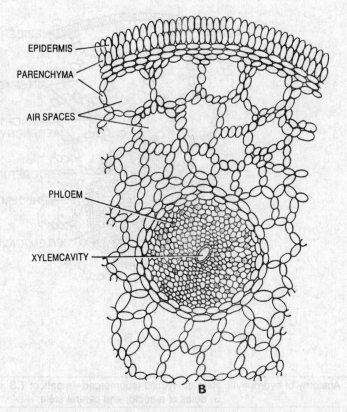

B

Fig. 6.5. Anatomy of hydrophytic stem. T.S. of stem of *Potamogeton* (monocot). A, diagrammatic ; B, detail of a sector.

Cortex. The cortical region is wide and represented by thin walled parenchyma cells having large intercellular or air spaces. The connecting bands of spaces usually consist of single row of cells. In the cortex, the bigger air spaces are found towards periphery whereas smaller air spaces are confined towards centre. The innermost layer of the cortex is represented by well defined endodermis.

Stele or vascular system. The outer portion of the stele is composed of a very wide zone of phloem while xylem is represented by a central cavity formed by reduction. No true vessels. On the whole the stelar system is very much reduced.

Hydrophytic Features

(1) The big intercellular or air spaces are present.
(2) Only thin walled parenchyma is present.
(3) No sclerenchyma or mechanical tissues are met with.
(a) The phloem is well developed.
(b) The xylem is represented by a cavity.
(c) No true vessels are found.

5. V.S. of Leaf of *Potamogeton* (Monocot)

This is a dorsiventral leaf having two distinct faces, (*i*) upper and (*ii*) lower.

Epidermis. The upper epidermis consists of a single row of thin walled cells arranged tangentially and having stomata at various places. Distinct substomatal chambers are found below the stomata.

The lower epidermis also consists of a single row of tangentially arranged thin walled compact cells, having no stomata, as the lower epidermis remains in direct contact of water.

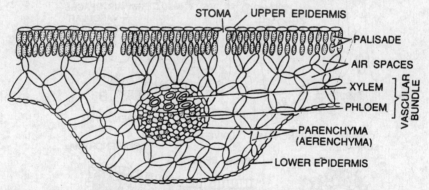

Fig. 6.6. Anatomy of hydrophytic leaf. T.S. of *Potamogeton* (monocot) leaf. Detail of central portion.

Palisade. Below the upper epidermis one or two layers of well developed palisade tissue are found. These cells contain abundance of chloroplasts.

Parenchyma. The general body of the leaf is composed of thin walled parenchyma arranged in uniseriate rows of cells and having large intercellular or air spaces.

Midrib or Vascular System

In the central region of the leaf the midrib is found. It consists of xylem and phloem. The xylem is found towards the upper epidermis and phloem towards lower epidermis. The vascular system is much reduced.

Hydrophytic Features

(1) The large air spaces are found.
(2) The stomata are confined on upper epidermis.

(3) The palisade is present towards upper side.

(4) No mechanical tissues are found.

(5) The vascular system is very much reduced.

6. V.S. of leaf of *Typha* (Monocot)

It is a dorsiventral leaf having two surfaces. It remains in direct contact of water.

Epidermis. The upper epidermis consists of a single row of cells. The stomata are confined to the upper surface. The lower epidermis is also single layered, and having no stomata.

Palisade. Just beneath the upper epidermis a few layers of palisade tissue are found having abundance of chloroplasts.

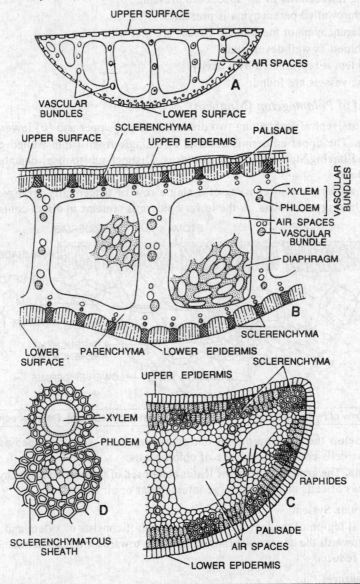

Fig. 6.7. Anatomy of aquatic leaf of *Typha* (monocot). A, T.S. of leaf, diagrammatic ; B, T.S. of leaf, semidiagrammatic ; C, T.S. of leaf, showing detail of a corner ; D, a vascular bundle.

Spongy tissue, idioblasts and air spaces. The general body of the leaf consists of spongy parenchyma with large air spaces. Minute crystals of calcium oxalate are found, projecting in the intercellular spaces from the connecting parenchymatous strands. The walls of idioblasts are pitted wherein contact with adjacent cells. Diaphragms are present in large air spaces.

Vascular system. The vascular system is poorly developed and represented by closed bundles. Normally towards upper and lower side double or mixed inversely oriented bundles are found. Each vascular bundle consists of phloem and poorly developed xylem. True vessels are altogether absent.

Hydrophytic Features

   (*i*) The air spaces are present.
   (*ii*) The raphides are present to give support to the framework of thin walled spongy parenchyma.
   (*iii*) Stomata are present only on the exposed (upper) surface.
   (*iv*) No mechanical tissues are developed.
   (*v*) Very much reduced vascular system.
   (*vi*) True vessels are absent.
   (*vii*) Phloem is much developed in comparison to the xylem.

XEROPHYTES

At the other extreme of plant association, plants are known as xerophytes. The term, however, is applicable to a great number of plants, which vary in their structural peculiarities to adapt them to live under the conditions of water. Some plants live in very dry situations while on the other hand some are found living in conditions of fairly reasonable supply of water. The plants growing in dry situations develop a large and deeply penetrating root system capable of efficient absorption. Some plants develop in marshy places, which possess higher osmotic concentration and due to this higher concentration within plants, the absorption of water from the marshy soil takes place (*e.g. Molinia*). Usually the xerophytic plants possess succulent and small leaves having less surface exposed to wind gusts. Sometimes the leaves contain abundance of mucilage, which tends to reduce transpiration. In addition to these morphological adaptations, the plants possess many anatomical xerophytic features. They are as follows :

Epidermis and thick cuticle. In the xerophytic plants, the epidermis becomes somewhat specialised. Usually the epidermal cells become cutinized and radially elongated. Sometimes it becomes multilayered, *e.g., Nerium* leaf. The cuticle varies in its thickness from species to species. Sometimes it is slightly thicker than normal, as in semixerophytic plants and on the other hand, in extreme xerophytes the cuticles may be as thick as, or thicker than, the epidermal cells. Sometimes a waxy substance is produced on the cuticle, *e.g., Calotropis*.

Hypodermis. Many xerophytic plants possess single or multilayered hypodermis immediately beneath the cutinized epidermis. Sometimes the hypodermis becomes lignified. In many plants, the mucilage, gums and tannings are common in this layer.

Structure of stomata. The stomata are very minute openings formed in the epidermal layer in green aerial parts of the plant. The stomata are used for interchange of gases, and evaporation of the surplus water. They are most abundant in the lower epidermis of dorsiventral leaf. In the isobilateral leaves, they are usually evenly distributed on all sides. Some of the xerophytic plants possess less stomata, either by reduction of leaf surface or of stomatal number per unit area. The reduce excessive transpiration, usually the stomata in pits are produced. Commonly these stomata may be termed 'sunken stomata'. They occur in *Hakea, Agave,* etc. In the oleander (*Nerium*) and *Banksia* the stomata are found in groups and in irregular depressions on the leaf surface. Usually the depressions contain hairs which also protect the stomata from direct attack of wind gusts, *e.g., Banksia, Nerium*, etc.

Sclerenchyma. The xerophytes commonly have a large proportion of sclerenchyma in their leaf structure than the mesophytes. This tissue is either found in groups or in continuous sheets. The sclerenchyma layers check excessive transpiration to some extent and also strengthen the plant body. The xerophytes which possess heavy sclerification of the leaves may easily be called **sclerophyllous,** *e.g., Dasylirion.*

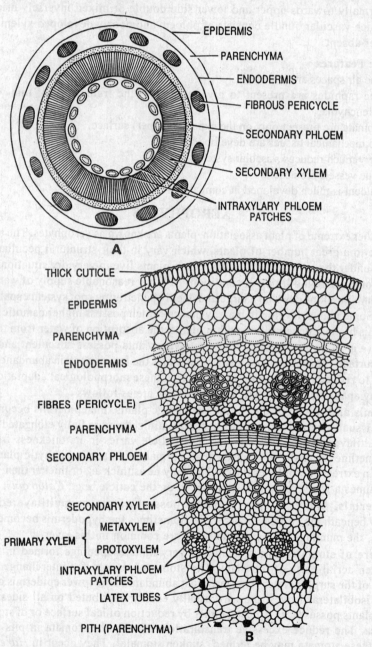

EPIDERMIS

PARENCHYMA

ENDODERMIS

FIBROUS PERICYCLE

SECONDARY PHLOEM

SECONDARY XYLEM

INTRAXYLARY PHLOEM PATCHES

A

THICK CUTICLE

EPIDERMIS

PARENCHYMA

ENDODERMIS

FIBRES (PERICYCLE)

PARENCHYMA

SECONDARY PHLOEM

SECONDARY XYLEM

METAXYLEM

PRIMARY XYLEM { PROTOXYLEM

INTRAXYLARY PHLOEM PATCHES

LATEX TUBES

PITH (PARENCHYMA)

B

Fig. 6.8. Anatomy of xerophytic stem. T.S. of *Calotropis* (Asclepiadaceae-dicot) stem. A, diagrammatic ; B, detail of a sector.

Hairs. Many xerophytes, especially of alpine heights, possess a matting of hairs on the epidermis. These hairs are mostly confined on the lower surface of leaves. Hairs may also be abundant over the entire aerial part of the plant. They prevent rapid evaporation through stomata. Xerophytes, which possess abundance of hairs, are called **trichophyllous.**

Rolling of leaves. Many xerophytic grasses have the stomata confined to ventral surface, and when there is a deficiency of water the leaves roll up so that all stomata are on the inner surface of the rolled leaf. The air enclosed in the rolled leaf soon becomes saturated with water and the outward diffusion of water stops. *Ammophila arenaria* or sand dune grass is a good example of rolling leaf.

Reduced leaf surface. Many xerophytes possess very reduced needle-like or scaly leaves, *e.g.*, *Casuarina*, etc. Here the reduction is because of the relatively small total surface of the leaf. Xerophytes with reduced leaves are termed '**microphyllous**'.

Water storage tissue. Many fleshy xerophytes possess water storage tissue in them. The xerophytic plants possess succulent stems or leaves, which consist largely of special parenchymatous tissue used for water storage. The examples are *Cactus, Aloe, Opuntia,* etc. These plants possess spread type of root system. In rainy season water is quickly absorbed and stored and then expanded slowly during the period of drought.

Abundant palisade. In the stems of many xerophytes, the palisade tissue is found (*e.g.*, *Capparis*). In the leaves the palisade is compact and found in abundance.

Latex tubes. In many xerophytic stems and leaves the laticiferous canals are found. Due to viscosity of latex the transpiration is checked up to a certain extent.

Vascular system. It is well developed in xerophytes.

7. T.S. of Stem of *Calotropis* (Dicot)

Epidermis. The epidermis consists of radially elongated epidermal cells and covered with very thick cuticle. A thin waxy layer is also found above the cuticle.

Parenchyma. Below the epidermis, multilayered parenchyma is present. The cells are thin walled, rounded and isodiametric. Intercellular spaces are very common.

Endodermis. The last layer of the cortex is endodermis containing starch grains. The cells are barrel shaped and arranged tangentially quite close to each other.

Pericycle. Beneath the endodermis a parenchymatous zone of pericycle is present which is interrupted by unlignified group of fibres. The cells of parenchyma are polygonal and thin walled.

Secondary phloem. Just below the pericycle region, secondary phloem is present. The secondary phloem is found in the continuous strand around the axis ; sieve tubes, companion cells, and phloem parenchyma present. Sometimes at certain places crushed primary phloem is also visible.

Cambium. Beneath the secondary phloem cambium zone is found. The cambial strip is found in continuous strand round about the whole axis.

Xylem. Below the cambium a continuous strand of secondary and primary xylem is present. The primary xylem consists of wide metaxylem and narrow protoxylem vessels, whereas secondary xylem is represented by xylem parenchyma (prosenchyma,) which are lignified tissue.

Intraxylary phloem. The patches of intraxylary phloem are also found around the pith region.

Pith. The central region of the stem is filled up with thin walled, polygonal, parenchymatous cells, which represent the medulla (pith).

Latex tubes. The latex tubes or laticiferous canals are also visible in different parenchymatous regions.

Anomalous Structure

The intraxylary phloem strands are present around the periphery of pith region.

Xerophytic Characters

    (*i*) Very thick cuticle with waxy layer is present on the surface of the stem.

    (*ii*) The epidermis consists of radially elongated epidermal cells.

    (*iii*) The latex tubes are present.

    (*iv*) The sclerenchymatous tissue is well developed.

8. V.S. of Leaf of *Agave* (Monocot)

Epidermis. The leaf is isobilateral and approximately possesses the same type of anatomy on both the sides. Towards the upper surface, the upper epidermis is found whereas towards the lower surface, the usual lower epidermis is present. The anatomy of both upper and lower layers of epidermis is same. It consists of radially elongated and compact epidermal cells having no intercellular spaces. The epidermis on both the sides is covered with a thick cuticle. The sunken stomata are present. The guard cells contain many chloroplasts. Below each stoma sub-stomatal chamber is always found which helps in exchange of gases.

Chlorenchyma. Just beneath the epidermis (on both sides) one or two layers of chlorenchyma are present usually having elongated or oval cells containing chloroplasts with well defined intercellular spaces.

Parenchyma. The ground tissue of the leaf consists of thin walled, rounded parenchymatous cells having well defined intercellular spaces.

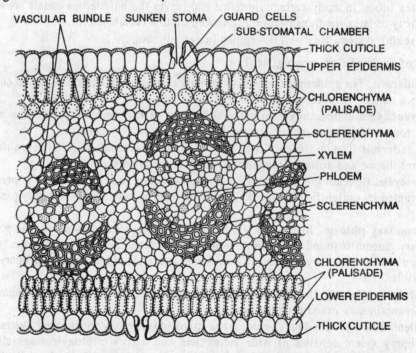

Fig. 6.9. Anatomy of xerophytic leaf. T.S. of *Agave* (monocot) leaf. Detail of a portion.

Vascular system. The vascular system is well developed and consists of many vascular bundles. The central bundle is bigger than the rest. The fibers are found on both the sides of each vascular bundle. The xylem is found towards upper side whereas the phloem towards lower side.

Xerophytic Features

    (*i*) The thick cuticle is found on both the surfaces.

(*ii*) The epidermis consists of elongated epidermal cells.
(*iii*) The sunken stomata are present on both surfaces.
(*iv*) The sclerenchyma is developed.

9. V.S. of Leaf of *Nerium* (dicot)

Epidermis. The leaf is dorsiventral and consists of upper and lower epidermis. The upper epidermis is multilayered and usually consists of two or three layers of barrel-shaped compact cells having no intercellular spaces among them. The outermost layer is covered with a well defined, thick cuticle. Generally the stomata are not found on the upper surface. The lower epidermis consists of a single row of barrel-shaped cells, arranged closely to each other, and protected with a well defined cuticle. At certain places the irregular depressions are formed due to incurve of the lower epidermis. The stomata are found in the depression which are commonly protected with trichomes (hairs) growing around the sides. Due to the presence of these hairs, the rate of transpiration is sufficiently reduced as the stomata are not attacked by the direct gusts of wind.

Mesophyll. It is distinguished into palisade and spongy tissue. Immediately beneath the upper epidermis one or two layers of palisade are found, containing abundance of chloroplasts. Towards lower surface, the spongy tissue is well developed. The intercellular spaces among spongy tissue are well developed and quite big in size. The cells contain abundance of chloroplasts but comparatively lesser than those of palisade tissue.

Vascular system. It is very well developed and consists of mid-rib and lateral veins. The phloem is always found towards lower side and xylem towards upper side,

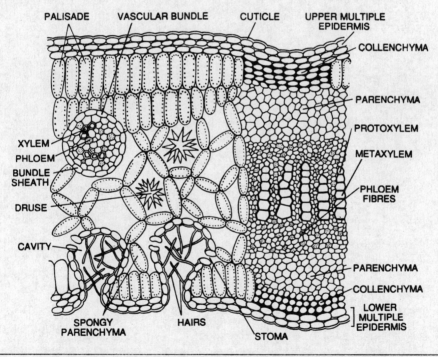

Fig. 6.10. Anatomy of xerophytic leaf. T.S. of *Nerium* (dicot) leaf, detail of a portion.

Xerophytic Features

(*i*) The thick cuticle is present on upper and lower epidermis.
(*ii*) A multilayered upper epidermis is found to check excessive transpiration.
(*iii*) The stomata are found in the depressions which are confined on the lower surface of leaf. They are also protected with hairs to check the direct attack of wind gusts.
(*iv*) The vascular system is well developed.

Fig. 9.V.a. Anatomy of Nerium type leaf. T.S. of Nerium (dicot) leaf, detail of a portion.

Sclerenchyma. Beneath the epidermis one or two layers of sclerenchyma are usually found.

Palisade. Usually in the ridges of the stem few layers of palisade tissue are present. These are loose, elongated and with a large number of discoid chloroplasts.

Xerophytic Features

(*i*) A thick cuticle is present above the epidermis.

(*ii*) The stomata are found in the depressions.

(*iii*) Usually hairs are present in the furrows which protect the stomata.

(*iv*) The palisade tissue is found even in the stem.

(*v*) The vascular system is well developed.

(*vi*) The mechanical tissues are developed.

12. T.S. of Stem of *Capparis* (Dicot)

Epidermis. The epidermis consists of radially elongated epidermal cells, arranged very close to each other, having no intercellular spaces. The epidermis is covered with very thick cuticle. These two devices are meant to check excessive transpiration — a xerophytic character.

Palisade. Below the epidermis two or three layers of palisade tissue are found which contain a large number of chloroplasts. These tissues help in carbon assimilation. In *Capparis aphylla* the leaves are altogether absent and the phenomenon of photosynthesis is completed by the palisade tissue of the stem — a xerophytic character.

Endodermis. The last but one layer of the cortex is endodermis which consists of thin-walled and barrel-shaped cells.

Pericycle. The sclerenchymatous pericycle in patches is found just below the endodermis. These patches are alternated with thin walled parenchymatous cells.

Secondary phloem. Beneath the sclerenchymatous pericycle and parenchyma secondary phloem in continuous ring is present. The phloem is represented by sieve tubes, companion cells and phloem parenchyma.

Cambium. Below the phloem multilayered cambial zone is found. The cells are thin walled, rectangular and arranged in radial rows.

Xylem. The xylem may be divided into primary and secondary xylem. The primary xylem consists of large cavities of metaxylem and narrow vessels of protoxylem which are arranged in radial rows. The secondary xylem is represented by xylem parenchyma (prosenchyma).

Medullary rays. The medullary rays are usually two or three layered. The cells are arranged radially. These rays connect the pith with outer tissues and are usually found in between the vascular bundles.

Pith. In the central region of the stem pith is found which consists of thin walled parenchymatous cells.

Xerophytic Characters

(*i*) A very thick cuticle is found over epidermis.

(*ii*) Epidermis consists of radially elongated epidermal cells. The stomata (sunken) are also found on the epidermis.

(*iii*) The palisade tissue is found in the outer cortical region of the stem.

(*iv*) The mechanical tissue (sclerenchyma) is well developed.

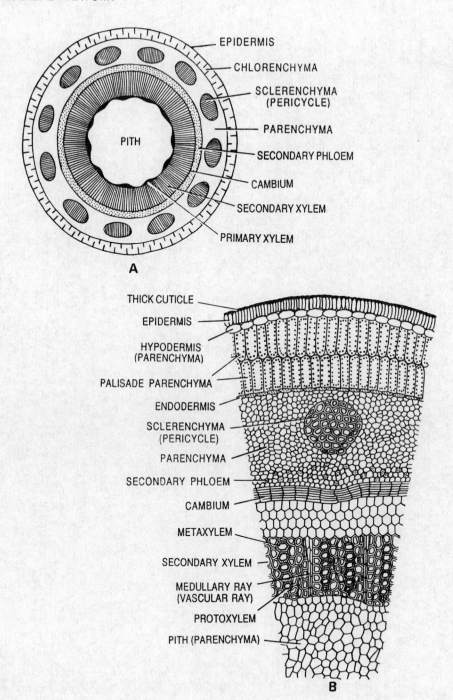

Fig. 6.13. Anatomy of xerophytic stem. T.S. of *Capparis* (dicot) stem. A, diagrammatic ; B, detail of a sector.

Fig. 9.13. Anatomy of xerophytic stem: T.S. of Casuarina (dicot stem) A. diagrammatic, B. detail of a sector.

Vascular bundles. The vascular bundles are conjoint, collateral, endarch and open.

Xylem. The xylem is traversed by rays 2-3 cells wide in *Rhizophora mucronata.* The vessels possess scalariform perforation plates.

Crystals. The crystals are generally clustered.

Secretory elements. Vertically elongated secretory cells containing tannin and/or oil present in the cortex and the pith.

Anatomy of leaf. The leaves are usually dorsiventral. Hairs are mostly unicellular with thick or thin walls. The cuticle is well developed and often quite thick on both the leaf surfaces. **Cork warts** occur as small black spots on the lower side of the leaf. The **epidermis** is single layered and consists of rectangular cells. The cells of upper epidermis possess some rod-shaped and cubical crystals of calcium oxalate. The **hypodermis** towards the upper surface is 2 or more layered. The **stomata** are confined to the lower surface. They are depressed and often provided with a front cavity. The **mesophyll** consists of palisade and spongy tissue. Palisade tissue consists of 1 - 4 layers. Spongy tissue usually possesses large intercellular spaces. Aqueous tissue and muclilage cells are also present beneath the upper epidermis. H-shaped sclerenchymatous idioblasts occur in the palisade tissue, and variously branched ones in the spongy mesophyll.

Anatomy of root. The well-known breathing roots (pneumatophores) of members of the Rhizophoraceae inhabiting mangrove swamps have large intercellular spaces of the spongy cortex which facilitate gaseous exchange in the special habitat in which the plants grow. The **Cork** consists of suberized cells. The cork layer remains interrupted by lenticels at several places. In some cases the cork consists of alternating layers of suberized and ordinary parenchymatous cells in the aerial portion. Next to the cork there lies a thick **cortex** containing abundant, large, intercellular spaces, arranged radially around the stele. Intercellular spaces are large in the subterranean than in the aerial parts of the roots. The cortex may be subdivided into two portions — the secondary cortex and the primary cortex. The **secondary cortex** consisting of few layers is found just beneath the cork. The **primary cortex** lies next to the secondary cortex. The primary cortex is broad and lacunar. The primary cortex in the terrestrial part of the root is composed of cells of two kinds - (a) radially elongated cells connected with one another tangentially by short lateral arms ; (b) rows of vertically elongated cells which show small, circular lumina in transverse section. Sclerenchymatous **idioblasts** also occur in the cortex. H-shaped sclerenchymatous idioblasts project into the cortical intercellular spaces in the aerial part of the root, but are less numerous below ground.

The endodermis is conspicuous. Numerous secretory cells are found in the pericyclic region. The xylem is well formed and strongly lignified. The outer pith is sclerenchymatous whereas the central region of pith is parenchymatous. Several oil cells are present here and there in the pith region.

CHAPTER 7

Soil Science

The Soil

The word soil is derived from a Latin word '*solum*' meaning earthy material in which plants grow. The study of soil is known as **Soil Science** or **Pedology** (*pedos* = earth) or **Edaphology** (*edaphos* = soil). Soil makes natural habitat for plants and animals. It provides water and nutrients to the living organisms. Knowledge of soil is helpful for agricultural practices, such as cultivation, irrigation, artificial drainage and use of fertilizers. The study of soil is also important in geological, petrological, mineralogical and palaeobotanical studies. According to R.F. Daubenmire, "Soil is the upper part of earth crust in which plants are anchored." In other words, soil can be defined as that region on the earth surface where geology and biology meet each other.

Soil Profile

Weathering of parental rocks results in the development of several loose layers or horizons of weathered materials. Biological system, addition of organic matter (humus) and interaction between organic and mineral compounds make the horizons more distinct. The complete succession of horizons down to the level of undifferentiated parent materials is called **soil profile.** In brief, it is vertical section of earth crust showing different layers or horizons of soil.

Morphological Characteristics of Soil Profile

Several morphological characteristics have been recorded in respect of the horizons, such as colour, texture, structure, consistence, concretions, calcareousness, roots, etc.

Colour. This is one of the most noticeable characteristics of a soil. As a soil profile is examined, the definite changes are observed in colour from the surface through the subsoil and underlying parent material. The colours of the surface and subsoil are as follows :

Surface. The colour is dark, moderately dark, light or very light.

Subsoil. The colour may be dull, mottled or bright.

As a rule, the surface is darker than the subsoil, since it contains more organic matter. Subsoil colour is less affected by organic matter than surface colour.

Texture. The texture of the soil particles, formed from weathering, varies greatly in size. They are classified on the basis of their size into gravel, sand, silt and clay. Most soils are the mixtures of the various sized particles except that many contain no gravel, and some very little sand. If a soil contains sufficient quantities of at least two sizes of particles, it is known as **loam,** silty loam or clay loam, depending on the size of the particle, that predominates in the mixture. On the other hand, if a mixture consists mostly of one size of particles, it is not known as loam.

Weight of soil after heating = Z – X gm

Amount of humus in the soil sample = (Y – X) – (Z – X) gm

Percentage of humus in the soil sample $= \dfrac{(Y-X)-(Z-X)}{(Y-X)} \times 100$

Note and compare the variation in humus contents of different samples taken from polluted and unpolluted soils. Also correlate the pollutional factors prevailing in these soils.

EXERCISE 2

Object : To test the presence of phosphate, sulphate and chloride in the soil.

Requirements : Soil samples, conical flask, distilled water, beakers, test tubes, sulphuric acid, silver nitrate, hydrochloric acid (conc.), burner, $BaCl_2$, ammonium molybdate, nitric acid (conc.), NH_4NO_3.

Preparation of Water Extract : Take about 250 gm of soil sample in a conical flask, add 500 ml distilled water and shake it thoroughly. Wait for about 10 hours. Soluble inorganic salts will be dissolved in water during this period. Pour the water slowly in a beaker and collect the filtrate. This is called *water extract.*

(1) *Phosphate :* Take 10 ml of water extract in a test tube and add in it a few drops of ammonium molybdate solution, nitric acid (conc.) and NH_4NO_3. Development of yellow colour indicates the presence of phosphates in the soil.

(2) *Sulphate :* Take about 20 ml of water extract in a beaker and add in it 2 to 5 ml hydrochloric acid (conc.). Boil it and then add $BaCl_2$ solution. Development of white precipitate indicates the presence of sulphates in the soil.

(3) *Chloride :* Take about 20 ml of water extract in a beaker and neutralize its carbonate and bicarbonate by adding about 10 ml N/10 H_2SO_4. Add silver nitrate to the solution. Appearance of white precipitate indicates the presence of chlorides in the soil.

EXERCISE 3

Object : To demonstrate and determine the biomass, percentage of moisture in soil, plants and animal material.

Biomass. The quantity of living material in unit area of land is called the *Standing crop.* This can be expressed in terms of number or weight. The standing crop in terms of weight is also called the *biomass.* Biomass is usually expressed in terms of dry weight at any one time.

Method. Lay a few quadrats of 25 cm. × 25 cm. each in the grassland at random. Clip all the above ground portions and collect them in a polythene bag, and in another bag collect the fallen leaves and other plant part parts. In a third bag collect the animals, ants and other insects. Dig the soil in the form of a monolith up to 25 cm., wash the monolith and take out all the underground plant parts. Dry all the materials in an oven at 70°C for 24 hours, and express the biomass in terms of dry weight per square metre.

The energy status of organic materials can be measured by burning the same in a bomb calorimeter and determining the amount of energy thus liberated.

Soil moisture. About 100 gms. of soil sample is to be collected in polythene bags each from surface and at desired depth from different parts of the field and brought to the laboratory. Weigh a certain quantity of soil in a pre-weighed beaker and place in an oven maintained at 105°C. After 8 hours remove the sample from the oven and quickly weigh again. The soil moisture content is calculated as the percentage of moisture on the basis of oven dry weight of the soil.

Plant and animal moisture. Collect plant and animal materials from the area in polythene bags separately and put in oven at 80°C and calculate the percentage of moisture on the basis of oven dry weight materials.

EXERCISE 4

Object : To study the biotic components of a pond ; collection and identification of plants and animals.

Requirements : Collection nets with different meshes, specimen tubes, glass jars of different sizes, hand lens, plant grappler, metre scale, iron chain, scissors and forceps, centrifuge.

Method : The hydrophytes of the pond margin or marsh and shallow regions can be hand-picked or lifted and collected in polythene bags. Iron hooks tied to long string can be used to drag submerged plants of deeper area. For plankton, special type of plankton bottle with nylon net and long handle-rod is used. The plankton net is wielded several times so as to obtain a concentrated collection of microorganisms. Identify the collection with the help of suitable key or literature for plants and animals and list them in sequence.

The biomass of macroproducers and macroconsumers per unit can also be estimated by suitable sized quadrat (preferably 25 cm. square) and can be expressed in fresh weight as well as dry weight as described in gm./m^2 or gm./cubic metre.

For microproducers and microconsumers collect the sample without much disturbance of the sampling of site in some glassware. Take about 10 ml. of this sample in test tube and centrifuge it. Drain out the water and take fresh and dry weights. Express in gm./litre.

EXERCISE 5

Object : To study the environmental factors of a pond.

A. To determine the pH of pond water.

Method : The same techniques employed for measuring the pH of the soil can be used. Samples should be collected at different times and at different places. Along with this the temperature of the sample should also be recorded.

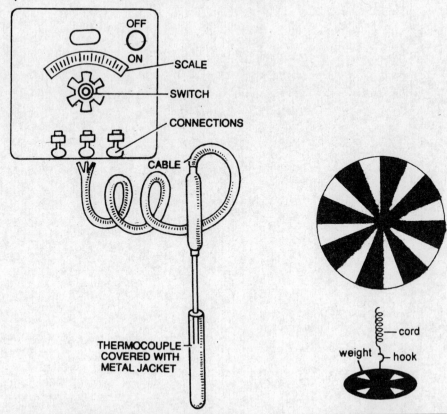

Fig. 7.1. Thirmister. An apparatus to measure the temperature of water of a pond.

Fig. 7.2. Secchi disc.

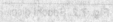

Fig. 7.1. Thermister. An apparatus to measure the temperature of water of a pond.

Fig. 7.2. Secchi disc.

(iii) Consumers : Primary consumers, e.g. Birds, tortoises, etc.

(c) Decomposers : Fungi and bacteria.

EXERCISE 8

Object : To measure temperature and pH of the water of a pond.

Requirements : Maximum-minimum thermometer or thermister or thermopile.

Method : 1. **Temperature.** The temperature of the pond can be determined by any of the following apparatuses :

(a) *Maximum-Minimum Thermometer.* It contains two indicators. With the help of a magnet they are set to the present atmospheric temperature. Quickly lower down the thermometer to the desired depth in the pond. Keep it there for 10 minutes. Bring out the thermometer quickly and note the readings of both the indicators. One of the two indicators, one remains at the point and the other moves to some extent giving the reading of temperature at that particular depth of the pond.

(b) *Thermister.* It is an instrument which gives correct reading of temperature in centigrade. It contains a long cable. At the one end of the cable is attached a thermocouple. A milliampere... is pre-set which is calibrated in C° and gives direct reading. Quickly lower the thermocouple to the desired depth and note the temperature.

(c) *Thermopile.* It is also one of the good apparatuses for measuring the temperature of a pond. After lowering to the desired depth, bring it out when it is filled completely with water. With the help of a good sensitive thermometer, note the temperature of the water.

2. **pH :** pH of the pond water can be tested by pH meter, pH paper or B.D.H. Universal indicator.

EXERCISE 9

Object : To measure the temperature of soil and air. (Fig. 7.5).

Fig. 7.5. Soil Thermometer. An apparatus to measure the soil temperature.

Method : Use ordinary thermometer and soil thermometer for air and soil respectively, on surface and 10 cm. depth in sun and shade.

(*iii*) *Consumers of 3rd order* (Tertiary consumers); *e.g.* Birds, big fishes, *etc.*

(*c*) **Decomposers :** Fungi and bacteria.

EXERCISE 8

Object : To measure temperature and pH of the water of a pond.

Requirements : Maximum-minimum thermometer, or thermister, or thermoflask.

Method : 1. Temperature : The temperature of the pond can be determined by any of the following apparatuses :

(*a*) *Maximum-Minimum Thermometer* : It contains two indicators. With the help of a magnet they are set to the present atmospheric temperature. Quickly lower down the thermometer to the desired depth in the pond. Keep it there for 10 minutes. Bring out the thermometer quickly and note the readings of both the indicators. Out of the two indicators, one remains at the point and the other moves to some extent giving the reading of temperature at that particular depth of the pond.

(*b*) *Thermister* : It is an instrument which gives correct reading of temperature in centigrade. It contains a long cable. At the end of the cable is attached a thermocouple.

A milliammeter is present which is calibrated in C° and gives direct reading. Quickly lower the thermocouple up to a desired depth and note the temperature.

(*c*) *Thermoflask* : It is also one of the good apparatuses for measuring the temperature of a pond. After lowering to the desired depth, bring it out when it is filled completely with water. With the help of a good sensitive thermometer, note the temperature of the water.

2. pH : pH of the pond water can be tested by pH meter, pH paper or B.D.H. Universal Indicator.

EXERCISE 9

Object : To measure the temperature of soil and air. (Fig. 7.5)

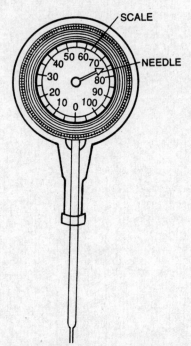

Fig. 7.5. Soil Thermometer. An apparatus to measure the soil temperature.

Method. Use ordinary thermometer and soil thermometer for air and soil respectively, on surface and 10 cm. depth in sun and shade.

EXERCISE 10

Object : To measure humidity and light intensity. (Fig. 7.6)

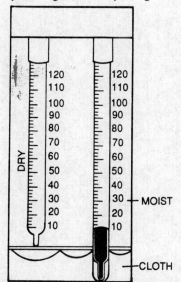

Fig. 7.6. Psychrometer (thermohydrograph). An apparatus for measuring humidity.

Method. Humidity can be measured by wet and dry bulb thermometer, or thermohydrograph (which records continuously temperature and humidity) Measurement of *light intensity* is carried out in Lux unit, at different places by means of photometer or Lux-meter (Fig. 7.7).

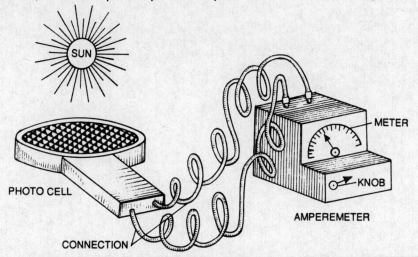

Fig. 7.7. Luxmeter (photometer). An apparatus for measuring light intensity. The unit of light intensity is lux (1 lux = 1 lumen per m² = approximately 0.1 foot candle; 1 foot candle = 1 lumen per ft²).

EXERCISE 11

Object : To determine soil texture; presence of carbonate and nitrate; pH value and base deficiency including spot test.

Method. (1) *Soil texture.* Examine the soil under hand lens for large particles. Squeeze small amount of air dry soil as well as moist soil between thumb and finger and try to judge the texture with the help of key given below.

EXERCISE 15

Object : To determine the presence of nitrate in the soil samples.

Requirements : White spot plate or white tile, diphenylamine, H_2SO_4, water, soil samples.

Method : Take small amount of soil on a white spot plate and add conc. 2 drops of 0.02% diphenylamine solution in conc. H_2SO_4. Blue colour will be formed. Distinguish the grades of blue colour by an imaginary scale of 1-5 and record the data in tabular form as under.

TABLE 7.3

Soil sample	Depth of the blue colour produced
1	+ + + +
2	+ + +
3	+ + + + +
4	+ + +
5	+

Results : Nitrate contents are highest in soil sample No. 3 and lowest in sample No. 5.

EXERCISE 16

Object : To determine the soil pH.

pH is a property to know the chemical nature of soil. If a reaction is predominated by hydrogen ions, it becomes acidic. Results are alkaline in the reverse condition. pH of the soil can be estimated by pH meter or pH paper. One more satisfactory way for determining pH is the use of Universal indicator.

Requirements : Soil, BDH Universal Indicator, test tube, water.

Method : 1. Mix the soil in some water, shake and add BDH Universal Indicator. Compare the colour of the solution with the chart on the bottle of indicator and note the pH.

2. Mix thoroughly the soil in a test tube with equal amount of barium sulphate and about 20 ml of water. Take a few drops of supernagant liquid on a porcelain tile and add equal amount of Universal indicator and compare the colour of the soil with the chart for pH given on the bottle of Universal Indicator.

EXERCISE 17

Object : To determine base deficiency of given soil samples.

Requirements : Test tube, soil samples, alcoholic solution of ammonium thiocyanate, and hydrogen peroxide.

Combar's Test : Shake thoroughly a little amount of soil with a saturated alcoholic solution of ammonium thiocyanate in a test tube. Let the soil settle. Add a drop of hydrogen peroxide. Red colour will develop. The darkness of the red colour and its depth can be noted in 5 degrees as given in the following Table 7.4.

TABLE 7.4

Soil sample	Depth of the red colour produced
1	+ + + +
2	+ + + +
3	+ + + + +
4	+ + + +
5	+ + + + +

Results : Base deficiency is minimum in soil sample number 3 and maximum in sample numbers 5.

EXERCISE 15

Object : To determine the presence of nitrate in the soil samples.

Requirements : White spot plate or white cavity tile, diphenylamine, H_2SO_4, water, soil samples.

Method : Take small amount of soil on a white spot plate and add only 2 drops of 0.02% diphenylamine solution in conc. H_2SO_4. Blue colour will be formed. Distinguish the grades of blue colour by an imaginary scale of 1-5 and record the details in tabular form as under :

TABLE 7.3

Soil sample	Depth of blue colour produced
1	3 or +++
2	2 or ++
3	5 or +++++
4	4 or ++++
5	1 or +

Results : Nitrate contents are highest in soil sample No. 3 and lowest in sample No. 5.

EXERCISE 16

Object : To determine the soil pH.

pH is a property to know the chemical nature of soil. If a reaction is predominated by hydrogen ions, it becomes acidic. Results are alkaline in the reverse condition. pH of the soil can be estimated by pH meter or pH paper. One more satisfactory way for determining pH is the use of Universal Indicator.

Requirements : Soil, BDH Universal Indicator, test tube, water.

Method : 1. Mix the soil in some water, shake and add BDH Universal Indicator. Compare the colour of the solution with the chart on the bottle of indicator and note the pH.

2. Mix thoroughly the soil in a test tube with equal amount of barium sulphate and about 20 ml of water. Take a few drops of supernatant liquid on a porcelain tile and add equal amount of Universal Indicator, and compare the colour of the soil with the chart for pH given on the bottle of Universal Indicator.

EXERCISE 17

Object : To determine base deficiency of given soil samples.

Requirements : Test tube, soil samples, alcoholic solution of ammonium thiocyanate and hydrogen peroxide.

Comber's Test : Shake thoroughly a little amount of soil with a saturated alcoholic solution of ammonium thiocyanate in a test tube. Let the soil settle. Add a drop of hydrogen peroxide. Red colour will develop. The darkness of the red colour and its depth can be noted in 5 degrees as given in the following Table 7.4 :

TABLE 7.4

Soil sample	Depth of the red colour produced
1	1 or +
2	3 or +++
3	5 or +++++
4	2 or ++
5	4 or ++++

Results : Base deficiency is minimum in soil sample number 1 and maximum in sample number 3.

SOIL SCIENCE

EXERCISE 18

Object : To determine the water-holding capacity of the soil.

Requirements : Soil sample, filter papers, brass or tin cigarette box with perforated bottom, balance with weighing box, water, oven, petri dish.

Method : 1. Dry the soil in the oven and crush it.

2. Take a brass or tin box (or a cigarette can) with perforated bottom and place a filter paper inside the box at its perforated bottom. Weigh this box with paper.

3. Now fill the box gradually with the dry soil and place this soil-filled box in a petri dish containing water. Wait for about 8-10 hours and then once again weigh the container.

4. Now put the container in an oven at 105°C for about 24 hours and weigh it again.

5. Take a filter paper (similar to the one used earlier in the container), dip it in the water and find out the amount of water absorbed by a filter paper.

6. Calculate the water-holding capacity by the following formula :

$$\text{Water-holding capacity} = \frac{\text{Amount of water in the soil}}{\text{Weight of the oven dry soil}} \times 100$$

Calculations :

Weight of wet soil + container + wet filter paper = 110 gm

Weight of box = 40 gm

Weight of wet filter paper = 1 gm

Weight of wet soil = (1) – (2 + 3) = (110) – (40 + 1) = 69 gm

Weight of oven dry soil + box + dry filter paper = 89 gm

Weight of dry filter paper = 0.5 gm

Weight of oven dry soil = 5 – (2 + 6) = 89 – (40 + 0.5) = 48.5 gm

Water in the soil = (4 – 7) = (69 – 48.5) = 20.5 gm

$$\text{Water-holding capacity} = \frac{\text{Weight of water in the soil}}{\text{Weight of the oven dry soil}} \times 100$$

$$= \frac{20.5}{48.5} \times 100 = 42.26\%$$

Biotechnology:
Plant Tissue Culture

PLANT TISSUE CULTURE

Plant tissue culture is the maintenance and growth of plant cells, tissues and organs on a suitable culture medium *in vitro*, *e.g.*, in a test tube or any other suitable vessel.

Plant tissue cultures are often classified according to the type of *in vitro* growth, such as callus and suspension cultures, or the explant used for culture initiation, *e.g.* embryo culture, anther culture, etc.

An **explant** is the part of a plant that is excised from its original location and used for initiating a culture.

Surface sterilisation and sterilisation. It is essential that the explants, glassware, culture containers or vessels, media and the instruments used for plant tissue culture must be free from microbes.

Hence the explants are treated with specific anti-microbial chemicals, and the process is called **surface sterilisation.** Suitable sized plant material (explant) is sterilised as follows :

(*i*) Bring the explant to be sterilised in well sterilised laboratory and prepare pieces for sterilisation.

(*ii*) Clean the working area and hands with alcohol, put on mask and cap, and light the spirit lamp.

(*iii*) Keep 3 or 4 petridishes in a line, add disinfectant (*e.g.*, mecuric chloride 0.01 to 0.1% aqueous solution, or 20% sodium hydrochloride) in first plate and autoclaved distilled water in subsequent plates.

(*iv*) Place plant pieces in first plate and immerse the material with the help of sterilised forceps for 5–10 minutes depending upon the disinfectant used.

(*v*) Transfer material from first to second petriplate, rinse gently and pass to third and fourth plates, one by one with thorough rinsing.

(*vi*) Finally drain the distilled water, and prepare suitable sized explants.

A quick dip in 70% ethanol (15–30 seconds), is always advantageous, before surface sterilisation with disinfectant.

(iv) The microorganisms present in the medium might harm the beginning many be destroyed by sterilizing the properly clogged culture vials. It can be done by maintaining the temperature at 120°C for about 15 minutes.

(v) The microorganisms may also be carried along with tissue that is being cultured. To prevent this, the explant material from where the tissue is to be excised is surface sterilized. The material may be surface sterilized with saturated chlorine water and then thoroughly washed with sterilized distilled water, and to remove all traces of chlorine. The material is fairly hard as are some fruits and seeds, it may be surface sterilized by flaming in alcohol.

Fig. 8.2 Development of tobacco plants from single cells. A callus is raised from a small piece of tissue grown from the pith (A). By transferring the liquid medium and shaking the culture flasks (B). The callus is dissociated into a single cell (C) is mechanically removed from the flask and is placed on a slide in a drop of culture medium (D). A microcolony is formed around the culture cell using the large-cover slip. Large callus (E) developing on the cell mass or developing on and transferred to a semi solid medium where it grows into large callus (E) and eventually into plantlet plants (F, G), then transferred to soil (F). These plants grow to maturity, flower and set seeds (I).

(vii) finally, precautions must also be taken to prevent the entry of microorganisms, whether the vial is removed to transfer the tissue to the nutrient medium solution. For this all operations from surface sterilization of the tissue up to inoculation are done in an aseptic environment.

Aeration

Proper aeration of the cultured tissue is also an important aspect of culture technique. If the tissue is grown on the surface of a semi-solid medium it acquires enough aeration without special device for liquid medium special device. Filter paper bridge is used. Here two legs remain dipping in the medium and the horizontal part supporting the tissue raised above the level of the medium.

Cellular Totipotency

This is the capacity of mature cells showing that when freed from the plant body, they had the ability to reorganize themselves into the new individuals. Steward and his co-workers showed that the phenomenon in the carrot cultures. Here the small pieces of mature clumpt root, were grown on a (*a*) The microorganisms present in the medium right from the beginning many be destroyed by sterilizing the properly plugged culture vials. It can be done by maintaining the temperature at 120°C for about 15 minutes.

(*b*) The microorganisms may also be carried along with tissue that is being cultured. To prevent this, the plant material from which the tissue is to be excised is surface sterilized. The material may be surface sterilized with saturated chlorine water and then thoroughly washed with sterilized distilled water and to remove all traces of chlorine. If the material is fairly hard, as are some fruits and seeds, it may be surface sterilized by rinsing in alcohol.

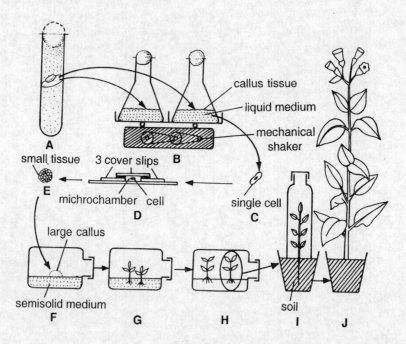

Fig. 8.2. Development of tobacco plants from single cells. A callus is raised from a small piece of tissue excised from the pith (*A*). By transferring it to a liquid medium and shaking the culture flasks ; (*B*), The callus is dissociated into a single cell; (*C*), is mechanically removed from the flask, and is placed on a slide in a drop of culture medium; (*D*), a microchamber is formed around the culture drop using the three-cover slips; (*D*), a small tissue; (*E*) derived from the cell through repeated division is then transferred to a semi-solid medium where it grows into large callus (*E*) and eventually differentiated plants (*F, G*), when transferred to soil; (*H*), these plants grow to maturity, flower and set seeds (*I*).

(*c*) Finally, precautions must also be taken to prevent the entry of microorganisms while the plug of a culture vial is removed to transfer the tissue to the nutrient medium (inoculation). For this, all operations from surface sterilization of the tissue up to inoculation are done in an aseptic environment.

Aeration

Proper aeration of the cultured tissue is also an important aspect of culture technique. If the tissue is grown on the surface of a semi-solid medium it acquires enough aeration without special device for liquid medium, special device "filter paper bridge" is used. Here, two legs remain dipping in the medium and the horizontal part carrying the tissue is raised above the level of the medium.

Cellular Totipotency

This is the capacity of mature cells showing that when freed from the plant body, they had the ability to reorganize themselves into the new individuals. Steward and his co-workers, showed this phenomenon in the carrot cultures. Here the small pieces of mature carrot root, were grown in a liquid medium supplemented with coconut milk, in special containers. These cultures were shaken generally which freed all the cell clusters into the medium. Some of them developed into rooting clumps. When these were transferred to the tubes containing a semi-solid medium, they gave rise to whole plant that flowered and set seeds. On the basis of these experiments, it can be inferred that, at least theoretically, every living plant cell, irrespective of its age and location, is totipotent. However, this phenomenon cannot be compared with the mode of the development of the zygote, wherein the divisions give predictable manner. But in case of cultured cells, the isolated single cells of tobacco divide, quite irregularly to form a mass from which roots and shoot buds differentiate eventually.

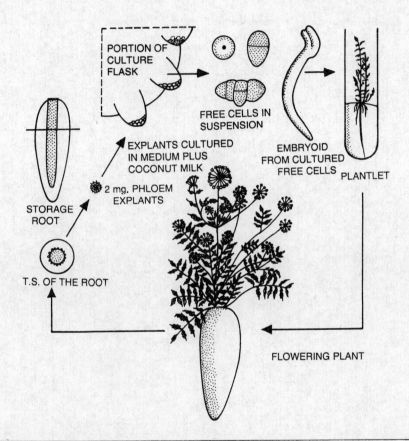

Fig. 8.3. An experiment to demonstrate the totipotency of plant cells. Slices of the carrot root were cut and small pieces of tissue were taken from the phloem region. These were inoculated into a liquid medium in special flasks, the tissue grew actively and single cells and small cell aggregates dissociated into the medium. Some of the cell clumps developed roots, and when transferred to a semisolid medium, these rooted nodules formed shoots. These plants could be transferred to soil.

However, Guha and Maheswari, while culturing mature anthers of *Datura innoxia* with an aim of understanding the physiology of meiosis, accidentally noticed that on basal nutrient medium containing kinetin, coconut milk, or grape juice numerous embryo-like structures appeared from the inside of anthers, which eventually, developed into plants. Later on, these workers confirmed the origin of the embryoids from pollen grain. As expected, the plantlets of pollen-origin were haploid.

Applications of Tissue Culture

(a) The technique provides a way for rapid multiplication of desirable and rare plants.

(b) As the experiments reveal, we may obtain healthy stocks from virus infected plants through shoot-tip culture.

Fig. 5.4. Different methods of regeneration from explant and cell/suspension cultures.

callus, in cell suspensions and protoplasts cultures, or directly from cells of organised structures, such as stem segments or zygotic embryo.

Advantages of plantlet regeneration. There are several advantages of plantlet regeneration through plant biotechnological methods using organogenesis or embryogenesis, in comparison to conventional methods of propagation. The advantages include the efficiency of process, *i.e.*, formation of plantlet in fewer steps, with reduction in labour, time and cost, and the potential for the production of much higher number of plantlets, and their morphological and cytological uniformity. Till now about 150 species from angiosperms and gymnosperms have been reported to produce somatic embryos in culture.

Shoot and root regeneration. Shoot regeneration is promoted by a cytokinin, such as BAP (benzylaminopurine). While root regeneration is promoted by an auxin, such as NAA (naphthalene acetic acid). Thus, shoot and root regenerations are generally controlled by auxin-cytokinin balance. Usually, an excess of auxin promotes root generation, and that of cytokinin promotes shoot generation.

Callus cultures are first kept on a BAP (cytokinin) containing medium. After sometime shoots regenerate from callus cells. When the shoots become 2-3 cm long, they are excised and transferred to an auxin-containing medium. After sometime, roots regenerate from the lower ends of these shoots to give rise to complete plantlets.

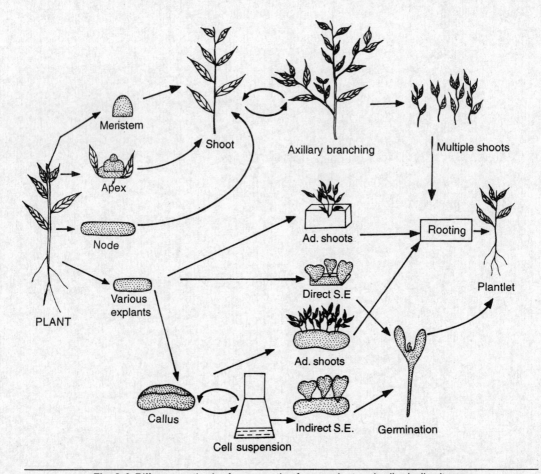

Fig. 8.4. Different methods of regeneration from explant and callus/cell cultures.

Somatic embryo regeneration. Plant cells are totipotent and can produce complete new plants under favourable conditions of nutrients and plant growth regulators. Steward and Reneirt, almost simultaneously reported for the first time, somatic embryo formation in carrot cell suspension cultures in 1958. These somatic embryos were similar to zygotic embryos in development and structure.

A somatic embryo develops from a somatic cell. The pattern of development of a somatic embryo is similar to that of a zygotic embryo.

Somatic embryo regeneration is induced usually by a relatively high concentration of an auxin like 2, 4-D (2, 4-dichorophenoxyacetic acid). The young embryos develop into mature embryos either in the same medium or on another medium. Mature somatic embryos germinate to yield complete plantlets.

During somatic embryo generation in cell suspension cultures, embryos of different sizes are produced. For any experimental or micropropagation method, embryos of uniform size are required. This can be achieved by sieving or fractionation of suspension with appropriate sieve size.

Somatic embryo regeneration is a versatile technique for micropropagation of plant species. A large number of herbaceous dicots and monocots have been regenerated through somatic embryogenesis.

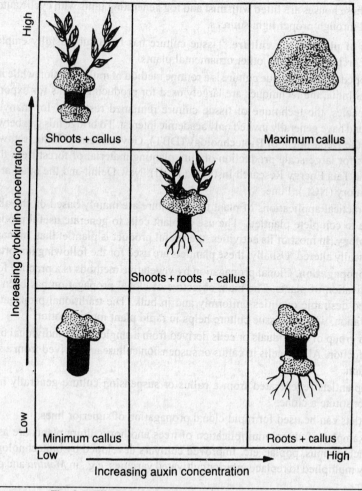

Fig. 8.5. Effect of a combination of auxin and cytokinin ratio.

Establishment of plantlets in the field. Plantlets are produced through rooting of isolated shoots or germination of somatic embryos. Now, the plantlets can be removed from culture vessels and established in the field. This stage is concerned with transfer of plantlets in pots, their **hardening** and establishment in soil. Hardening of plants imparts some tolerance to moisture stress and plants become autotrophic from heterotrophic condition. During hardening, plantlets are kept under a reduced light and high humidity for a suitable period of time. Hardening procedures make the plantlets capable of tolerating the relatively harsher environments outside the culture vessels.

Hardened plants are then transferred to glass or poly-houses with normal environmental conditions. Generally the poly-houses are erected by mounting polythene or polycarbonate sheets on metal frame support. Now, plants are irrigated frequently and their growth and variation monitored regularly. Plants are generally transferred to fields, *e.g.*, plantation crops, after 4-6 weeks of acclimatization.

In India, there are now many commercial companies which produce millions of plantlets through micropropagation.

Large glass houses and green houses are essential components of micropropagation industry. Hardening and acclimatization of delicate *in vitro* raised plantlets is carried out in these glass houses. Now a days chambers made of polycarbonate and polypropylene sheets are used for creating large working place. These houses are fitted with mist and fog generating units with cyclic auto-regulation. Light is provided through proper light sources.

Application of plant tissue culture. Tissue culture has been successfully employed for the multiplication of orchids and many other ornamental plants.

In the developed countries tissue culture is a routine method of multiplication while in developing countries, such as India, the techniques are largely used for producing plants for export markets.

With tree species, the technique of tissue culture remianed restricted for many years to the laboratory stage and have generally invited only academic interest. To bridge this gap between research and application, the Department of Biotechnology (DBT), Government of India, set two pilot-scale national facilities for large-scale production of elite planting material of forest trees through tissue culture, one at the Tata Energy Research Institute (TERI), New Delhi, and the other at the National Chemical Laboratory (NCL), Pune.

However, practical applications of plant tissue culture are mainly based on the ability of plant cells to give rise to complete plantlets. The use of plant cells to generate useful products is called **plant biotechnology.** In most of its activities, the useful product is plantlet that, in many cases may have been genetically altered. Usually, these plantlets are used for the following important purposes:

(i) **Clonal propagation.** Clonal propagation by vegetative methods is a practice followed since man started cultivation of plants. The main objective of clonal propagation has been to reproduce plants of selected desirable qualities uniformly and in bulk. The traditional propagation methods, require long duration, whereas tissue culture helps in rapid plant multiplication.

A **clone** is a group of individuals or cells derived from a single parent individual or cell through a asexual reproduction. All the cells in callus or suspension culture are derived from a single explant by mitotic division.

Hence, all plantlets regenerated from a callus or suspension culture generally have the same genotype and constitute a clone.

These plantlets can be used for rapid clonal propagation of superior lines.

Selected examples of clonal multiplication of trees and horticulture plants are as follows : oil palm, citrus peach, prunus, poplar, etc. Improved cultivars developed by biotechnological methods are then clonally multiplied to replace inferior cultivated varieties, *e.g.*, in *Mentha* and other aromatic plants.

(ii) **Somaclonal variation.** Genetic variation present among plant cells of a culture is called **somaclonal variation.**

In vitro cell and tissue cultures of plant give rise to genetic variation spontaneously. While spontaneous variation is not desired during propagule multiplication, it has been useful in providing some genetic variants among crop species. The observed frequencies of such somaclonal variants vary widely and are probably related to both time and culture. Several point mutations have been observed, the majority of analysed spontaneous genetic variants from somatic cultures appear to have resulted from induction of aneuploidy, loss of interchanges or intra-chromosomal segment duplication, deletions or structural arrangements.

Spontaneous or mutagen induced genetic variation in somatic cell culture coupled with *in vitro* selection techniques have been effective in isolating desired novel genetic variants with cellular level expression while in heterozygous condition. The somaclonal variation has been used to develop several useful varieties of crop plants.

(*iii*) **Transgenic plants.** A gene that is transferred into an organism by genetic engineering is called **transgene**. An organism that contains and expresses a transgene is called **transgenic organism.**

The plants, in which a functional foreign gene has been incorporated by any biotechnological methods that generally not present in plant, are called **transgenic plants.** However, a number of transgenic plants carrying genes for traits of economic importance have either been released for commercial cultivation or are under field trials.

However, transgenes can be introducd into individual plant cells. The cells containing and expressing transgenes can be easily selected *in vitro*. Ultimately, plantlets can be regenerated from these cells. These plantlets yield highly valuable transgenic plants.

Some of the commercially grown transgenic crop plants in developed countries are : 'Flavr Savri' and 'Endless Summer' tomatoes, 'Freedom II' squash, 'High lauric' rapeseed and 'Roundup Ready' soybean. So far more than 60 transgenic dicot plants including herbs, shrubs and trees, and several monocots, such as maize, oat, rice, wheat, etc., have been produced. In future the number of these crops certainly will go up. These transgenic plants contain certain selected traits such as herbicide resistance, insect resistance, virus resistance, seed storage protein, modified ripening, modified seed oil, agglutinin, etc.

Meristem Culture

The meristem is a dome of actively dividing cells about 0·1 mm in diameter and 0·25 mm in length. Shoots of all flowering plants grow by virtue of their apical meristems. The totipotency of the plant cells forms the basis of meristem culture.

Here, one can use an explant containing pre-existing shoot meristems, and produce shoots from them. Such cultures are known as **meristem culture.** The explants generally used in meristem culture are shoot tips or nodal segments.

These explants may be cultured on a medium containing a cytokinin, usually BAP (benzylaminopurine). Cytokinins promote axillary branching by overcoming apical dominance. Hence, they support multiple shoot development from each explant.

When axillary branching takes place, individual shoots are cultured, whereas when axillary branching does not take place, the single shoot is cut into nodal segments, which are then cultured. Shoots of 2-3 cm are excised and rooted on a suitable medium.

The *in vitro* culture of meristem and shoot tip involves several phases such as initiation of culture and establishment of explant, growth and differentiation, proliferation of shoots and finally plantlet fomation by rooting of shoots.

The plantlets thus obtained are subjected to hardening and ultimately established in the field.

Uses of meristem cultures. Meristem cultures are used for rapid clonal multiplication. Development of virus free plants is one of the most significant application of meristem culture. Generally this technique has applications in diverse areas such as clonal multiplication of vegetatively propagated crop plants, virus elimination and germplasm preservation.

Embryo Culture

Interspecific crosses may fail due to several reasons, but when the development of embryo is arrested owing to the degeneration of the endosperm, or when the embryo aborts at an early stage of development, embryo culture is the only technique to recover hybrid plants. It is being used extensively in the extraction of haploid barley (*Hordeum vulgare*) from the crosses *H. vulgare* × *H. bulbosum*. Embryo culture is also a routine technique employed in orchid propagation and inbreeding of those species that show dormancy. Das and Burman (1992) developed the method of regeneration of tea shoots from embryo callus.

Excision of young embryos from developing seeds and their cultivation on a nutrient medium is called **embryo culture**. *In vitro* older embryos are more easily cultured than young embryos.

The objective of embryo culture is to allow the young embryos to complete development and ultimately, give rise to seedlings.

More recently, a number of hybrids have been successfully raised through embryo culture : *Hordeum vulgare* × *Secale cereale*, *H. vulgare* × *Agropyron repens*, *H. vulgare* × *Triticum aestivum*, interspecific hybrids in *Abelmoschus* and *Secale.*

In some interspecific crosses, the endosperm of developing hybrid seeds degenerates at an early stage. Here, young embryos also die on the degeneration of endosperm. Hence such interspecific crosses cannot be normally made. In such cases, young hybrid embryos are excised and cultured *in vitro* to obtain hybrid seedlings.

The orchid industry owes a great deal to the technique of embryo culture. The culture of orchid embryos was initiated at the Singapore Botanic Garden in 1928. Orchids lack stored food. Here, embryo culture allows development of seedlings from most of the embryos. In such cases, embryo culture is also used for rapid clonal propagation.

Embryo culture has helped in overcoming self-sterility of seeds, especially of crop plants propagated vegetatively, when the seeds do not germinate in nature. In a wild relative of commercial banana, *Musa balbisiana,* for example, the seeds do not germinate under natural conditions. However, if the embryos are excised and grown on a simple culture medium of mineral salts, seedlings are readily obtained.

Indian work. Sometimes some interspecific hybrids of *Oryza* show quite a low percentage of seed germination under normal conditons because the hybrid embryos succumb at an early stage of their development. The scientists raised seedllings of certain interspecific crosses in *Oryza* by culturing the excised embryos on Nitsch's medium . The embryo culture technique has also been successfully employed in *Colocasia esculenta* where the seeds fail to germinate in nature. They grew the excised embroys on synthetic media and obtained seedlings which on transplanting in soil gave rise to normal healthy plants.

Rangaswamy and Rangan (1963) have cultured the embroys of a stem parasite, *Cassytha filiformis,* in the absence of the host, on a modified White's medium supplemented with IAA. The embryos of *Cuscuta reflexa,* a total stem parasite, were also cultured. Somewhat similar results have been obtained with the embryos of *Dendrophthoe falcata*, a partial stem parasite. Like the embryos of stem parasites, those of some root parasites have also shown considerable capacity for proliferation. In cultures of seeds of *Orobanche aegyptiaca,* a total root parasite, the ovoid unorganized embryos produced a massive callus capable of continuous growth followed by differentiation into shoot tips.

Anther Culture and Haploid Production

Anther, a male reproductive organ, is diploid (2n) in chromosome numbers. As a result of microsporogenesis, tetrads of microspores or pollen grains are formed from a single spore mother cell (2n), which are haploid (n).

In nature, haploid plants originate from unfertilised egg cells. However, in laboratory, they can be produced from both male and female gametes. In many plant species, haploids are produced when their anthers are cultured on a suitable medium. This process is called **anther culture.**

The first successful pollen cultures were established by Tulecke in the 1950's using mature pollen grains of certain gymnosperms. In 1964, Guha and Maheshwari discovered that when excised anthers of *Datura innoxia* were cultured intact in a mineral salt medium in conjunction with coconut milk and other complex organic substances and growth hormones, embryo-like outgrowths appeared from the sides of the anther in about 6-7 weeks. In subsequent studies, they confirmed the haploid nature of the embryoids and their origin from microspores.

Investigations have shown that for some reason, anthers from flowers of the Solanaceae respond best to excision and culture by production of embryoids. Convincing demonstration of the direct transformation of microspores into embryoids has been provided by several workers in different species of the genera of Solanaceae, *i.e., Datura, Nicotiana, Atropa, Lycium, Petunia, Solanum, Capsicum* and *Hyoscyamus.* It has been observed that embryoids go through the globular, heart-shaped and torpedo stages typical of the ontogeny of normal diploid zygotic embryos before they finally elongate and form shoot and root meristems. Embryoids have also been obtained form cultured anthers of certain cereals like rice. All in all therefore, the capacity of microspores in cultured anthers to form haploid embryoids and plants can now scarcely be questioned.

In some other plants, haploids do not arise directly from the microspores, but do through the intervention of a callus. The microspores first develop into multicellular bodies which later give rise to an exceedingly dense callus. Subculture of the callus in an embryogenesis-inducing medium containing specific concentration of auxins and a cytokinin led to the initiation of haploid seedlings. There, thus seem to exist the following alternative pathways for haploidy in anther cultures :

  1. Microspore → callus → embryogenesis → plantlet *e.g.,* Solanaceae

  2. Microspore → callus → embryogenesis → plantlet *e.g., Oryza, Brassica, Hordeum, Coffea, Populus.*

  3. Microspore → callus → plantlet, *e.g., Datura metelloides.*

In several species, the pollen grains can be isolated and cultured to obtain haploids. In many species of plants, haploids can also be produced by culturing unfertilised ovaries or ovules.

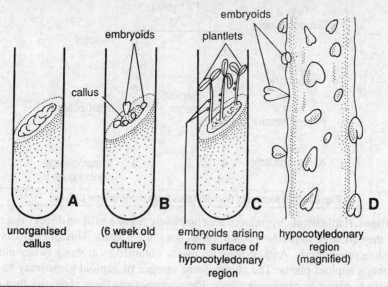

Fig. 8.6. Embryoid formation in tissue culture of butter cup. A, an unorganized callus ; B, six-week old culture showing numerous embryoids arising from the cells ; C, the embryoids have developed into plantlets and a fresh crop of embryoids is seen arising from the surface of the hypocotyledonary region of these plants; D, the embryoid-bearing portion enlarged from C.

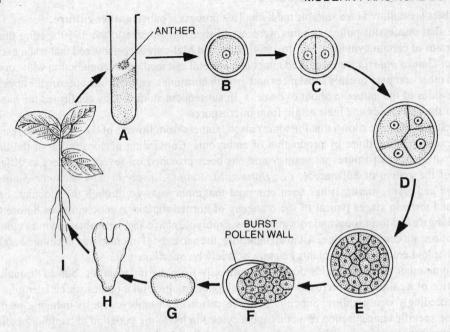

ANTHER

BURST
POLLEN WALL

Fig. 8·7. Diagram showing the development of haploid plants from the pollen grains of tobacco. The anther of the right stage is excised from the flower bud and cultured on a suitable medium (A). Some of the pollen inside the anther undergoes repeated division (B-D), forming a multicellular tissue within the parent wall (E). Eventually, the pollen wall bursts, releasing the tissue mass directly develops into an embryoid and germinates to form a haploid plant.

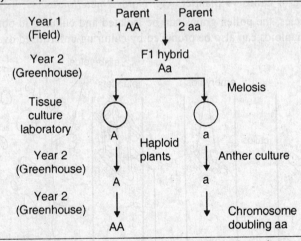

Year 1
(Field)

Parent 1 AA

Parent 2 aa

Year 2
(Greenhouse)

F1 hybrid
Aa

Tissue culture laboratory

Melosis

A   a

Year 2
(Greenhouse)

Haploid plants

Anther culture

A   a

Year 2
(Greenhouse)

AA

Chromosome doubling aa

Fig. 8.8. Production of homozygous lines using anther culture.

Applications. Haploids, such produced are completely sterile and of no direct value. But they are important as they are used to produce homozygous lines in 2-3 years. This strategy can be of much value in breeding programmes. Anthers from F₁, plants, obtained by crossing two or more lines, are cultured to obtain haploid plants. The chromosome number of haploid plants may be doubled by using colchicine to obtain homozygous plants. The progeny from these plants are then subjected to selection to isolate superior homozygous lines.

Thus, haploid plants are very useful in (i) direct screening of recessive mutation in diploid or polyploid, screening of recessive mutation is not possible, and (ii) development of homozygous diploid plants following chromosome doubling of haploid plant cells.

In China, the most widely grown wheat is a doubled haploid produced through homozygous diploid lines. Anther culture of rice is also successfully grown. Haploid plants have been produced in tobacco, wheat and rice through pollen culture which are used for the development of disease resistant and superior diploid lines.

At present, more than 247 plant species and hybrids belonging to 38 genera and 34 families of dicots and monocots have been regenerated using anther culture technique. They include economically important crops and trees, such as rice, wheat, maize, coconut, rubber plantation, etc.

Protoplast Culture and Somatic Hybridisation

An even more advanced technique of free cell culture is that involving the culture of isolated protoplasts. Essentially, the method consists of, first, breaking down the cell wall mechanically or

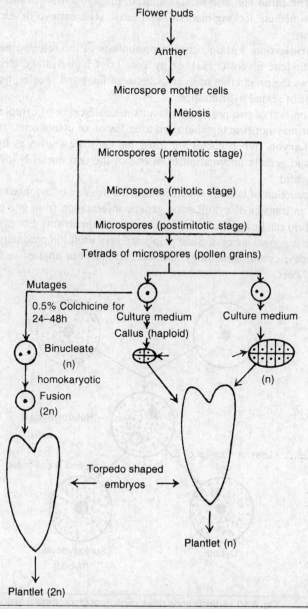

Fig. 8.9. Methods of anther culture, and production of haploid and diploid plants *in vitro.*

chemically using enzymes and thus freeing the protoplasts which are then cultured like whole cells using appropriate culture media. The cells are, in other words, rendered naked and then cultured.

When cell wall is mechanically or enzymatically removed, the isolated protoplast is known as 'naked plant cell' on which most of recent researches are based.

Plant cell wall acts as physical barrier and protects cytoplasm from microbial invasion and environmental stress. Cooking (1960), for the first time isolated the protoplasts of plant tissues by using cell wall degrading enzymes, *viz.*, cellulose, hemicellulose, pectinase and protease extracted from a saprophytic fungus *Trichoderma viride*. Later on protoplasts were cultured *in vitro*.

Protoplast culture and regeneration. The protoplasts regenerate a cell wall, undergo cell division and form callus. The callus can also be subcultured. Embryogenesis begins from callus when it is placed on nutrient medium lacking mannitol and auxin. The embryo develops into seedlings and finally mature plants.

Somatic hybridisation. Fusion between protoplasts of the selected parents is induced by a solution of polyethylene glycol (PEG), or by very brief high voltage electric current. Somatic hybridisation allows the production of hybrids between lines and species, that cannot be produced normally by means of sexual hybridisation.

Fusion of cytoplasm of two protoplasts results in coalescence of cytoplasm. The nuclei of two protoplasts may or may not fuse together even after fusion of cytoplasms. The binucleate cells are known as **heterokaryon.** When nuclei are fused the cells are known as **hybrid,** and when only cytoplasms fuse and genetic information from one of the two nuclei is lost is known as **cybrid,** *i.e.,* cytoplasmic hybrid.

However, production of cybrids which contain the mixture of cytoplasms but only one nuclear genome can help in transfer of cytoplasmic genetic information from one plant to another. Thus, information of cybrid can be applicable in plant breeding experiments. For example, in China, cybrid technology in rice is a great success. Such plants are very useful in producing hybrid seeds without emasculation. Today, cybrid technology has successfully been applied to carrot, mustard, citrus, tobacco and sugar beet.

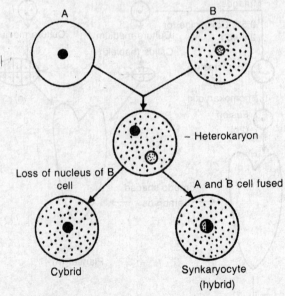

Fig. 8.10. Hybrid/cybrid production through protoplast fusion.

Somatic hybrids may also be used for gene transfer, transfer of cytoplasm and production of useful allopolypoloids.

Tissue and protoplast cultures have been used in genetic engineering for the transfer of DNA and extrachromosomal bodies — plasmids, mitochondria, chloroplasts, *nif* (nitrogen fixing) genes from the nitrogen fixing bacterium *Klebsiella pneumoniae* to a strain of the colon bacterium *Escherichia coli.* Isolated protoplasts have great advantage in all the afore mentioned uses. For transformation purposes cultured apical meristems are also usable because these can easily be regenerated into whole plants and also because intact DNA taken up by plants appears to be rapidly transported to meristematic regions, where growth and differentiation are centred.

Root culture. Excised roots were the first plant organs of higher plants to be successfully brought into sterile culture. In addition to the usual requirements for a carbon source and mineral nutrients most isolated roots grown in sterile culture required to be supplied with certain vitamins. This is because, in the intact plant, certain vitamins, are synthesized in the leaves and the roots are dependent upon shoots for the supply of these substances which they are unable to synthesize themselves. For example, tomato roots require only sucrose, mineral nutrients and thiamin, and given all these, will grow successfully in culture for many years. But excised roots of some monocotyledonous plants fail to grow even when supplied with a full complement of b-vitamins and other vitamins. In some of these (*e.g.*, rye), an exogenous auxin supplement to the nutrient medium allows growth to proceed. In order to maintain the culture, the excised roots must be regularly subcultured on to a fresh medium, by excising a piece of root bearing a lateral which then proceeds to grow rapidly and maintain the culture.

As a rule, excised root of most species produce only root tissues in culture. There are exceptions, however, where they regenerate shoot buds as well as further roots, *e.g.*, *Convolvulus, Taraxacum* and *Rumex.*

Generally excised root is cultured in liquid medium. The techniques of root culture give certain important informations such as, (*i*) nutritional requirements, (*ii*) infection by *Rhizobium* and nodulation and (*iii*) physiological activities.

Culture of Shoot Apices and Leaves

Like roots, isolated shoot apical meristems and leaf primordia can also be grown in sterile culture. These are often preferred in fact, because these frequently produce roots and can hence eventually develop into complete plants. The shoot apices and leaves of vascular cryptogams, such as ferns, are relatively more autotrophic than those of angiosperms. Thus, even a small fern apex can be grown on a medium containing only carbohydrate source and mineral nutrients. Small angiosperm apices (less than 0.5 mm in diameter) require a general source of organic nitrogen and certain specific amino acids and vitamins in addition to the basic medium, but larger apices will grow on a simple medium. The simpler requirements of larger apices may be due to the fact that they carry larger leaf primordia, which apparently can supply some of the requirements of the apex for vitamins and other organic nutrients.

Isolated young leaves of the fern *Osmunda cinnamomea* and of the sunflower (*Helianthus annuus*) and tobacco (*Nicotiana tabacum*) have been successfully grown on a simple medium containing only sucrose and inorganic salts. Such isolated leaf primordia continue to grow and develop into normally differentiated leaves, although the latter are usually very much smaller than normal leaves developed *in vivo, i.e.,* on the plant.

Culture of Ovaries

Rau (1956) attempted to culture pollinated ovaries of *Phlox drummondii* and studied the influence of extraneous chemicals on the pattern of development of the endosperm and embryo. The addition of colchicine to the medium caused aberrant divisions, fusion and aggregation of endosperm nuclei and finally a degeneration of the endosperm. In 12 to 14 days old cultures the embryo also aborted and the seeds were malformed.

Nirmala Maheshwari and Lal (1961) excised the flowers of *Iberis amara* one day after pollination and planted them on agar nutrient media. Fruits of normal size were obtained in two weeks on a medium containing Knop's mineral salts + Nitsch's trace elements + sucrose + B vitamins. The seeds formed *in vitro* contained viable embryos. Removal of the sepals slowed down the growth of the ovaries showing that the calyx is by no means an unessential structure but has an important role in the physiology of the fruit.

Pollinated ovaries of a few other plants have also been reared into fruits, but when unpollinated ovaries are taken, the fruits are either not formed or are seedless.

Johri and Sehgal (1963) cultured the ovaries of *Anethum graveolens* at the zygote stage on White's basal medium containing yeast extract and /or casein hydrolysate thirteen to twenty weeks later, a polyembryonate mass developed by the proliferation of the zygotic proembryo and ruptured the pericarp. Further growth resulted in the production of multiple shoots some of which flowered in the test tube after about seven months. Thus this was possible to obtain several seedlings from a single fertilized ovule.

However, it is easier to maintain ovules in sterile culture when they are left *in situ* within the ovary. The physiological requirements of fertilized ovules do not appear to be species specific, since young ovules of widely different species have grown to mature seeds following transplantation on to the placenta of *Capsicum* fruits.

Culture of Ovules and Parts of Ovules

White (1932) was the pioneer to culture the ovules. White and La Rue cultured ovules of *Erythronium* and *Antirrhinum* on White basic medium containing indole acetic acid IAA.

Nirmala Maheshwari and Lal (1961) cultured the ovules of *Papaver somniferum* excised six days after pollination when they contained only a 2-celled proembryo and a free nuclear endosperm. These grew to maturity in twenty days and even germinated and produced seedlings in the culture tubes.

Several genera, such as *Citrus, Eugenia* and *Mangifera* show the occurrence of nucellar embryos. Since they have the same genetical composition as the maternal parent, they are of much importance for the clonal propagation of desirable varieties. Rangaswamy (1961) reported that if the nucellar tissue of *Citrus microcarpa* is grown on a suitable nutrient medium containing casein hydrolysate, it proliferates profusely and on subculturing produces embryo-like regenerants termed **"pseudobulbils"**, which can develop into seedlings so that an indefinite number of new plants can be obtained from a single nucellus.

A. N. Rao (1963) successfully germinated seeds of an interspecific hybrid of *Vanda* on a simple agar nutrient medium. Some of the fertilized ovules directly produced seedlings; others gave rise to a callus from which new plants arose subsequently.

Culture of Endosperms

It is somewhat more difficult to raise tissue cultures from the endosperm. However, Rangaswamy and Rao (1963) established a continuously growing tissue from the mature endosperm of *Santalum album* when they cultured it along with the embryo on White's medium containing yeast extract, kinetin and 2, 4-D. On the other hand, the endosperm failed to callus when it was grown without the embryo. Johri and Bhojwani (1965), also cultured the endosperm of *Exocarpus cupressiformis* on White's medium containing indole actic acid IAA, kinetin and casein hydrolysate. If merely the endosperm devoid of the embryo was grown, it did not proliferate. In their experiments, the shoots were differentiated and not the roots.

BIOTECHNOLOGY

Biotechnology is that portion of microbiological science which deals with the possible utilisation of microorganisms in industrial processes, or in processes in which their activities may become of indusrial or technical significance. Thus, biotechnology may be defined as the use of microorganisms, animal or plant cells, or their components to generate products and services useful to human beings. However, the use of complete animals and plants is not generally included in biotechnology.

For several decades it has been known that numerous kinds of yeasts, moulds and other lower fungi, and several types of groups of bacteria have direct relation, to certain types of economic processes carried out in connection with industrial or factory operations, such as brewing, wine making, cheese making, etc. However, people did not know that microorganisms were involved in these processes. Microorganisms were used for the first time to produce some organic compounds like citric acid in the beginning of twentieth century. Thereafter, microorganisms were employed to generate a variety of products, including antibiotics. In all such processes, only the natural capabilities of the organisms and cells are exploited. All such activities carried over by microorganisms were grouped under **old biotechnology.**

In recent years revolution in biology has occurred due to the potential of biotechnology. Techniques have been developed to produce rare and medicinally valuable molecules, to change hereditary traits of plants and animals, to diagnose diseases, to produce useful chemicals, and to clean up and restore the environment. Thus, biotechnology has great impact in the fields of health, food, agriculture and environment protection.

During 1970, the technique of recombinant DNA technology was developed. Recombinant DNA technology is popularly known as genetic engineering. Recombinant DNA technology is responsible for the isolation of desired gene from any organism, and its transfer and expression into the organism of choice. In most of the developed countries, the recombinant DNA technology has become one of the major thrusts. The United Nations Industrial Development Organisation (UNIDO) has recognised the potential of genetic engineering and biotehnology for promoting the economic progress of the developing countries.

Transgenic microorganisms are produced to obtain novel pharmaceutical proteins, such as human insulin is commercially produced from a transgenic *Escherichia coli* (bacterium) strain, that contains and expresses the human insulin gene. Proteins poduced by transgenes are called **recombinant proteins.**

Many valuable recombinant proteins, also have been produced by use of transgenic animal cell lines and transgenic plants. However, the recombinant proteins cannot be naturally produced by the concerned cells or organisms. The production technologies based on genetic engineering are grouped under **modern biotechnology.**

In India, in 1988, a full fledged Department of Biotechnology (DBT) has been set up, in the Ministry of Science and Technology for planning, promotion and coordination of various biotechnological programmes.

Recombinant DNA technology has made it easier to detect the genetic diseases and cure before the birth of a child. In genetic engineering programmes, it has become possible to map the whole genome of an organism. Gene bank and DNA clone bank have been constructed to make available different types of genes of its known function.

Table 8.3. Area of Biotechnology

Area of interest	Products
1. Recombinant DNA technology (genetic engineering)	Fine chemicals, enzymems, vaccines, growth hormones, antibiotics, interferon.
2. Treatment and utilisation of biomaterials (biomass)	Single cell protein, mycoprotein, alcohol and biofuels.
3. Plant and animal cell culture.	Fine chemicals (alkaloids, essential oils, dyes, steriods), somatic embryos, encapsulated seeds, interferon, monoclonal antibodies.
4. Nitrogen fixation	Microbial inoculants (biofertilizers).
5. Biofuels (bioenergy)	Hydrogen (via photolysis), alcoholos (from biomass), methane (biogas produced from wastes and aquatic weeds).
6. Enzymes (biocatylysts)	Fine chemicals, food processing, biosenser, chemotherapy.
7. Fermentation	Acids, enzymes alcohols, antibiotics, fine chemicals, vitamins, toxins (biopesticides).
8. Process engineering	Effluent, water recycling, product extraction, novel reactor, harvesting.

Genetically Modified Crops

The plants, in which a functional foreign gene has been incorporated by any biotechnological methods that generally not present in plant, are called **transgenic plants**. A transgenic crop that contains and expresses a **transgene** (*i.e.*, functional foreign gene). Generally, transgenic crops are called **genetically modified crops** or **GM crops**.

The techniques used for production of transgenic crops have two great advantages. They are as follows :

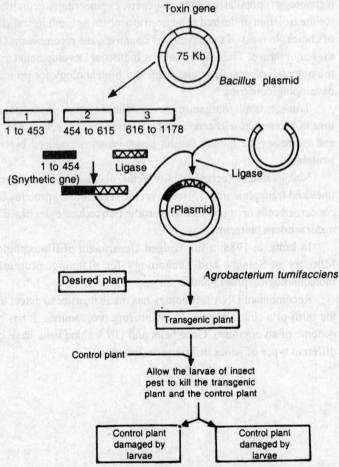

Fig. 8.11. Construction of a transgenic plant and expression of **Bt** gene against insect larvae.

(*i*) Any gene (from any organism or chemically synthesised) can be used as a transgene.

(*ii*) The change in genotype can be controlled to some extent as only the transgene is added into the crop genome.

In contrast, breeding activities can use only those genes which are present in such species that can be hybridised with them. Moreover, changes occur in all those traits for which the parents used in hybridisation differ from each other.

However, when a transgene is introduced into the genome of an organism, it can achieve one of the following characteristics :

(*i*) Produces the desired protein.

(*ii*) Produces a protein which itself produces the desired phenotype.

(*iii*) Modifies an existing biosynthetic pathway, and therefore, a new end product is obtained.

Some examples are mentioned here :

For example, **hirudin** is a protein that prevents blood clotting. The gene encoding hirudin was chemically synthesised. Thereafter, this gene was transferred into *Brassica napus,* where hirudin accumulates in seeds. Now, the hirudin is purified and used medicinally. Here, the transgene product itself is the desired product.

The other example is of a soil bacterium *Bacillus thuringiensis* which produces a crystal (Cry) protein. The Cry protein is toxic to larvae of certain insects. There are several different types of Cry proteins, and each of them is toxic to a different group of insects. The gene encoding Cry protein is *cry* gene, which has been isolated and transferred into several crops. A crop, that expresses a *cry* gene is usually resistant to the group of insects for which the concerned Cry protein is toxic. This is a case where the transgene product is directly responsible for the production of the phenotype of interest. Here this is noteworthy that the symbols for a gene (*cry*) and for its protein (Cry) product are the same. However, transgene symbol which has small letters is written in italics (*cry*), whereas the first letter of protein symbol is capital and written in Roman (Cry).

Insect-resistant transgenic plants. The *Bt* gene of a bacterium, *Bacillus thruingiensis* has been found to encode the toxins called endotoxins which have cidal effect of certain insect pests. These toxins are of different types, such as beta-endotoxin and delta-endotoxin. Preparations of *Bt* gene in powder form have been made available in market for commercial use.

The other approach has been isolation of the toxin gene *Bt 2* from *Bacillus thruingiensis* and its introduction into Ti-DNA plasmid of *Agrobacterium tumefaciens.* Thus, Ti-plasmid mediated transformation of several plants has been done, *e.g.*, tobacco, cotton, tomato, corn, etc.

Tomato variety 'Flavr Savr' is an example where expression of a native tomato gene has been blocked. Expression of native gene can be blocked by several methods. For example, fruit softening is promoted by the enzyme **polygalacturonase**, which is responsible for degrading pectin. Production of polygalacturonase was blocked in the transgenic tomato variety 'Flavr Savr'. Hence, fruits of this tomato variety remian fresh and retain their flavour for a longer period in comparison of the fruits of normal tomato varieties. The fruits of this transgenic variety have a superior taste and increased total soluble solids.

Genetically modified crops (GM crops) are already in cultivation in advanced countries, such as U.S.A. and many European countries.

However, in India, some insect resistant cotton varieties expressing *cry* genes have reached onto farmers for cultivation.

It is thought that transgenic crops may be harmful to the environment because of the following reasons :

(*i*) The transgene may be transferred through pollen from GM crops to their wild relatives and such a gene transfer may make the weeds more persistent and damaging.

In such cases, transgenic crops should not be grown in close vicinity of their wild relatives.

(*ii*) The transgenic crops may themselves become persistent weeds.

(*iii*) In view of this, such crops may damage the environment in some mysterious manner. Investigations are on to check such menace.

Genetically Modified Food

The food prepared from the produce of genetically modified crops (GM crops) is called **genetically modified food** (GM food).

The GM food differs from the food prepared from the produce of conventionally developed used during gene transfer by genetic engineering or recombinant technology.

(*iii*) GM food contains the antibiotic resistance gene itself.

It has been argued that the above mentioned features of GM foods may be harmful and problem making if such foods are consumed. These problems may be as follows :

(*i*) The transgene product (GM food) may cause toxicity and produce allergies.

(*ii*) The enzyme produced by the antibiotic resistance gene may cause allergies, as it is a foreign protein.

(*iii*) The bacteria present in the intestine of the humans may take up the antibiotic resistance gene that is present in the GM food. These bacteria will become resistant to the concerned antibiotic and become unmanageable.

The biotechnologists involved in the production of transgenic crops are aware of above men tioned aspects, and effortrs are being made to use other genes in place of antibiotic resistance genes.

Ban on genetic food. It is a growing concern all over the world that the genetic food may pose risks to human health, ecology and the environment. However, it has forced the governments of many countries to rethink on introduction of such crop. For the first time the European Commission's Scientific Advisors have recommended that a genetically engineered potato be withheld from the market because they cannot guarantee its safety. The United States, the world's biggest producers of genetically modified foods, has also threatened New Zealand to ban his genetically engineered foods.

Sustainable Agriculture

In modern days, in agricultural practices non-renewable resources are utilised which cause pollution. However, such practices cannot be continued indefinitely. This means, they are not sustainable.

Sustainable development may be defined in several ways. **Sustainable agriculture** primarily have renewable resources, which cause minimum pollution and maintain the optimum yield level.

Any such development which reduces the use of non-renewable resources, and level of pollution, will definitely enhance the sustainability of agriculture.

Biotechnology contributes in several ways for enhancement of the sustainability of agriculture. They are as follows :

Biofertilizers. The term 'biofertilizers' denotes all the 'nutrient inputs of biological origin for plant growth' (Subba Rao, 1982). However, microorganisms employed to enhance the availability of nutrients like nitrogen, and phosphorus to crops are called biofertilizers.

As we know, nitrogen is available in atmosphere in high amount in the form of gas. It is converted into combined form of organic compounds by some prokaryotic microorganisms through biological reactions. The phenomenon of fixation of atmospheric nitrogen by biological means is known as **'diazotrophy'** or 'biological nitrogen fixation' and these prokaryotes as 'diazotrophs' or 'nitrogen fixers' (nif). They may be in free living or in symbiotic forms.

Examples of nitrogen-fixing microorganisms are bacteria and cyanobacteria (blue-green algae). Some of these microorganisms are free-living, while others form symbiotic association with plant roots. **Rhizobia** form root nodules in leguminous crops, while cyanobacteria form symbiotic association with the pteridophyte *Azolla.*

On the other hand, insoluble forms of soil phosphorus are converted into soluble forms by certain microorganisms. This makes the phosphorus available to the plants.

Phosphate is made soluble by some bacteria and by some fungi that form association with roots of higher plants. The fungus and plant root association is called *mycorrhiza*. Here the fungi absorb their food from the roots and in response are beneficial to the plants. The mycorrhiza may be external or internal. The external mycorrhiza also called 'ectophytic mycorrhiza' are confined to the outer region of the roots, whereas the internal mycorrhiza are found deeply in the root cells. These fungi solubilise phosphorus, produce plant growth promoting substances and protect host plants from soil pathogens.

Advantages. Biofertilizers make a low cost and easy technique and can be used by small farmers.

It is free from pollution hazards and increases soil fertility. Cyanobacteria secrete growth promoting substances, amino acids, proteins, vitamins, etc. They add sufficient amount of organic matter in soil.

Rhizobial biofertilizer can fix 50-150 kg N/ha/annum.

Azolla supplies N, increases organic matter and fertility in soil and shows tolerance against heavy metals.

The biofertilizers increase physico-chemical properties of soil, such as soil structure, texture, water holding capacity, etc.

The mycorrhizal biofertilizers make the host plants available with certain elements, increase longevity and surface area of roots, reduce plant response to soil stresses, and increase resistance in plants. In general, plant growth, survival and yield are increased.

However, extensive efforts are made to enhance the effectiveness and the contribution of biofertilizers to agricultural production.

Biopesticides. Biopesticides are those biological agents which are used to control weeds, insects and pathogens. There is a vast majority of microorganisms, such as viruses, bacteria, fungi, protozoa and mycoplasma known to kill the insect pests. The suitable preparations of such microorganisms for control of insects are called 'microbial insecticides'. The microbial insecticides are non-hazardous, non-phytotoxic and selective in their action. Pathogenic microorganisms which kill insects are viruses (DNA containing viruses), bacteria (*e.g.*, *Bacillus thuringiensis*), and fungi (*e.g.*, *Aspergillus, Fusarium,* etc.). Now a days, some of the biopesticides are being used even at commercial scale.

For example, *Bacillus thuringiensis* is a widely distributed soil bacterium, and can be isolated from soil, litters and dead insects. It is a spore forming bacterium and produces several toxins. Spores of this bacterium produce the insecticidal Cry protein. Therefore, spores of this bacterium kill larvae of certain insects. After ingestion of spores, larvae are damaged, as the rod-shaped bacterial cell secretes at the opposite end, a single large crystal (Cry) in the cell. This crystal is toxic and proteinaceous in nature. The commercial preparations of *B. thuringiensis* contain a mixture of spores, Cry protein (toxin) and an inert carrier.

Bacillus thuringiensis, was the first biopesticide to be used on a commercial scale. Certain other bacteria and fungi are also used for control of some weeds and diseases of various crop plants.

Microbial pesticides are produced by many multi-national companies by using viruses, bacteria and fungi. *B. thuringiensis* preparations have been produced in U.S.A., France, Russia and U.K. in the form of wettable powder and water suspensions.

A number of **viruses** have been discovered which belong to groups Baculoviruses and cytoplasmic polyhedrosis viruses (CPV). Preparations of viruses or their products have been developed as effective biopesticides and being successfully used for the control of insect pests in agriculture and horticulture.

Recent studies on the use of **mycopesticides** for the control of insect pests are of much value. Mode of action of these fungi is different from viruses and bacteria. The infective conidia, spores, etc., of the antagonistic fungi reach the haemocoel of the insect either through integument or mouth. They multiply in haemocoel followed by secretion of mycotoxins which result in death of insect hosts.

The use of biopesticides may reduce the application of synthetic chemicals for control of diseases, insect pests and weeds. The synthetic insecticides, generally affect non-target organisms, and many beneficial organisms for agriculture, are killed. In turn, they cast hazardous effects on human health, and therefore, use of biopesticides has been suggested.

Disease-resistant Varieties

Genetic engineering has been also used in the development of such crop varieties which are resistant to certain diseases. Usually, plant diseases are caused by fungi, bacteria, viruses and nematodes.

The most successful approach for the production of virus resistant plants is the transfer of the virus coat protein gene into the plants. The genetic material of viruses is found enclosed in a protein coat.

The gene that encodes coat protein is isolated from the genome of the virus that causes concerned disease. Now this gene is transferred and expressed in the host of the concerned virus.

Expression of the coat protein produces resistance in the host to this virus. This approach has been used in producing a virus-resistant variety of squash. Such disease-resistant varieties are used to minimise the use of chemicals which are generally used for control of crop diseases. This approach also reduces pollution. Such varieties are successful in reducing yield losses due to various crop diseases, thus they enhance agricultural production.

Single Cell Protein (SCP)

The dried cells of microorganisms, such as algae, bacteria, actinomycetes and fungi, used as food or feed are collectively known as **microbial protein.** Since the time immemorial a number of microorganisms have been used as part of human diet. Microorganisms are widely used for preparation of a variety of fermented foods, such as cheese, butter, leavened bread, *idlis* and several other bakery products. Some other microorganisms have long been used as human food, *e.g.*, the blue green alga (cyanobacteria), *Spirulina*, and the fungi commonly called edible mushrooms.

The term 'microbial protein' was replaced by a new term 'single cell protein' (SCP) during first International Conference on 'microbial protein' held in 1967, at Masachusetts, U.S.A. In recent years, NBRI, Lucknow and CFTRI, Mysore, have established centres for mass production of SCP from *Spirulina* (cyanobacteria).

Substrates used for production of SCP. A variety of substrates are used for SCP production. Algae which contain chlorophylls, do not require organic wastes. They use free energy from sunlight and carbondioxide from air, while bacteria and fungi require organic wastes, as they do not contain chlorophylls, the major components of substrates are the raw materials which contain sugars, starch, lignocellulose from woody plants and herbs having residue with nitrogen and phosphorus contents and other raw materials.

Nutritional value of SCP. SCP is rich in high quality protien and poor in fats. They are ideal for human food. SCP provides a valuable protein-rich supplement in human diet.

Now a days, many pilot plants for the production of *Spirulina* powder have been established in Japan, U.S.A. and European countries. In India, food grade *Spirulina* at two main centres, one at MCRC, Chennai and the other at Central Food Technology and Research Institute (CFTRI), Mysore. The products are marketed in India and abroad.

The use of *spirutina* (SCP) should help bridge the gap between the requirement and the supply of proteins in the human diet. *Spirulina* (SCP) is a rich source of protein, amino acids, vitamins, minerals, crude fibres, etc., it is used as supplemented food in diets of under-nourished children, adults and old aged people in developing countries. *Spirulina* is also popular as health food.

SCP as therapeutic and natural medicine. *Spirulina* posseses many medicinal properties. It has been recommended by medicinal experts for reducing body weight, cholesterol and for better health. It lowers sugar level in blood of diabetics. It is a good source of β-carotenes, and helps in monitoring healthy eyes and skin.

Biopatent

Dictionary meaning of **patent** is, 'an official right to be the only person to make, use or sell a product or an invention'. Thus, a patent is the right granted by a government to prevent others from commercial use of his invention.

A patent is granted for :
- (i) an invention, including a product,
- (ii) an improvement in an earlier invention,
- (iii) the process of generating a product, and
- (iv) a concept or design.

Initially, patents were granted for industrial inventions by a particular company, such as patent medicines, etc.

But, now a days, patents are also being granted for biological entities and for products derived from them, such patents are called **biopatents**, e.g., *neem* and its products; *haldi* and its products.

However, industrialised countries, such as U.S.A. , Japan and European Union Countries, are awarding Biopatents.

Biopatents are awarded for the following :
- (i) strains of microorganisms,
- (ii) cell lines,
- (iii) genetically modified strains of plants and animals,
- (iv) DNA sequences,
- (v) the proteins enclosed by DNA sequences
- (vi) various biotechnological products
- (vii) production processes
- (viii) products, and
- (ix) product applications.

On the basis of ethical and political reasons, such biopatents have been opposed from time to time by different societies of the world. However, arguments in favour of biopatents are given primarily of increased economic growth.

Many biotechnological patents are quite broad in their coverage. For example, one patent covers 'all transgenic plants of family Brassicaceae/mustard family. Such broad patents are unacceptable and not fair, as they would enable financially powerful corporations to have their monopoly control over biotechnological processes. Such powerful corporations try to control the direction of whole agricultural research, including plant breeding. Such a position seems to be a threat to the food security of the world.

Biopiracy

When big organisations and multinational companies exploit patent biological resources or bioresources of other nations without proper authorisation from the countries concerned; such exploitation is called **biopiracy.**

The advanced or industrialised nations are generally rich in technology and financial resources. However, they are poor in biodiversity and traditional knowledge related to bioresources. While developing nations are poor in technology and financial resources, but quite rich in biodiversity and traditional knowledge related to bioresources.

Biological resources or **bioresources** are those organisms which can be used to derive commercial benefits from them.

Traditional knowledge related to bioresources is the knowledge developed by various communities from time immemorial, regarding the utilisation of the bioresources, e.g., use of plants and other organisms in healing art. Such traditional knowledge of a particular nation can be exploited to develop modern commercial processes. Here, the traditional knowledge is primarily used in the direction to be followed which saves a lot of time, and bioresources are easily commercialised.

Institutions and multinational companies of industrialised advanced nations are collecting and exploiting the bioresources, as follows :

(*i*) They collect and patent the genetic resources themselves. For example, a patent granted in U.S.A. covers entire 'basmati' rice germplasm indigenous to our country.

(*ii*) The bioresources are analysed for identification of valuable biomolecules. A **biomolecule** is a compound produced by a living organism.

(*iii*) Useful genes are isolated from the bioresources and patented, and thereafter, used to generate useful commercial products.

(*iv*) Sometimes, even traditional knowledge itself of other countries may be patented.

For example, a plant, *Pentadiplandra brazzeana* of West Africa, produces a protein called **brazzein.** This protein is approximately two thousand times as sweet as sugar. Moreover, this is a low calorie sweetner.

Local people of West Africa have known and used the super-sweet berries of this plant for centuries. However, the protein brazzein was patented in U.S.A. , where the gene encoding this protein was also isolated, sequenced and patented.

It is proposed to transfer the brazzein gene into maize and express it in maize grains. These grains (kernels) will be used for the extraction of brazzein, which can give a serious jolt to the countries exporting large quantities of sugar.

Bioresources of third world countries have always been commercially exploited by the industrialised nations without an adequate compensation. This exploitation has increased a lot with the development of biotechnological techniques. Some developing nations coming forward and raising voice to make laws to prevent unauthorised exploitation of bioresources and traditional knowledge.

Biowar

This word denotes, the use of harmful bacteria as weapons of war. The biological weapons are generally used against humans, and their crops and animals. A **bioweapon** is a device that carries and delivers to the target organisms, a pathogen or a toxin derived from it.

The **bioweapon agent**, is kept in a suitable container so that it remains acitive and virulent during delivery. The container with bioweapons could be delivered to the target by several ways, including missiles and aircrafts.

For example, anthrax is an acute infectious disease caused by the spore-forming bacterium *Bacillus anthracis*. Spores of *B. anthracis* can be produced and stored in a dry form keeping them viable for several decades in storage or after release. A cloud of anthrax spores, if released at a strategic location to be inhaled by the individuals under attack may act as an agent of effective weapon of **biowar**. For example, the anthrax bacteria were sent through letters after September 2001, in U.S.A.

An attack with bioweapons using antibiofic-resistant strains would initiate the incidence and spread of communicable diseases, such as anthrax and plague, on either an endemic or epidemic scale.

Bioweapons are low cost weapons, and cause far more casualities than chemical or conventional weapons. Bioweapon agents are microscopic and invisible with naked eyes, and therefore, difficult to detect.

Such type of biowar and use of bioweapons against civilised human society is a major threat for all inhabitants of this planet, the earth.

The possible defences against bioweapons include use of gas mask, vaccination, administration of specific antibiotics, and decontamination. However, biologists should play an important role in creating awareness about the impact of misuse of biology on the human society and the whole Biokingdom.

Bioethics

Ethics includes 'moral principles' that control or influence a person's behaviour. This is connected with beliefs and principles about what is right or wrong, morally correct or acceptable. This includes a set of standards by which a community regulates its behaviour and decides as to which activity is legitimate and which is not.

Thus, **bioethics** makes a set of standards which is used to regulate our activities in relation to the whole biokingdom.

Now a days, biotechnology, particularly recombinant DNA technology, is used for exploitation of the biological world by various ways. Biotechnology has been used in various ways, from 'unnatural' to 'detrimental' to 'biodiversity'. The major bioethical ways concerning to biotechnology, are as follows :

1. Use of animals in biotechnology is cruelty towards animals which causes great suffering to them.

2. When animals are used for production of certain pharmaceutical proteins, they are treated as a 'factory' or 'machine'.

3. Introduction of a transgene from one species into another species threats integrity of species.

4. Transfer of human genes into animals or *vice-versa* is great ethic threat for humanness.

5. Biotechnology is only used for fulfilment of the motive of selfishness by humans. This is used only for the benefit of human beings.

6. However, biotechnology poses unforeseen risks to the environment and biodiversity.

Besides ethical arguments, techniques of biotechnology are used in the production of things on a much larger scale and at a much faster rate. Each society has to evaluate bioethical issues and take right decision about their application.

TERMS TO REMEMBER

Anther culture. Haploids are produced, when anthers are cultured on a suitable medium.

Bioethics. A set of standards which may be used to regulate own activities in relation to the biological world.

Biofertilizers. Microorganisms employed to enhance the availability of nutrients.

Biomolecule. A compound produced by a living organism.

Biopatents. The patents granted for biological entities and products derived from them.

Biopesticides. Biological agents used for control of weeds, insects and pathogens.

Biopiracy. Exploitation of bioresources of other nations without proper authorisation from the countries concerned.

Bioresources. All these organisms that can be used to derive commercial benefits.

Biotechnology. Use of organisms, and their cells or components to generate products and services useful to human beings.

Biowar. Use of biological weapons against humans, or their crops and animals.

Bioweapon. A device that carries and delivers to the target organisms a pathological agent or a toxin derived from it.

Bioweapon agent. A biological agent or toxin.

Brazzein. A plant, *Pentadiplandra brazzeana* produces a protein called brazzein, which is about 2000 times as sweet as sugar. A low-calorie sweetener.

Callus culture. Cell division in the explant forms a callus, an unorganised mass of cells is called callus culture.

Clone. A group of individuals or cells derived from a single parent individual or cell through asexual reproduction.

Embryo culture. Excision of young embryos from developing seeds and their cultivation on a nutrient medium.

Explant. A plant part, excised from its original location and used for initiating a culture.

G.M. crop. Genetically modified crop or transgenic crop that contains and expresses a transgene.

G.M. food. The food prepared from genetically modified (transgenic) crops.

Hardening. The procedure done, when plantlets are transferred from culture vessels and established in the field.

Hirudin. A protein that prevents blood clotting.

Meristem culture. Use of an explant that contains pre-existing shoot meristems and produce shoots from them.

Mycorrhiza. The fungus and plant root association.

Plant tissue culture. Maintenance and growth of plant cells, tissues and organs on a suitable culture medium *in vitro*.

Protoplasts. The plant cell lacking cell wall.

Recombinant proteins. Proteins produced by transgenes.

Regeneration. Development of an organised structure (*e.g.,* root, shoot, embryo) from cultured cells.

Rhizobia. The bacteria which form root nodules in legume crops.

Somatic hybrid. A hybrid produced by fusion of somatic cells of two varieties or species.

Subculturing. When tissues/cells are regularly transferred into new culture vessels containing fresh media, the process is called subculturing.

Suspension culture. It consists of single cells and small groups of cells suspended in a liquid medium.

Sustainable agriculture. Primarily use renewable resources, cause minimum pollution and obtain optimum yield level.

Totipotency. The ability of plant cells to regenerate into complete plants is called totipotency.

Transgenic crop. A crop that contains and expresses a transgene.

CHAPTER 9

Biotechnology: Genetic Engineering, Cloning and Genomics

As we know, genes regulate growth and differentiation, and all fundamental life processes are also regulated by them. Ageing and cancer result from differential gene expression. Several other pathological disorders are also caused by some defective gene. Thus, it becomes quite important to understand the structure of genes and their organization and how their expression is regulated. However, in microorganisms, it is easy to study the organization and expression of genes. This is because several mutants, with altered characteristics can be isolated. In bacteria, conjugation and transduction experiments can also be carried out, where the functional characters could easily be related to specific genes and their arrangement.

In this chapter, we will learn about the tools and techniques of molecular biology for cleaving and rejoining DNA sequences from two or more different organisms.

Such genetically modified DNA fragments are known as recombinant DNA molecules. This process involves manipulation or engineering of the DNA (genes) involved in the process and thus the term **'genetic engineering'** has been coined.

The recombinant DNA molecules can be cloned and amplified virtually to an unlimited extent.

Application of DNA manipulation or genetic engineering ranges from cloning genes to cloning organisms including transgenic microbes, agriculturally important crops and farm animals.

Thus by the process of genetic engineering we can get genetically modified food products, human gene products, pharmacologically and therapeutically useful products.

Gene therapy or gene replacement can be used in the treatment of hereditary diseases which are otherwise incurable.

In modern days, DNA fingerprinting has been successfully used in forensic investigations.

Now human genome has been worked out, which reveals the blue print of our life itself.

The latest of this series is claim of first human clone, which was announced by Brigitte Boisselier, head of a company known Clonaid on December 26, 2002, a baby girl called Eve by scientists.

GENETIC ENGINEERING

Genetic engineering is considered as a kind of biotechnology.

This is a process in which the alteration of the genetic make up of cells is done by deliberate and artificial means.

This process involves transfer or replacement of genes to create recombinant DNA.

This can be done by cutting DNA molecules at specific sites to get fragments containing desirable and useful genes from one type of cell.

Thereafter, these genes can be inserted into a suitable carrier or vector.

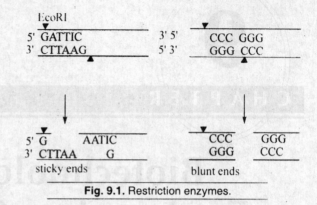

Fig. 9.1. Restriction enzymes.

Now, these recombinant DNA can be put into completely different cell of a bacterium or plant or animal cell.

By this technique they acquire useful characteristics, such as disease resistance or to make useful enzymes, hormones, vaccines, etc.

Tools and Techniques of Genetic Engineering

Genetic engineering involves cutting and pasting fragments of DNA may be cut and pasted in the vector, a plasmid or a virus whose DNA then becomes the recombinant DNA.

Tools of genetic engineering. The three tools for recombinant DNA technology are as follows :

1. Cell culture containing cells with the desired DNA segment (gene).

2. DNA modifying enzymes such as : (*a*) Restriction endonuclease from various bacteria. It cleaves double stranded DNA but only at a limited number of sites (*b*) DNA ligase from *Escherichia coli* which joins DNA molecules. (*c*) DNA polymerase from *E. coli* which synthesises a new strand of DNA complementary to an existing DNA or RNA template.

DNA segment can be excised by **"molecular scissors"** or **'chemical scalpels'** which are known as **restriction enzymes** in biotechnological language.

Restriction enzymes, synthesized by microbes as a defense mechanism, are specific endonucleases, which can cleave double-stranded DNA.

However, they can do this only at limited number of sites depending on the number of recognition sequences in DNA.

With the use of **restriction enzymes** it is possible to cut a DNA sequence. For example, a restriction enzyme EcoR1 will cut DNA only if

sequence $\dfrac{\text{GAATC}}{\text{CTTAG}}$ is present in the

double stranded DNA. Hundreds of such restriction enzymes with different sequence specificities have been isolated from several bacteria and are commercially available. These enzymes are known as **restriction enzymes**

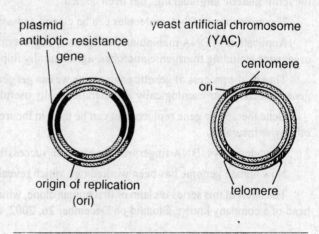

Fig. 9.2. Plasmid and yeast artificial chromosome

because they restrict infection by bacteria by certain bacteriophages, by degrading the viral DNA without affecting the bacterial DNA. Thus, such enzymes are helpful in breaking DNA molecule at a specific point. In recombinant DNA technology, they are used to cut DNA into specific fragments that contain specific genes.

DNA synthesising enzymes. DNA synthesising enzymes, such as **DNA polymerase** or **reverse transcriptase** to make DNA complementary to an existing DNA or RNA template respectively called c DNA (complementary or copy DNA) are also required.

Because of the presence of an universal genetic code, the DNA polymerases (synthesising enzymes) can accurately transcribe a DNA sequence from one organism to another organism, and finally molecular sutures, the **DNA ligase** enzymes to join DNA fragments.

This happens so by the formation of phosphodiester bond, again.

Any pair of fragments produced by the same restriction enzyme, from any DNA source (*e.g.*, fruit fly, any other animal or human), can be joined together.

3. **Cloning vectors.** The desired gene is inserted in the vectors or gene carrier to form DNA. Vectors carrying recombinant DNA (r-DNA) divide and thus help in producing several copies of the r-DNA.

There are five cloning vectors which are used in experiments with *E. coli* animals/humans are:

(*a*) plasmids (*b*) bacteriophages (viruses that infect bacteria) (*c*) plant/animal viruses (*d*) transposons (jumping genes) and (*e*) artificial chromosomes of bacteria, yeast and mammals.

The most commonly used vectors are plasmids and viruses.

Recombinant DNA (r-DNA) technique. The sequence of steps in r-DNA technology are as follows :

(*i*) Cell culture of cells with the required DNA sequences is obtained through tissue culture technique. (*ii*) Specific restriction endonuclease is selected from the specific bacterium. (*iii*) Restriction endonuclease cuts the specific DNA (desired gene) at the two ends which becomes the **restriction fragment**. (*iv*) Same restriction endonuclease cuts a matching DNA sequence from a plasmid. (*v*) Ligase enzyme which acts as a molecular glue joins the restriction fragment in the place vacated by the cut DNA segment of the plasmid. The plasmid DNA now

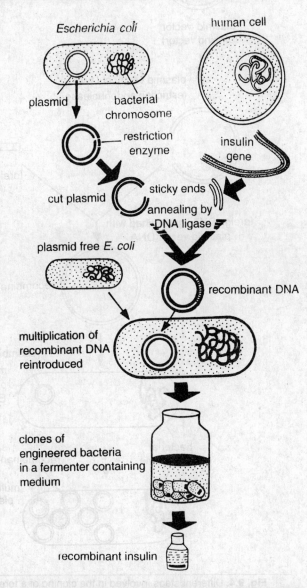

Fig. 9.3. Steps showing gene transfer for the production of human insulin.

contains foreign DNA and its DNA is called **recombinant DNA** (r-DNA). (*vi*) Recombinant plasmids containing recombinant DNA are now inserted into a host cell, *e.g.*, *E. coli*. This is commonly done by a process called **electroporation** in which transient temporary pores are created in the cell membrane of the host for the uptake of foreign DNA molecules. (*vi*) Host bacterium divides to give multiple copies of the recombinant DNA which may be preserved in a DNA library which is also called genomic DNA library.

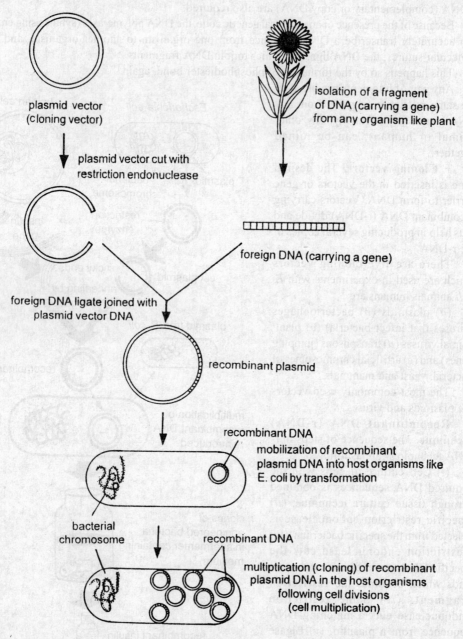

plasmid vector
(cloning vector)

plasmid vector cut with
restriction endonuclease

isolation of a fragment
of DNA (carrying a gene)
from any organism like plant

foreign DNA (carrying a gene)

foreign DNA ligate joined with
plasmid vector DNA

recombinant plasmid

recombinant DNA
mobilization of recombinant
plasmid DNA into host organisms like
E. coli by transformation

bacterial
chromosome

recombinant DNA

multiplication (cloning) of recombinant
plasmid DNA in the host organisms
following cell divisions
(cell multiplication)

Fig. 9.4. Different steps involved in the cloning of a foreign DNA fragment into a plasmid vector (diagrammatic representation).

Genomic DNA library. A gene library contains several copies of many of the desired genes or DNA fragments. These may be present in bacterial clones with **recombination DNA** or by obtaining **complementary DNA** (c- DNA) by obtaining a DNA from an RNA template by using the enzyme reverse transcriptase. A collection of different c-DNA fragments is a c-DNA library. Gene libraries are maintained through special techniques.

Gene Transfer

Gene transfer can be done by two methods :

    (*i*) indirect method through vectors or carriers and

    (*ii*) direct or vectorless transfer method.

The first method includes (*a*) plasmids and viruses and (*b*) natural genetic engineer.

(*a*) **plasmids and viruses.** Recombinant DNA technology involves the transfer of desired genes into vectors such as plasmids or viruses. Cloning of the recombinant DNA (r-DNA) then provides multiple copies.

Natural genetic engineering tumor inducing (ti) plasmid. For example, *Agrobacterium tumefaciens* is a plant pathogenic bacterium which can transfer part of its plasmid DNA as it infects host plants. Species of *Agrobacterium* produce crown galls or plant tumors in several dicot plants such as tobacco, tomato, potato, etc.

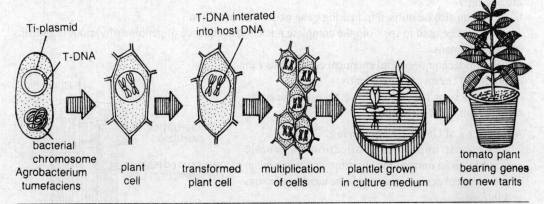

Fig. 9.5. *Agrobacterium*. Tumor inducing (Ti) plasmid-mediated genetic transformation in plants.

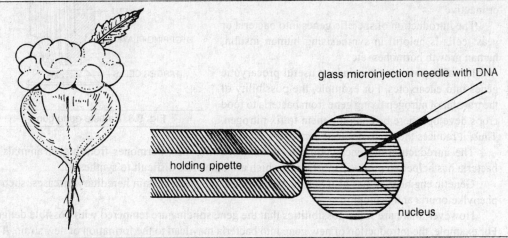

Fig. 9.6. Tumor inducing (Ti) plasmid. Crown caused on turnip by bacteria (*Agrobacterium tume-faciens*) carrying Ti plasmid.

Fig. 9.7. Microinjection. Micropipette is used for injecting DNA into the nucleus of a cell.

These bacteria contain large Ti-plasmids (*i.e.,* tumor-inducing plasmids in *Agrobacterium tumefaciens*) which pass on their tumour causing gene into the genome of the host plant. Thus, galls are formed on the host plant and therefore, these bacteria are known as *natural genetic engineers of plants.* Ti-plasmids can be used as gene vectors for delivering useful foreign genes into target plant cells and tissues. Ti-plasmid vectors can be used for genetic transformation of many important dicot (*e.g.,* potato, tomato, cotton, sunflower, etc.) and monocot (*e.g.,* wheat, rice, etc.) plants.

The **vectorless gene transfer** includes the following four important methods :

(*a*) **Electroporation.** In which temporary holes produced in plasma membrane of the cell mediate entry of foreign DNA.

(*b*) **Chemical mediated gene transfer**. In which certain chemicals (*e.g.,* polyethylene glycol) help in the uptake of foreign DNA into host cell.

(*c*) **Microinjection.** Introduction of foreign genes into plant or animal cells using micropipettes.

(*d*) **Particle gun.** In which Tungsten particles coated with foreign DNA are bombarded into target cells.

APPLICATIONS OF RECOMBINANT DNA TECHNOLOGY

The technique of recombinant DNA can be used as follows :

It can be used to elucidate molecular events in the biological process of cellular differentiation and ageing.

This can also be utilised in making gene maps with precision.

This can be used to spell out the complete nucleotide sequence of genome of various organisms including humans.

By this technique, useful chemical compounds can be produced cheaply and efficiently.

Vaccines for hepatitis B have been produced by recombinant DNA technology.

Application of Genetic Engineering

The most important application of genetic engineering is to unravel the structure and mechanism of expression of genes. For example the concept of exons and introns.

The operon concept of gene makes the genes active or inactive.

The introduction of specific genes into bacteria or yeast cells is helpful in synthesising human insulin, human growth hormones, etc.

It makes possible to introduce useful procaryotic genes into eucaryotes. For example, the possibility of the transfer of nitrogen fixing gene from bacteria to food crops develops there by enabling them to fix nitrogen. Thus, it reduces the need of nitrate fertilizers.

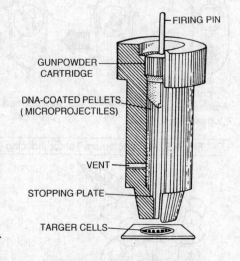

Fig. 9.8. Particle gene gun.

The introduction of genes coding for vitamins, antibiotics, hormones from higher animals to bacteria has helped to produce substances which are otherwise difficult to synthesise.

Genetic engineering has also helped man to use therapy for certain hereditary diseases, such as phenylketonuria and hemophilia.

However, there are some possibilities that the gene splicing are tempered with possible danger. For example, the introduction of new gene into bacteria may lead to the formation of new strain. The new strain may be virulent and may be responsible for epidemics.

A large number of drugs are becoming ineffective due to various microorganisms developing resistance due to uncontrolled recombinant DNA.

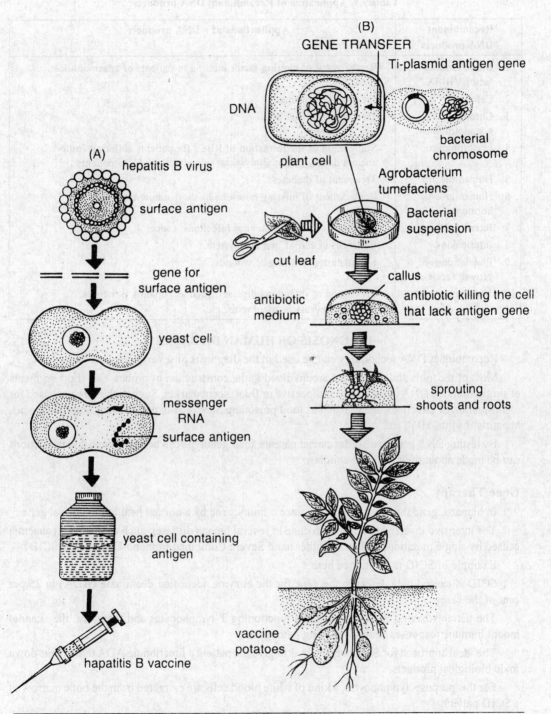

Fig. 9.9. Production of vaccines by rDNA technology. A, injectible hepatitis vaccine, B, edible vaccine.

The pathogenic microorganisms produced as a result of genetic engineering if used in biological warfare may be responsible for causing destruction of human race and other living beings.

Table 9.1. Application of Recombinant DNA products

Recombinant DNA products	Applications of r DNA products
1. Blood clotting factor VIII/IX	Replacement of clotting factor missing in patients of anaemophilia A / B.
2. Calcitonin	Treatment of rickets.
3. Chronic gonadotropin	Treatment of infertility.
4. Erythropiotin	Stimulation of the formation of RBCs for patients suffering from anemia during kidney dialysis or side effects of AIDS patients .
5. Human insulin	Treatment of diabetes.
6. Human growth hormone	Replacement of missing hormone in short stature people.
7. Interferon	Treatment of pathogenic viral infections, cancer.
8. Interleukins	Enhances action of immune system.
9. Platelet derived growth factor	Stimulation of healing of wounds.
10. Vaccines	Prevention of infectious diseases, such as hepatitis B, herpes, influenza, pertussis, meningitis, etc.

DIAGNOSIS OF HUMAN DISEASES

Recombinant DNA technology can be used in the diagnosis of several diseases.

Most of the tools and techniques are involved in the construction of probes, *i.e.*, short segments of single stranded DNA attached to a radioactive or fluorescent marker. Such probes are now used for identification of infectious agents, such as food poisoning *Salmonella*, pus forming *Staphylococcus*, hepatitis B virus, HIV, etc.

By testing DNA genetic disorder carrier parents, their genotype can be determined and predictions can be made about their afflicted children.

Gene Therapy

In humans, gene therapy is used to replace a faulty gene by a normal healthy functional gene.

The intensive investigation has been done in several human diseases, such as sickle cell anaemia caused by single mutations and on the other hand Severe Combined Immuno-Deficiency (SCID)

Example of SCID is mentioned here :

SCID is caused by a defect in the gene for the enzyme adenosine deaminase (ADA) in 25 per cent of the cases.

The patients having SCID do not have functioning T-lymphocytes and therefore, they cannot mount immune responses against invading pathogens.

The ideal approach for SCID treatment is to give the patient a functioning ADA that breaks down toxic biological products.

For this purpose, lymphocytes, a kind of white blood cells are extracted from the bone marrow of a SCID patient.

Now, a good copy of human gene encoding this enzyme (ADA) is introduced into these cells. This is done by exploiting the properties of special viruses called **retroviruses**, as vector.

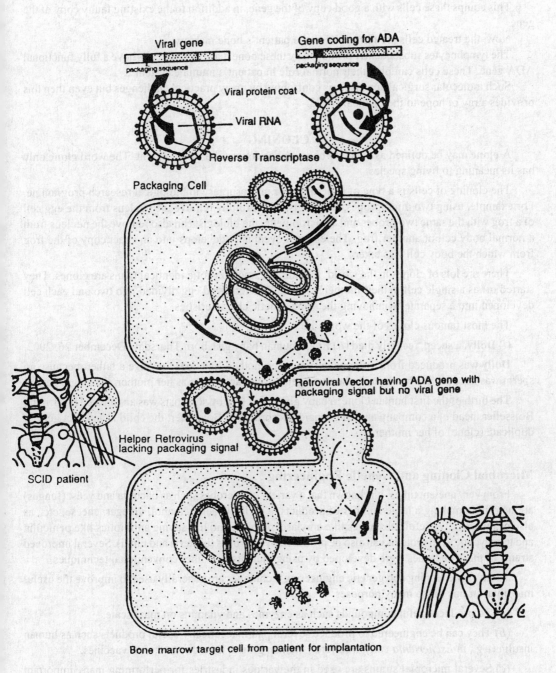

Fig. 9.10. Gene Therapy to treat Severe Combined Immuno-Deficiency (SCID).

This vector (retrovirus) is engineered to incorporate the ADA gene which has the packing sequence but no viral genes.

Now, co-infection of the bone marrow stem cells, removed from a SCID patient, with this vector and helper virus produces new virus particles with ADA gene inserted inside, but lacks the packing sequence.

This equips these cells with a good copy of the gene, in addition to the existing faulty copy of the gene.

Now, the treated cells are reinjected to the patient's bone marrow.

The lymphocytes subsequently produced by these bone marrow stem cells have a fully functional ADA gene. These cells can play their normal role in patient's immune system.

Such molecular surgical approach, is confronted by many practical challenges but even then this provides a ray of hope to the medical world.

CLONING

A **clone** may be defined as exact carbon copy or copies of a single parent. The word **clone** only has its meaning to living species.

The cloning of cells is a type of experiment of microsurgery in biological research programme. For example, using two microprobes, a biologist can carefully remove the nucleus from the egg cell of a frog with the same two probes and a micropipette, the biologist can also remove the nucleus from a normal body cell of another frog. The egg cell eventually develops into an exact copy of the frog from which the body cell was taken.

There are lots of clones in the world, for example, monozygotic identical twins are clones. They started off as a single cell in their mother's womb. The fertilized egg divided into two and each cell developed into a separate twin having the same genetic characteristics.

The most famous clones of the world are :

(*i*) **Dolly**, a sheep, recently died (*ii*) **Eve**, a human baby girl, born Thursday, December 26, 2002.

Dolly was produced from a single cell from her mother. She does not have a father, because no sperm was needed. She has exactly the same genetic characteristics as her mother, the single parent.

The birth of the first human clone, a baby girl called **Eve** by scientists was announced by Brigitte Boisselier, head of a company named Clonaid. According to Boisselier, the child is an exact genetic duplicate (clone) of her mother.

Microbial Cloning and Genetic Engineering

From very ancient times, it is known that a variety of microbes such as bacteria and yeast (fungus) are helpful in making a large number of products, *e.g.*, lactic acid, ethanol, vinegar, cheese, etc., as also of industrially useful substances like amylase, protease and life-saving antibiotics like penicillin and tetracycline. Cell proteins can also be produced by microbes (bacteria and fungi). Several improved strains of these microbes were developed by using mutants and other conventional techniques.

Today, gene cloning and genetic engineering techniques are generally used to improve the useful microbial strains for so many purposes.

(*a*) To produce useful compounds such as enzymes and vitamins on mass scale.

(*b*) They can be engineered to produce several pharmaceutically useful products such as human insulin (*e.g.*, in *Escherichia coli*), interferon, human growth hormone and viral vaccines.

(*c*) Several microbial strains are used in the various industries for performing many important functions such as the removal of undesired lignin (*e.g.*, *Trametes*).

(*d*) Microbes (*e.g.*, heavy-metal accumulating bacteria like *Pseudomonas*) can be used to purify polluted environment (called bioremediation).

(*e*) Certain microbes such as *Trichoderma* (fungus) and *Rhizobium* (bacterium) are used for bio-control (against plant diseases and pests) and as biofertilisers respectively.

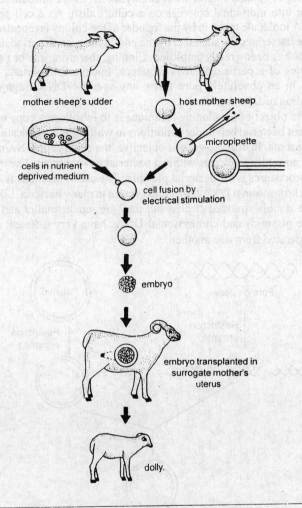

mother sheep's udder

host mother sheep

micropipette

cells in nutrient
deprived medium

cell fusion by
electrical stimulation

embryo

embryo transplanted in
surrogate mother's
uterus

dolly.

Fig. 9.11. Dolly. Steps in cloning of sheep.

Table. 9.2 Application of Genetically Engineered Microbes

Microbes	Applications
1. *Bacillus thuringiensis* (a soil bacterium)	Production of endotoxin (Bt toxin), a biodegradable insecticide for plant protection.
2. *Escherichia coli.* (a gut bacterium)	Production of human insulin, human growth factor interferons and interleukin.
3. *Pseudomonas fluorescence* (a bacterium)	Prevention of frost damage to the plants.
4. *Pseudomonas putida* (a bacterium)	Scavanging of oil spills. Digests hydrocarbons of crude oil.
5. *Rhizobium meliloti* (bacterium)	Nitrogen fixation by incorporating "nif" gene in cereal crops.
6. *Trichoderma* (a fungus)	Produces enzyme chitinase for biocontrol of fungal diseases in plants.

In the process of DNA cloning fragments of eukaryotic DNA are introduced into bacterial cells, which are then grown into individual colonies on a culture dish. As a cell proliferates to form a colony, the single DNA molecule taken in by the founder of the colony is repeatedly replicated by the enzymes present in the bacterial cells such that by the end of the growth period, the number of copies of the foreign sequence has been greatly amplified. Cloning, therefore, can be used as a technique to produce large quantities of a particular DNA sequence, but more important, it can be used as a technique to isolate, in an absolutely pure form, any specific DNA fragment among a large, heterogeneous population of DNA molecules.

Gene cloning. The object of the cloning technique is to introduce a copy of a eukaryotic DNA fragment into a recipient bacterial cell under conditions in which it will replicate autonomously from that of the host chromosome. In order to get this objective, the eukaryotic DNA must be linked to the DNA of a **vector** that normally replicates within a bacterial environment. The most common vector employed in cloning procedures is the bacterial **plasmid**. The use of plasmids is as follows: Plasmids are nonessential extrachromosomal DNA molecules present in many bacteria. Like the main bacterial chromosome, they are double-stranded circles, but they are much smaller and of variable genetic constitution. Since the plasmids and chromosomal DNAs have very different physical properties, they can be readily separated from one another.

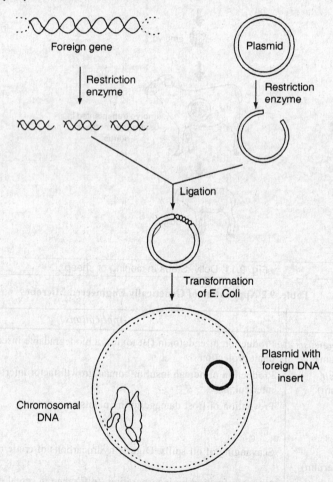

Fig. 9.12. Plasmid. Vectors and transformation.

The foreign DNA to be cloned is inserted into the plasmid to form the recombinant DNA molecule. This modified plasmid is then added to a bacterial culture as naked DNA, and in the presence of

$CaCl_2$, a small percentage of the bacteria will pick up one of these molecules from the medium. Once a plasmid is taken up, it will replicate autonomously within the recipient and will be passed on to its progeny during cell division. A wide variety of plasmids have been isolated, many of which carry genes for resistance to antibiotics. If these plasmids are added to a bacterial culture and the cells are then treated with specific antibiotics, only these bacteria which have taken up the plasmid will be able to survive.

How is the DNA of the vector combined with that form the eukaryotic genome? Recombinant DNA molecules can be formed in several ways.

Recombinant DNAs can be constructed between DNA fragments having blunt ends. This can be done by enzymatically adding a string of A- or C- bearing nucleotides to one strand of the fragment and a complementary string of T- or G- bearing nucleotides to the opposite strand of the vector, mixing the two populations, and sealing the molecules with the ligase.

Cloning genomic fragments. When working with genomic DNA, one has to isolate a particular gene or genes, such as those which code for the histones, from among the thousands of unrelated sequences. The first step in this type of experiment is to fragment the DNA with restriction endonucleases. These enzymes recognize sequences from 4 to 6 nucleotides in length. Once the DNA is fragmented, the fragments are combined with the DNA of the vector, and the diverse population of recombinant DNA molecules is subjected to the DNA cloning procedure. Since a given bacterial cell takes up only one plasmid, all the cells of a given colony will contair copies of the same recombinant DNA molecule.

Cell cloning. The bacterial cell is at one and the same time is the somatic and the germ cell. Having selected a single bacterium, one can grow large populations of cells, all identical in morphology and biochemistry. In modern times by means of refined culture techniques the cell cloning has become possible, and the pure populations of cells have been grown from a single isolated cell.

The smallest viable unit of plant one can at present envisage as reproducing, growing and developing in culture is a single cell. Several workers established method which would allow the growth of isolated plant organs and tissues *in vitro*, in culture.

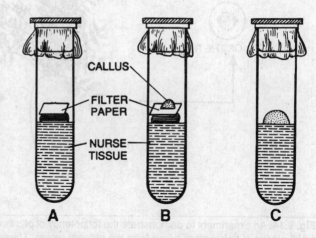

Fig. 9.13. Nurse-tissue technique to raise single-cell clones. A, a single cell from the callus is placed on filter paper lying on the top of a large callus (nurse tissue); B, the cell divides and forms a small tissue; C, this tissue is transferred from the filter paper to the medium directly where it is able to grow further.

Cell cloning is based on the property of **totipotency** in plants or **pluripotency** in animals. Totipotency is the potential ability of a plant cell to grow into a complete plant, whereas pluriopotency is the potential ability of a cell into develop any type of the cell in the animal body, *e.g.,* nerve cells, kidney cells or heart cells.

Virtually all plants are totipotent but in animals only fertilized egg and stem cells in the embryonic blastocyst are totipotent.

Plant cloning. Cellular totipotency is the capacity of mature cells showing that when freed from the plant body, they have the ability to reorganize themselves into the new individuals. Steward and his co-workers, showed this phenomenon in the carrot cultures. Here the small pieces of mature carrot root, were grown in a liquid medium supplemented with coconut milk in special containers.

These cultures were shaken generally which freed all the cell clusters into the medium. Some of them developed into rooting clumps. When these were transferred to the tubes containing a semi-solid medium, they gave rise to whole plant that flowered and set seeds.

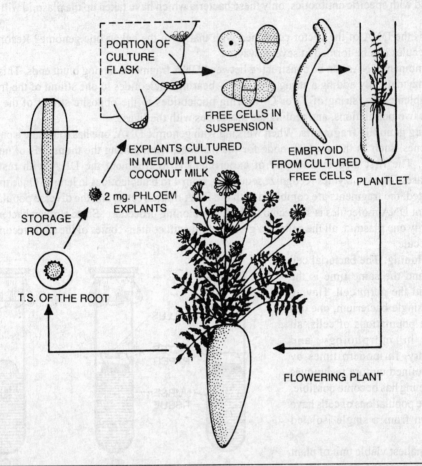

Fig. 9.14. An experiment to demonstrate the totipotency of plant cells. Slices of the carrot root were cut and small pieces of tissue were taken from the phloem region. These were inoculated into a liquid medium in special flasks, the tissue grew actively and single cells and small cell aggregates dissociated into the medium. Some of the cell clumps developed roots, and when transferred to a semisolid medium, these rooted nodules formed shoots. These plants could be transferred to soil.

Organismal cloning. It is characteristic of vegetative reproduction that a vegetative part, when removed from the plant and placed under suitable conditions, will replace the missing parts and produce a complete individual. It has been possible to grow several types of plant organs in sterile culture including roots, shoot apices, leaves, floral parts and fruits. The nutrient requirements for such organ culture vary considerably from species to species and according to the type of organ in question but certain general requirements can be recognised.

Intact higher plants are autotrophic, that is, they are able to synthesize all the organic substances required for their own life from water, carbon dioxide, oxygen and mineral nutrients. But since most sterile cultures are unable to carry on photosynthesis, it is clear that they will require atleast a carbon source, usually supplied in the form of a sugar as sucrose or glucose. In addition, sterile cultures require the same mineral nutrients as the intact plant, including both macronutrients (e.g., nitrogen, phosphorus, potassium and calcium) and micronutrients or trace elements (*e.g.*, Mg, Fe, Mn, Zn, etc.). In addition to the requirements for a carbon source and mineral nutrients, it is found that most isolated organs have also a requirement for certain special organic substances, such as vitamins, nicotinic acid, etc.

This type of reproduction is applied extensively to horticulturally important plants. Horticulturists usually refer to it as vegetative propagation. Its practical advantage is that a single individual can give rise to a large number of plants that will be uniform because all of them have the same genetic constitution, or genotype. Such a group of plants derived from a single one by vegetative propagation is called a **clone**. Now a days the organismal cloning is a common practice for the development of the clones of horticultural as well as forest plants.

Many orchids producing beautiful flowers on cloned plants. Scientists have genetically engineered agronomically important crop plants. Rapid production of such plants can be achieved using actively dividing meristematic cells, which occur at the apices of root and shoot of the plant.

For the agriculture, disease, drought, insect pest-resistant as well as herbicide-tolerant crops have been successfully produced by gene manipulation.

Genetically Modified Food (GMF), such as vitamin A-rich rice and lysine-rich pulse seeds are now becoming popular components of human staple food.

PLANT CLONING AND GENETIC ENGINEERING

In plants, agronomically important traits are governed by the genetic information stored in the nuclear and organellar (*i.e.*, chloroplasts and mitochondria) genome and gene transfer can be done in all these genomes. However, gene transfer in organelles specially in mitochondria is relatively difficult as compared to nuclear genetic transformation. The uptake of genes by cells in microbes and plants is termed as transformation.

Steps in plant genetic engineering. The important steps involved in plant genetic engineering are as follows:

1. The first step is the identification and isolation of agronomically important gene. 2. The second step is cloning the isolated gene in a plant transformation vector. 3. The third important step is introduction of the gene into plant protoplasts, cells or tissues using gene transfer methods.

4. Now comes culture and regeneration of complete plants from genetically transformed cells on suitable selection medium. 5. The last important step is demonstration of the integration and expression of foreign gene in the transgenic plants by using molecular techniques.

Applications of plant genetic engineering. Till now, the plant genetic engineering has been successful in producing disease and pest resistant as well as herbicide tolerant transgenic plants. For example, in tomato the slow ripening process of the fruits is developed; in soybean, corn and cotton herbicide tolerance is developed; in potato, tomato, tobacco and rice viral resistance is developed.

ANIMAL CLONING AND GENETIC ENGINEERING

Animal cloning. Animal cloning is more difficult than plant cloning because animal cells lose their totipotency on reaching the gastrula stage of animal development. However, animal tissue cultures from tumours and embryonic tissue cells have been successful. Standard techniques are available for isolating animal cells and tissues from different systems. Some more important examples of animal cloning are tissue culture, somatic cell fusion, cell cloning and creating transgenics.

Gene transfer in animals. Gene transfer in animals is mostly through direct methods such as electroporation or microinjection or using particle gun. In creating 'Dolly' the cloned sheep, fertilised egg of its mother was removed by microneedle and nucleus from an udder cell of a donor sheep was microinjected in the egg after removing egg nucleus. The egg developed into 'Dolly' with genes identical to its mother.

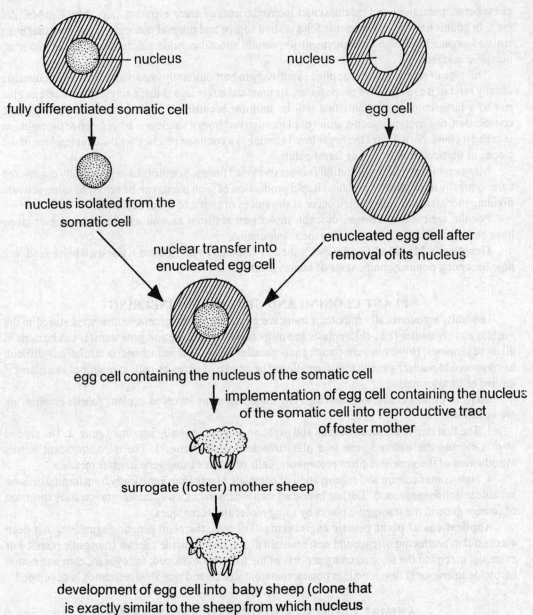

nucleus

nucleus

fully differentiated somatic cell

egg cell

nucleus isolated from the
somatic cell

nuclear transfer into
enucleated egg cell

enucleated egg cell after
removal of its nucleus

egg cell containing the nucleus of the somatic cell

implementation of egg cell containing the nucleus
of the somatic cell into reproductive tract
of foster mother

surrogate (foster) mother sheep

development of egg cell into baby sheep (clone that
is exactly similar to the sheep from which nucleus
from somatic cell was taken)

clones of sheep

Fig. 9.15. Steps involved in the cloning of the sheep **Dolly.**

Applications of animal cloning and genetic engineering. Examples of animal products (medicines) produced through genetic engineering are : (*i*) chick embryo fluid which produces vaccines for influenza, measles and mumps. (*ii*) duck embryo fluid which produces vaccines for rabies and rubella.

How sheep 'Dolly' cloned ? Ian Wilmut and his associates at the Roslin Research Institute, Scotland, took cells from ewe (mother sheep's udder). An udder cell is different from a skin cell or a muscle cell or a nerve cell.

They managed to store these udder cells in nutrient deprived culture. This checked the starved cells from dividing, and switched off their active genes.

Now, one udder cell complete with its nucleus was selected, as this nucleus carries the mother's genetic information.

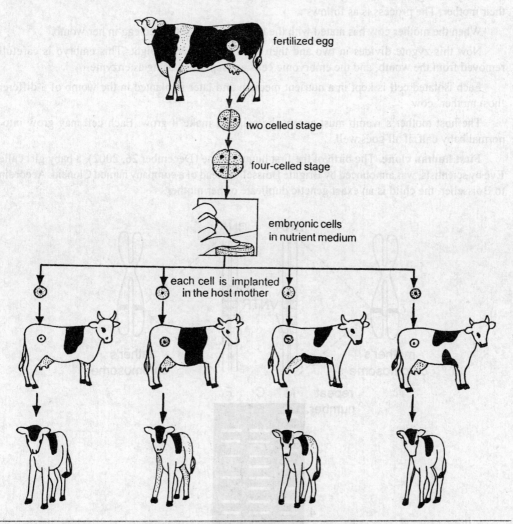

Fertilized egg

two celled stage

four-celled stage

embryonic cells in nutrient medium

each cell is implanted in the host mother

Fig. 9.16. Japanese method of cloning cattle.

Meanwhile, unfertilized egg cell was taken from a different ewe (host mother sheep). Its nucleus was sucked out leaving an empty cell containing all the necessary components to produce an embryo. This cell was now ready to receive udder cell nucleus.

They now fused udder cell nucleus with the empty egg cell by electrical stimulation. Then this egg cell had the mother's nucleus.

When a normal or altered egg is implanted in a different female is termed **'surrogate mother'**. This means, substitute mother.

Then the altered egg was cultured for six days. Out of many resulting embryos, one was implanted in the uterus of the surrogate mother, where it grew into a lamb.

Thus, **Dolly** was born genetically identical to mother sheep as her first cell nucleus came from mother's cell.

How calves are cloned in Japan ? Scientists from Japan have cloned cattle in a different way.

They have got success in growing as many as eight identical calves from one fertilized cell of their mother. The process is as follows :

When the mother cow has mated with the bull, she has a fertilized egg in her womb.

Now this zygote divides in two and then in four and then in eight. This embryo is carefully removed from the womb, and the embryonic cells are separated using as enzyme.

Each isolated cell is kept in a nutrient medium and later implanted in the womb of a different 'host mother' cow.

The host mother's womb must accept the cell and make it grow. Each cell may grow into a normal baby calf, if all goes well.

First human clone. The birth of the first human clone (December 26, 2002), a baby girl called **Eve** by scientists, was announced by Brigitte Boisselier, head of a company named Clonaid. According to Boisselier, the child is an exact genetic duplicate of her mother.

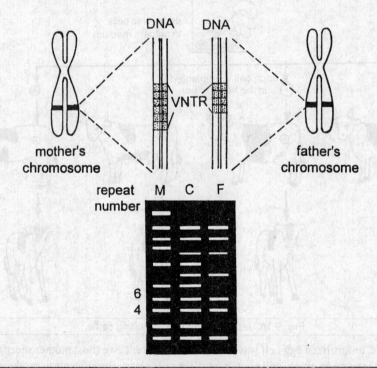

Fig. 9.17. Variable Number Tandem Repeats (VNTRs). M = mother C = child, F = father.

To clone, scientists slip the nucleus of an adult cell, like a skin cell, into an unfertilized egg from which its own genetic material has been removed.

Then, if stimulated to act like a fertilised egg, the newly altered genetic material can then direct the egg to divide and grow into an embryo, then a foetus, then a newborn, if all goes well. Yet, as scientists have discovered, only rarely does all go well.

In animal work so far only about 1 to 5 per cent of cloning attempts succeed, said Randall Prather, a cloning expert. That is, for every 100 eggs, one to five clones are born.

DNA FINGERPRINTING

Every individual organism is unique.

Each person has a unique DNA fingerprint.

A DNA fingerprint of a person is the same for every cell, tissue and organ.

DNA fingerprint cannot be altered by any` known treatment.

The ideal way to distinguish an individual from other people on Earth would be to describe entire genomic DNA sequence of the person.

The technique of DNA fingerprinting was used for the first time by English geneticist Alec Jeffreys, in 1984.

Important for DNA fingerprinting are short nucleotide repeats which vary in number from person to person and are inherited.

They are called **Variable Number Tandem Repeats** or **VNTRs.**

The VNTRs of two persons may be of the same length and sequence at certain sites, but vary at other sites.

For example, a child might inherit a chromosome with six tandem repeats from the mother

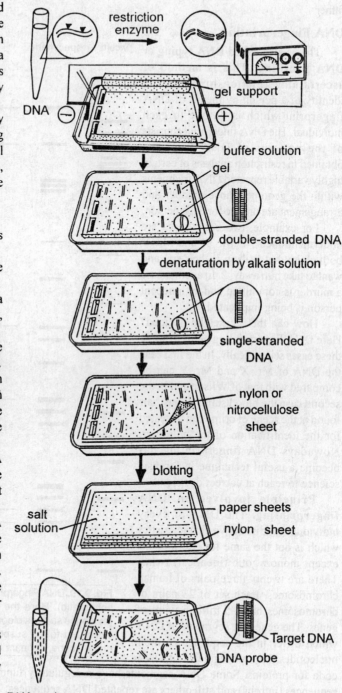

Fig. 9.18. Steps in technique of DNA fingerprinting.

and the same tandem repeated four times in the homologous chromosome inherited from the father.

However, the half of VNTR alleles of the child resemble that of the mother and half that of the father.

DNA Fingerprinting

This is also called **DNA typing** or **DNA profiling.** This is method of ascertaining relationships and the identity of a person by means of DNA fingerprint which is unique to each individual. The DNA fingerprint consists of the patterns of DNA fragment obtained in restriction analysis of certain highly variable repeated DNA fragments within the genome whose number and arrangement are unique for each person.

For example, two court cases are undermentioned : 1. Mr. X and Mr. Y both claim that Wilson is their son and want to take him away. 2. In another case a murder is committed and an innocent person is being implicated.

How can these cases be decided? Here DNA fingerprinting helps to solve these cases scientifically. In the first case the DNA of Mr. X and Mr. Y can be compared with that of Wilson and in the second case the blood stains or any hair found at the scene of crime can be tested for the identification of the murderer. Nowadays DNA fingerprinting has become a useful technique in forensic science to reach at correct decisions.

Principle involved in DNA fingerprinting. The DNA of every individual has distinctive characteristics which is not the same for two humans except monozygotic (identical) twins. There are twenty three pairs of human chromosomes. Each set of 23 pairs of chromosomes has 1.5 million pairs of genes. The genes are segments of DNA which differ in the sequence of their nucleotides. Not all segments of DNA

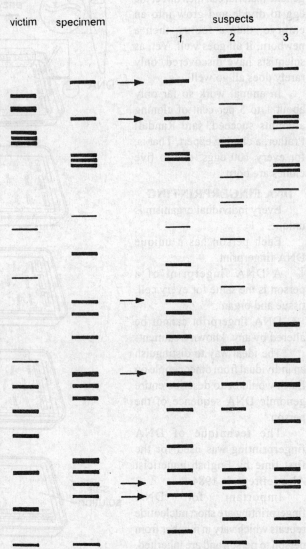

Fig. 9.19. DNA Fingerprints from a Murder Case (somewhat schematic). Here the DNA fingerprint of the specimen (evidence such as blood stain which does not belong to the victim but to the suspected murderer) obtained from the crime-scene, appears to match with that of suspect No. 1.

code for proteins. Some DNA segments have a regulatory function, while others are intervening sequences (introns) and still others are repeated DNA sequences. The non-repetitive or unique DNA sequences form almost half of the haploid genome (DNA in one set of 23 chromosomes) and except identical twins, no two humans have genomes with same DNA nucleotide sequences.

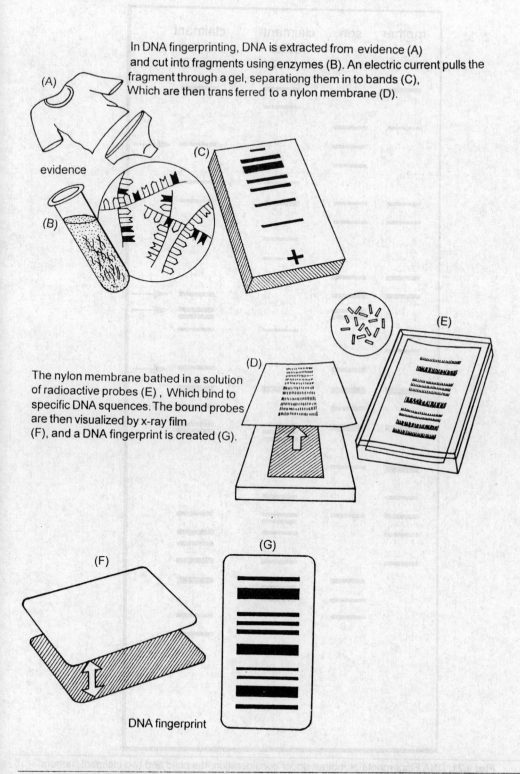

In DNA fingerprinting, DNA is extracted from evidence (A) and cut into fragments using enzymes (B). An electric current pulls the fragment through a gel, separationg them in to bands (C), Which are then transferred to a nylon membrane (D).

evidence

The nylon membrane bathed in a solution of radioactive probes (E), Which bind to specific DNA squences. The bound probes are then visualized by x-ray film (F), and a DNA fingerprint is created (G).

DNA fingerprint

Fig. 9.20. DNA fingerprinting. How technique helps us to settle criminal (murder) cases.

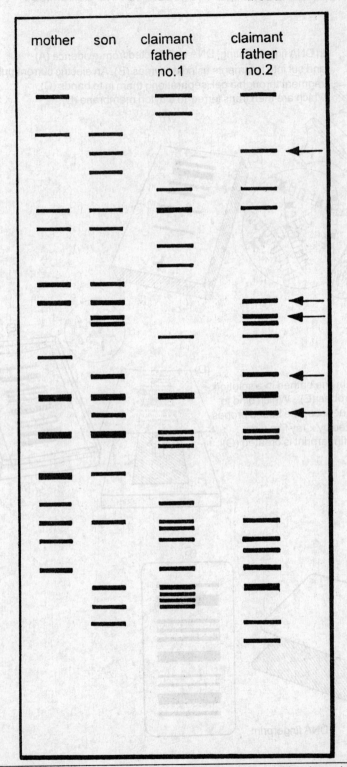

Fig. 9.21. DNA Fingerprints of mother under consideration, the child and two claimant "fathers" (somewhat schematic). Claimant No. 2 is proved to be the real (biological) father.

In DNA finger printing short repetitive nucleotide sequences are quite important as they vary from person to person. They are called the **Variable Number Tandem Repeats (VNTRs).** The VNTRs of two persons may be of the same length and sequences at certain sites and vary at other sites. When chromosomal DNA samples are digested with restricted enzymes, DNA from different individuals yield specific patterns when subjected to gel electrophoresis.

Mechanism of DNA fingerprinting. DNA fingerprints can be prepared from extremely minute amounts of blood, semen, hair bulk or any other cells of the body. The main steps are as follows.

The first step is called **extraction.** In this step DNA is extracted from any of the above mentioned cells. Thereafter many copies of this DNA are made by a technique called Polymerase Chain Reaction. Making of many copies of DNA is called **amplification.** Then DNA is cut with restriction enzymes into precise reproducible sequences, this is called **restriction digestion.**

In the next step DNA restricted sequences are then separated by gel electrophoresis, *i.e.,* separation of DNA sequences. Now separated DNA sequences are transferred from gel onto a trinitrocellulose or nylon membrane, *i.e.,* known as **Southern blotting** after the name of the inventor E. M. Southern.

Then an already available complementary DNA is made to hybridise with the isolated DNA, *i.e.,* **hybridisation.** Many such DNA strands with specific nucleotide sequences complementary to VNTR sequences are available, which are called **probes.**

Lastly, the membrane is exposed to X-ray film on which specific bonds can be seen as depicted in the figure.

Applications of DNA fingerprinting. 1. The tests for paternity can be done for identifying the true (biological) father. The bands of child's DNA should match the DNA prints of the biological parents. 2. Identification of the criminal is made possible by DNA fingerprinting. Here DNA finger prints of suspects and from blood or hair or semen picked up from the scene of crime are prepared and compared. The DNA fingerprint of the person matching the one obtained from sample obtained from site of crime can give clue to the actual criminal. 3. To verify whether a hopeful immigrant is, as he or she claims, really a close relative of already an established resident. 4. To identify social groups to rewrite biological evolution.

GENOMICS

All the DNA in the cells of an organism, such as cells from skin, muscle or brain and every thing including genes, is called its **genome**.

Human body contains 100 million cells of over 260 different kinds.

In all, there are 23 different chromosomes containing packed DNA in a haploid set of human genome.

Additional DNA is in cell's mitochondria which is inherited from one's mother.

In human genome, according to estimates there are about three billion of biochemical letters, *i.e.,* nucleotide base pairs (in human genome), and 30,000 genes per cell.

Human Genome Project

This project began in 1990. The main aims of the project are as follows :

1. To develop the ways of mapping the human genome.

2. To store this information in databases and to develop tools for data analysis.

3. To address the ethical, legal and social issues that may arise from this ambitious human genome project.

Genomic Revelations

The human gene count is approximately 30,000 to 40,000. This count is nearabout the same in mice.

Nine-tenths of human genes are identical to that of the mouse which is generally used for experimental purposes.

The fruit fly (*Drosophila melanogaster*) has about 13,000 genes per cell.

Escherichia coli has about 4,000 genes.

Humans are incredibly 99.9 per cent identical with *E. coli* at the DNA level. In other words, genomically humans and bacteria are similar.

However, most of human differences are shared among all ethnicities and races spread into the geographic regions around the planet.

Different human genes vary widely in the length often over thousands of base pairs.

White β -globin and insulin gene are less than 10 kilo base pairs.

The gene responsible for Duchenne Muscular Dystrophy on X chromosome is made up of 2400 kilo base pairs, most probably the longest gene known.

However, a lily has 18 times more DNA than a human, *i.e.,* 106 billion base pairs per cell.

Such large amounts of genes are split by long non-coding introns. Only less than 2 per cent of the genome is known to include the exons, the protein coding sequences. In fact, a lily produces fewer proteins than a human.

As already studied, clusters of VNTRs of variable lengths, arranged in tandem.

Approximately one million copies of short 5 to 8 base pair repeated sequence clustered around the centromeres and near the ends of the chromosomes represent, the **junk DNA**.

Fig. 9.22. Human genome.

Prospects and Implications of Human Genome

It is expected and seems possible that we will soon get snapshots of more than 1200 genes that are responsible for common cardiovascular ailments, endocrine diseases like diabetes, neurological disorders like Alzheimer's disease, deadly cancers and many other such diseases.

Even single gene defects may account for several inherited diseases.

Efforts are in progress to determine genes that will revert cancerous cells to normal.

The human genome will definitely make a halthier living.

The human genome also holds the prospects of vast database of knowledge about designer drugs, genetically modified diets and genetic identity.

Human Genome Revelations

The year 2003 marks fifty years of the discovery of the double-helix of DNA, twenty five years of the world's first test-tube baby and now the complete mapping of the human genome.

The Human Genome Project that commenced in 1990 under a US-UK led public consortium of academic centres headed by Francis Collins, has now announced that the map, valued at nearly $800 million, is complete two years ahead of schedule.

Three draft maps of human genome have already made public, and this is the final one, as the scientists say. This however, does not mean the end of genome mapping as the work will shift to other species.

Also, variations in the human genome will have to be studied and then there is the whole task of analysing the tomes of data generated by the map. For, it is in data-crunching that applications can be formulated.

It all began with the discovery of the structure of DNA by James D. Watson and Francis Crick. They made their stunning discovery public in an article that first appeared in **Nature** magazine on April 25, 1953.

Since then, biology, has got transformed into a dynamic field of study, generating whole new subjects : **genetics, biotechnology, proteomics, pharmacogenomics, bio-informatics** and **chem informatics**, among others.

The human genome map will serve as a ready-reckoner for human body functions. Its 35,000 - odd mapped genes are intended to unravel the nature and history of disease, *i.e.*, what makes us ill, and what makes us well ? The information generated will enable gene therapists formulate suitable treatments. It means analysing the 3.1 billion base or DNA letters responsible for heredity in humans.

The 'language of life' is a tool that has increasingly made designer drugs possible, especially to treat hereditary diseases. With the Canadians claiming they have now sequenced the SARS virus genome, hopes are up that a vaccine or cure could soon be found for the killer-pneumonia.

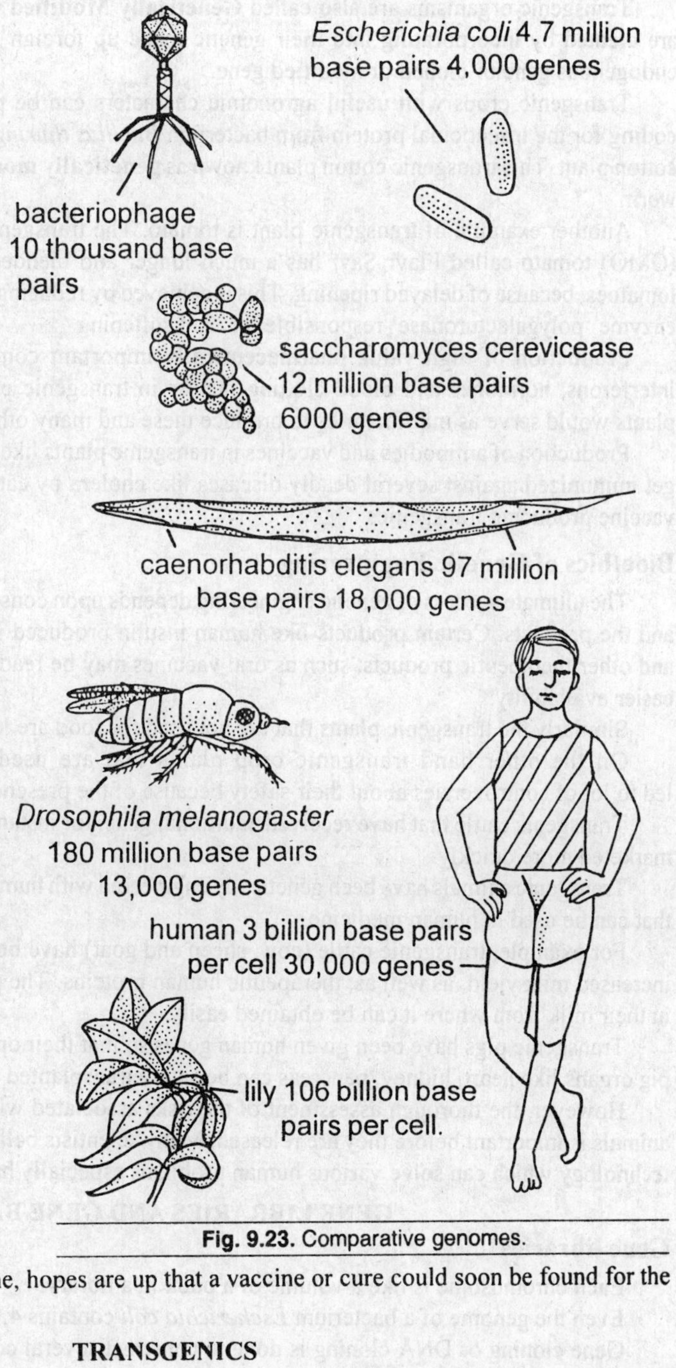

bacteriophage 10 thousand base pairs

Escherichia coli 4.7 million base pairs 4,000 genes

saccharomyces cerevicease 12 million base pairs 6000 genes

caenorhabditis elegans 97 million base pairs 18,000 genes

Drosophila melanogaster 180 million base pairs 13,000 genes

human 3 billion base pairs per cell 30,000 genes

lily 106 billion base pairs per cell.

Fig. 9.23. Comparative genomes.

TRANSGENICS

Any organism containing a foreign gene (segment of DNA) from a different species is a **transgenic organism**. As genes can be transferred to the genome of another organism only through genetic engineering, transgenics can be defined as ''genetically engineered organisms carrying gene/genes of another species in their genome''.

Transgenic organisms are also called **Genetically Modified Organisms** (GMOs). The GMOs are created by incorporating into their genetic make up foreign gene/genes or extra copies of an endogenous gene or cloned or modified gene.

Transgenic crops with useful agronomic characters can be produced. For example, the gene coding for the insecticidal protein from bacterium *Bacillus thuringiensis* has been transferred to the cotton plant. This transgenic cotton plant known as **genetically modified cotton** Bt is resistant to boll worm.

Another example of transgenic plant is tomato. The transgenic genetically modified organism (GMO) tomato called Flavr Savr has a much longer and blended with flavour than conventional tomatoes, because of delayed ripening. This is achieved by reducing the amount of cell wall degrading enzyme 'polygalacturonase' responsible for fruit softening.

Production of high value pharmaceutically important compounds such as human insulin, interferons, hormones and blood clotting factors in transgenic plants or seeds. In fact transgenic plants would serve as minifactories to produce these and many other compounds in huge quantities.

Production of antibodies and vaccines in transgenic plants like banana and tomato. Children may get immunized against several deadly diseases like cholera by eating banana or raw tomatoes from vaccine producing transgenics.

Bioethics of Genetic Engineering

The ultimate success of genetic engineering depends upon consumer acceptance of the technology and the products. Certain products like human insulin produced in genetically engineered bacteria and other therapeutic products, such as oral vaccines may be readily accepted by public because of easier availability.

Similarly the transgenic plants that are not used for food are less likely to cause public concern.

On the other hand transgenic crop plants that are used for human consumption have led to lot of controversies about their safety because of the presence of certain unwanted properties.

Transgenic cattle that have received additional gene, for instance, to increase growth rate, can be marketed more quickly.

Transgenic animals have been genetically engineered with human genes in order to make products that can be used in human medicine.

For example, transgenic cattle (cow, sheep and goat) have been produced with the intention of increased milk yield, as well as, therapeutic human proteins. The cattle secrete there useful proteins in their milk from where it can be obtained easily.

Transgenic pigs have been given human genes so that their organs carry human antigens. These pig organs like heart, kidney, pancreas can be safely transplanted into humans.

However, the thorough assessment of the risks associated with transgenics for both plants and animals is important before they are released. Many scientists believe that genetic engineering is the technology which can solve various human problems especially hunger and disease.

GENE LIBRARIES AND GENE BANKS

Gene libraries

Each chromosome is like a volume of a book in a library.

Even the genome of a bacterium *Escherichia coli* contains 4,000 genes.

Gene cloning or DNA cloning is done to construct several copies of the desired genes in large amounts. This precise technique allows specific DNA sequences to be separated from other sequences permitting detailed analysis or manipulation.

Gene libraries can also be created using RNA.

The enzyme Reverse Transcriptase, a RNA-directed DNA polymerase, is used to convert the RNA into complementary DNA (*i.e.,* cDNA), which can then be converted in the same way as DNA cloning.

Such gene libraries are maintained through special techniques.

Gene Banks

A gene bank is a repository of clones of known DNA fragments, genes, gene maps, seeds, spores, frozen sperms or eggs or embryos.

These stored genes may be used in genetic engineering and breeding experiments where species have become extinct.

These gene banks will be used increasingly as the rate of extinction increases, depleting the Earth's biodiversity and genetic variety.

Now the genomic information is available for a dozen of species. The most remarkable is the prospects and contribution of Human Genome Project.

The Human Genome Project that commenced in 1990, has now announced that the map, is complete two years ahead of schedule in year 2003.

TERMS TO REMEMBER

Bacteriophage. A virus capable of infecting a bacterium and replicating in it.

Bioethics. Considering of what is good or bad from morality point of view in the application of biological innovations specially on humans.

Biotechnology. The use of living cells or microorganisms (*e.g.*, bacteria) in industry and technology to manufacture drugs and chemicals or to break down wastes, etc. In recent years, it specially refers to the use of genetically modified cells and microorganisms.

Callus. Mass of undifferentiated cells that initially arises from plant cell or tissue in artificial culture.

Cellular totipotency. Ability of a plant or animal cell to repeatedly divide and differentiate into a complete organism on a defined nutrient medium under suitable laboratory conditions.

Cloning. Producing a population of identical DNA molecules, cells or individuals derived from a single such unit.

DNA fingerprinting. Also called DNA typing or DNA profiling. A method of ascertaining relationships and the identity of a person by means of DNA fingerprint which is unique to each individual.

DNA library. A collection of cloned DNA fragments, usually representing an entire genome present in an organism. Also called genomic DNA library.

DNA ligase. An enzyme that can seal one DNA fragment with another DNA segment both having sticky ends. Ligase is the 'molecular glue'.

Electroporation. Creation of transient (temporary) pores in the cell membrane of a host allow the entry of foreign DNA.

Enucleation. Removal of the nucleus from the cell used, in cloning.

Gene cloning. Also called DNA cloning. Technique for obtaining clones or identical copies of a particular DNA molecule.

Gene therapy. Replacement and alteration of a faulty gene. Technique used for hereditary disease.

Genetic engineering. A technique for artificially and deliberately modifying DNA (genes) to suit human needs.

Genome. Total number of genes contained in one haploid set of chromosomes of a diploid organism.

Genome library. DNA library consisting of fragments of chromosomal DNA.

Microinjection. Introduction of foreign genes into animal or plant cell by injecting DNA directly.

Molecular scissors. Restriction endonuclease enzyme.

Particle gun. A technique for bombarding microprojectiles (gold or tungsten particles) coated with foreign DNA with great velocity into the target cells.

Plasmid. Extrachromosomal small circular double stranded DNA molecules in a bacterial cell which have sequences matching those of the required gene and can be similarly cut by the same restriction enzyme. Plasmids are autonomous and replicate separately from the host chromosome.

Probes. DNA strands with specific nucleotide sequences complementary to VNTR (Variable Number Tandem Repeats) sequences.

Recombinant DNA or r DNA. DNA produced by joining together genes from different sources.

Restriction endonuclease. Any such enzyme which very specifically recognises a particular DNA sequence, and cuts it. These enzymes are the 'molecular scissors'.

Southern blotting. A technique named after the inventor, Southern, involving hybridisation of DNA with probes.

Surrogate mother. A female who grows someone else's zygote/embryo in her own uterus for full gestation period and delivers the baby.

Syndrome. A group of symptoms appearing together for a particular condition.

Transgenic. Genetically modified organism (GMO) carrying foreign genes. The introduced foreign gene is called **transgene**.

Vector. An intermediate carrier (in genetic engineering), a phage, plasmid or virus DNA into which another DNA is inserted for introduction into bacterial or other cells for amplification (DNA cloning).

UNIT–5

UTILIZATION OF PLANTS: ECONOMIC BOTANY

The economic botany deals with application of botanical knowledge to the well-being of mankind. The primary necessities of man are threefold—food, clothing and shelter. *The most essential need of man is food. The food primarily comes from plants in the forms of cereals (e.g., rice, wheat, maize, oat, barley and rye), millets (e.g., sorghum, pearl millet, finger millet, etc.), pulses, vegetables and fruits. For clothing again plants are indispensable. The plants that yield fibres are second only to food plants. From the times immemorial the man needed some form of clothing, and this need was fulfilled only by fibre-yielding plants. In this respect cotton occupies an all important position, supplemented by jute and some other fibres for coarse clothing. To meet an everincreasing demand for food and clothing an application of the knowledge of botany has been considered to be of great importance for better utilization of plant products. From the time immemorial shelter from the weather inclemencies and as a protection against natural enemy has been felt too much. In this respect the forest products have been of service to mankind from the very beginning of his history. The most familiar and most important, of these products is wood, which is used in all types of construction work. Other products like bamboo, reed, cane, thatch grass, etc., are of equal value for house making. With the advancement of civilization the need of man is also ever on the increase. To meet his requirements he has tried to tap plants as sources for his comforts and varied use by exploiting his scientific knowledge and has been successful in this direction to a great extent. Other useful plant products include—wood (for furniture, boat building, bridge building, railway sleepers, fuel, etc.), fibres (for gunny bags, rope, cordage, matting, canvas, carpet, etc.), drugs, tannins, dyes, paper, sugar, starch, gum, resin, rubber, vegetable fats, fatty oils, essential oils, tea, coffee, cocoa, tobacco, spices, condiments, cork, etc. Utility of bacteria, yeasts, other edible and antibiotics producing fungi, algae and lichens cannot be denied. It becomes quite evident that a knowledge of botany and its proper application led to the well-being of humanity in several ways. The more important plants and their products have been grouped in several important categories. In the present text the plants and their products have been grouped as follows:*

FOOD PLANTS

Cereals and millets. *Cereals: The cereals are the most important sources of plant food for man. They constitute the most important group in the food plants of India. The cereals are the members of family Gramineae. There are six true cereals rice, wheat, maize, barley, oat and rye. They contain a high percentage of carbohydrates, together with a considerable amount of proteins and some fats. Even vitamins are present.*

Millets: They are also known as small grains. They are considered to have been cultivated in India from prehistoric times. Some of the commonly grown millets in India are sorghum, pearl millet and finger millet.

Legumes and nuts. *Legumes:* The legumes or pulses are next in importance to cereals as sources of food. They belong to the family Leguminosae. They contain more protein material than any other vegetable products. Carbohydrates and fats are also present in the legumes. The pulses form an important item in India where the majority of the population consists of vegetarians. The important Indian pulses are gram, black gram, green gram, pea, pigeon pea, lentil, etc.

Nuts: A nut is a one-celled, one-seeded dry fruit with a hard pericarp. Only a few nuts of commerce fulfil this description, e.g., chestnut. The others included among nuts may be peanuts, almonds, coconuts, cashewnuts, walnuts, pistachio nuts, etc. These "so called" nuts make a valuable food material. The food value is due to a high protein and fat content.

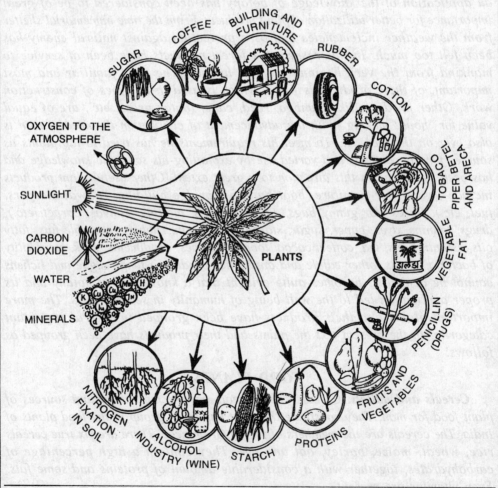

Plants and human welfare

Vegetables. The term vegetable is usually applied to edible plants which store up reserve food in roots, stems, leaves and fruits and which are eaten cooked, or raw as salad. The vegetables rank next to cereals as sources of carbohydrate food. The nutritive value of vegetables is tremendous, because of the presence of indispensable mineral salts and vitamins.

Fruits. Morphologically a fruit is the seed-bearing portion of the plant, and consists of the ripened ovary and its contents. Simple fruits are derived from a single ovary, and compound fruits from more than one. The aggregate fruits are formed from numerous carpels of the same flower, while composite fruits develop from ovaries of different flowers. In economic botany only those fruits are considered which are usually eaten without cooking. For convenience the fruits have been divided into two groups tropical fruits *(e.g., mango, citrus fruits, litchi, banana, guava, sugar apple, fig, papaya, pine-apple, etc.) and* temperate fruits *(e.g., apple, pear, plum, peach, strawberries, grape, etc.).*

PLANTS AND PLANT PRODUCTS OF INDUSTRIAL VALUE

Fibres and fibre-yielding plants. The fibre-yielding plants rank second only to food plants in their usefulness to human kind. The utilization of fibres is directly related to the advancement of civilization. As civilization advanced, the use of vegetable fibres increased greatly. They are of enormous value in our daily life. About two thousand species of the plants yield various fibres all over the world. The chief fibres of commercial importance have been classified in six groups— textile fibres *(e.g., cotton, flax, etc.),* brush fibres, filling fibres, rough weaving fibres, natural fabrics and paper-making fibres. The most important fibre-yielding plants belong to the families—Malvaceae, Tiliaceae, Linaceae, Leguminosae, Musaceae, Bombacaceae, Liliaceae, Palmae, Gramineae, Amaryllidaceae, Urticaceae, and Bromeliaceae.

Wood and cork. Wood: In modern days wood is the most widely used commodity outside of food and clothing. It is one of the most versatile of the raw materials of industry. Wood is cheaper, lighter, and more easily worked with tools. Moreover the wooden structure can be readily altered or rebuilt. Wood is very strong for its weight and unique in strength, elasticity and toughness. It is a bad conductor of heat and electricity and does not rust. The wood is also used in the form of thin sheets or veneers.

Cork: The cork consists of the outer bark of the tree. It is used for many purposes. In some cases the natural cork is utilized whereas in others composition cork, made of coarse pieces treated with adhesives and molded. The most important cork made articles are stoppers, hats, floats, mats, tiles, metal tops for sealing bottles, gaskets, inner soles for shoes, etc.

Tannins and dyes. Tannins: Tannins make a heterogeneous group of complex compounds of widespread occurrence in plants. They are organic compounds chiefly glucosidal in nature, which have an acid reaction and are very astringent. It is a colourless solid, dissolves in water to solutions of astringent tastes. They are of commercial importance because of their property of forming an insoluble colloidal compound (leather) with the hides of animals. They also react with the salts of iron to form dark-blue or greenish-black compounds, the basis of common inks.

Dyes: The dyes are coloured compounds capable of being fixed to fabrics and which do not wash out with soap and water or fade on exposure to light. Therefore, a coloured organic substance is not necessarily a dye. Natural dyes and stains, obtained from the roots, leaves, bark, fruit or wood of plants, have been used from ancient times.

Rubber and its products. Rubber is obtained from the latex, of various plants of tropical and sub-tropical regions. Most of the rubber plants belong to the angiospermic families—Euphorbiaceae, Moraceae and Apocynaceae. The most important rubber plant is Hevea brasiliensis of family Euphorbiaceae. Latex occurs in latex tubes or latex vessels of the plants. Latex is a varying mixture of water, hydrocarbons, resins, oils, proteins, acids, salts, sugar, etc., the substance used as the source of rubber. The Hevea or Para rubber tree is the source of 95% to 98% of the rubber production of the world. The most important rubber products are tyres and tubes for automobiles and cycles accounting for about 75% of the total rubber consumption, about 6% is used for footwear and about 4% for wire and cable insulations.

Fatty oils and vegetable fats. The fatty oils are liquid at ordinary temperatures and usually contain oleic acid. Chemically they consist of glycerin in combination with a fatty acid.

The fats are solid at ordinary temperatures and contain stearic or palmitic acid. When a fat is boiled with an alkali, it decomposes and the fatty acid unites with alkali to form soap.

Usually the fatty oils are stored up in seeds of the plants belonging to many angiospermic families. Sometimes, to a less extent they are also stored in fruits, stems and other plant organs. Several fatty oils are edible and used as cooking media. These edible oils contain both solid and liquid fats.

Sugars and starches. Sugars: The glucose manufactured by the green plant in photosynthesis, is almost universally present in plant cells. This basic material of metabolism, the glucose, has the formula $C_6H_{12}O_6$. Fruit sugar or fructose is another product of photosynthesis which has the same formula. The more complex sugars are built up from these simple sugars. The most important complex sugar is sucrose or cane sugar, which has the formula $C_{12}H_{22}O_{11}$. This sugar is accumulated in abundance in sugarcane and sugar beets. Today, the sugar industry is the second largest in India, next only to textiles.

Starch: Starch occurs in all green plants. It is a complex carbohydrate with the formula $(C_6H_{10}O_5)$ n. Like the sugars, they are derived also from glucose and constitute the first visible product of photosynthesis. This is the commonest type of reserve food in green plants and plays the most important role in their metabolism.

Commercial sources of starch are wheat, barley, maize, potatoes and arrowroot. In these plants starch occurs in the form of starch grains which vary in shape and size.

Pulp and paper. The paper is a cellulose product. Cellulose is the most complex carbohydrate and is universally present in the cell walls of plants. One of the important uses of cellulose is in the manufacture of paper. Paper can be made from any natural fibrous material.

Gums and resins. Gums: The true gums are formed as the result of disintegration of internal tissues, for the most part from the decomposition of cellulose. The gums are insoluble in alcohol but soluble in water, readily swell up in it, and form a viscous mass. They are colloidal in nature. They contain a large amount of sugar and are closely allied to the pectins. The gums are formed in various kinds of plants. Acacia senegal yields the best gum-arabic of commerce. The gums exude naturally from the stems, or in response to wounding. The commercial gums are the dried exudations of the plants.

Resins: They represent oxidation products of various essential oils and are very complex and varied in their chemical composition. They are mostly found in the stems of the trees, and occur in abundance in special canals or ducts. They are yellowish solids, insoluble in water but soluble in alcohol, turpentine and spirit. It normally oozes out through the bark and hardens on exposure to the air.

MEDICINAL PLANTS AND DRUGS

Medicinal plants. The branch of medical science, which deals with the drug plants, is known as pharmacognosy. This branch of medical science is concerned with the history, commerce, collection, selection, identification and preservation of crude drugs and raw materials. Most of the drugs are obtained from wild plants growing in all parts of the world, and especially in tropical regions. The medicinal value of drug plants is due to the presence in the plant tissues of some chemical substances that produce a definite physiological action on the human body. The most important of these substances are alkaloids. Some of these chemicals are powerful poisons and therefore the drugs should be prepared and prescribed only by expert physicians.

Fumitories and masticatories. From the time immemorial the human beings have smoked or chewed various substances for pleasure. For example, the bulk of tobacco is used for smoking in the form of cigarette, bidi, cigar, cheroot and chuttas and in pipe and hookah. Large quantities of tobacco are also consumed for chewing.

On the other hand betel leaves and arecanuts are widely used as a masticatory. The basic preparation for chewing purposes consists of betel leaf smeared with hydrated lime, and catechu to which scrapings of arecanut are added; flavourings such as coconut shavings, clove, cardamom, fennel, powdered liquorice, nutmeg, and also tobacco are used according to one's taste. Chewing of betel leaves with various adjuncts is an ancient practice in India and other countries of East Asia.

FOOD ADJUNCTS

Spices and condiments. *The spices cannot be grouped as foods, for they contain less nutritive value. They stimulate the appetite and increase the secretion and flow of gastric juices. They give a good flavour and aroma to food, and add greatly to the pleasure of eating. For this reason they are commonly known as "food adjuncts". The aromatic value of the spices is due to the presence of the essential oils. Sometimes the term "spice" is restricted to hard parts of plants, which are generally used in a pulverized state. Condiments are spices or other flavouring substances which possess a sharp taste, and are commonly added to food after it has been cooked.*

Vitamins. *The vitamins are absolutely essential for well-being of both plants and animals. They are formed by plants. They are necessary for normal metabolism, growth, development and reproduction. Vitamins are also essential for the prevention of several human diseases. Fruits, vegetables and seeds of various plants are good sources of vitamins. Seaweeds contain nearly all the known vitamins. The yeasts also contain several important vitamins.*

Non-alcoholic beverages. *The beverages containing caffeine are used all over the world for their stimulating and refreshing qualities. Caffeine is an alkaloid, which has definite medicinal values and acts as a diuretic and nerve stimulant. The most important non-alcoholic beverages are—tea, coffee and cocoa. Caffeine is harmful in large quantities, it is present in these beverages in very small amounts, not exceeding two per cent. The other beverages which do not contain alcohol are commonly known as* soft drinks. *They contain high sugar content and make a good source of energy. The fruit juices are the simplest soft drinks.*

LOWER PLANTS IN ECONOMIC BOTANY

Fungi. *Some fungi have been esteemed as articles of food from early times. Edible fungi have delicate flavours and are often valued delicacies. The important edible fungi are—*Agaricus *spp.,* Cantharellus *spp.,* Volvaria *spp.,* Lycoperdon *spp.,* Morchella *spp.,* Tuber *spp. and many others.*

The fungi, like yeasts are responsible for fermentation. The baking industry depends solely on the enormous budding of the yeast cells.

Penicillium is best known to the non-botanist because it is the source from which the antibiotic penicillin is extracted. The famous drug, ergotine is obtained from Claviceps purpurea, *the causal organism of plant disease, ergot of rye.*

Lichens. *As food lichens have been used from the earliest times as animal feed and also as food for human consumption in times of scarcity. Lichens were once employed for dyeing wool and silk and colouring materials derived from them were highly valued before the advent of synthetic dyes. Lichens were formerly used as sources of fermentable sugars for the production of ethyl alcohol. Several lichens possess medicinal properties.*

Algae. *From the earliest times several sea weeds have been used as direct source of food to human beings. High mineral content up to 5% of the wet material, in which all the mineral elements important in human and animal physiology are found, makes sea weeds a unique supplement for a well balanced diet. The sea weeds (marine algae) are the richest source of vitamins. The vitamins A, B and E are found in abundance in sea weeds. Several important foodstuffs prepared by algae are—suimono, mitsu, dulse, seatron, laver, kompu, carrageen, etc.*

10

CHAPTER

Food Plants

CEREALS

The cereals are the most important source of plant food for man. They constitute the most important group in the food plants of India. The cereals are the members of family Gramineae, and possess the characteristic fruit, the caryopsis. In this fruit the wall of the seed becomes fused with the ovary wall to form the husk. The term 'grain' is applied to this type of fruit. There are six true cereals—rice, wheat, maize, barley, oats and rye. Of which rice, wheat and maize, are most important, and they have played an important part in the development of civilization. Sometimes the millets and sorghums are erroneously referred to as cereals. Cereals contain a high percentage of carbohydrates, together with a considerable amount of proteins and some fats. Even vitamins are present.

RICE

Oryza sativa Linn; family—Gramineae (Poaceae); Eng.—rice; Hindi—*chaval, dhan*; Sanskrit—*dhanya, vrihi, nivara, syali*; Bengali—*chal*; Marathi—*tandula, dhan, bhat*; Gujarati—*choka, dangar*; Telugu—*vadlu, varidhanyamu, biyyamu*; Tamil—*nellu, arisi*; Kannada—*akki, bhatta, nelu*; Malayalam—*nellu ari*.

Uses. The chief use of rice is as food, and more people use it than any other cereal. The rice is generally eaten with pulses (legumes) or some other food rich in proteins. A diet of rice and soyabeans makes the food of millions. The rice straw is used for making straw boards, paper and mats. Rice bran oil is used for making soaps and cosmetics. Rice starch is much used in European countries. In several tropical countries intoxicating beverages are prepared from rice. Important beverage of Japan, *Sake* is prepared by fermenting rice. In India also in some parts of Orissa and Andhra Pradesh intoxicating beverages are prepared from rice.

This starch-rich food is eaten after boiling. It may also be converted into parched rice, beaten rice or rice flakes, and puffed rice; mixed with black gram (*urd*) powder, used for fermented preparations like *idli* and *dosa*. Broken grains obtained during milling, used as human and cattle food, for making alcoholic beverages, and as a source of starch and rice flour. Paddy husk is used as fuel; the bran is also used as cattle feed. The fatty oil obtained from bran is used for edible purposes.

WHEAT

Triticum aestivum Linn.; family—Gramineae (Poaceae); Hindi—*Gehu*; Sanskrit—*Godhuma*; Bengali—*Giun, gom, gam*; Marathi—*Gahum, gahung*; Gujarati—*Ghavum, gawn, govum*; Telgu—*Goodhumalu*; Tamil—*Godumai, godumbayarisi*; Kannada—*Godhi*; Malayalam—*Gendum, kotanpam, godamba*.

Uses. There are three main kinds of flour—*suji, maida,* and *ata* which are used for various purposes. The flour is used chiefly for making 'bread' and 'chapatis'. The flour is also used for making biscuits, cakes, pastry and similar articles. Wheat flakes are used as breakfast food.

Wheat is also used in the manufacture of beer and other alcoholic beverages. Wheat straw is used for seating chairs, stuffing mattresses, etc. It makes a good food for livestock. Wheat straw is also used as fodder.

This makes a staple food in most parts of the world. Properties of gluten in the grains are such that it produces bread-stuffs generally superior to those from any other cereal grains. By products of wheat milling, such as bran, germ and middlings constitute valuable feed for stock, readily eaten; supplementary feeds are provided to supply protein and minerals in which the straw is deficient. The straw is used as bedding for cattle; it is also used for padding, as in mattresses, for packing fragile goods, for thatching and many other purposes. It may be used also for production of furfuryl alcohol. Straw-pulp is utilized for the manufacture of paper, straw-board, and building-board.

Non-feed industrial uses of wheat include the manufacture of starch, industrial alcohol, malted wheat, and core-binder flour; only small quantities of wheat are used for starch and gluten manufacture. Grain is regarded as a stand-by for alcohol production. Low-grade flours are utilized in the preparation of pastes for wall papering and ply-wood adhesives, and in iron foundries as a core binder.

Wheat products include peeled wheat ; *Bulgur,* a parboiled wheat product; *Wurld wheat,* similar to *Bulgur,* but of lighter colour ; *Instant* or *agglomerated* flour; Farina or *semolina; Wheat flakes; Shredded wheat ; Puffed wheat ; Grape-nuts,* prepared from toasted slices of malted bread; *Gluten,* used in special breads; and *wheat germ,* rich in vitamin E.

MAIZE

Zea mays Linn., family—Gramineae (Poaceae) ; Eng.—Maize, corn, Indian corn; Hindi— *Makai, Makka, Bhutta* ; Bengali—*Janar, bhutta, jonar;* Marathi—*Maka, makai, buta;* Gujarati—*Makkari, makkai;* Telugu—*Mokka-janna, makka jonnalu;* Tamil—*Makka-cholam;* Kannada—*Mekkejola, musukojola, goinjol;* Malayalam—*Cholam;* Oriya—*Maka, buta;* Assam—*Gomdhan, makoi;* Manipur—*Chujak, nahom.*

Uses. The chief use is as a food for man and livestock. The grain is very nutritious, with a high percentage of carbohydrates, fats and proteins. Not only is the grain valuable as a stock feed, but the plant as a whole is an important fodder crop. The immature cobs are largely eaten after roasting. The grains are also used in making corn starch and industrial alcohol. The glucose is also manufactured from the grain. The corn oil is prepared which is used for soap making, lubrication and as salad oil. Corn flakes make a good breakfast food. The fibres in the stalks are utilized for making paper and yarn. Zein, the protein which occurs in maize grain, is utilized for making artificial fibres with good tensile strength and wool-like qualities.

Table 10.1

Cereals	Proteins (Gms)	Fat (Gms)	Calories	Calcium Mgs	Iron Mgs	Vit 'A' I.U.	Vit 'B' Ribof-lavin Mgs	Vit 'C' Mgs
Maize (Tender)	4.7	0.9	125	9	1.1	54	0.17	6
Maize (Dry)	11.1	3.6	342	10	2.0	1502	0.10	-
Ragi	7.3	1.3	328	344	17.4	70	0.10	-
Rice (milled)	6.8	0.5	345	10	3.1	-	0.03	-
Jowar	10.4	1.9	349	25	5.8	79	0.28	-
Wheat (whole)	11.8	1.5	46	41	4.9	108	0.12	-

It is of special importance in the hilly and sub-montane regions of the country where it forms the staple diet of the people, particularly in the winter months. In the northern parts, it is also extensively grown as a fodder.

Maize Products	Uses
1. **Maize grits**	Can be used directly for maufacture of breakfast foods like corn flakes. This can also be used in the manufacture of starch.
2. **Maize rice**	Can be used in replacement of rice or in conjunction with rice. This can also be used in the manufacture of starch.
3. **Poultry grits**	Can be used in replacement of rice and other cereals in breweries and distilleries.
4. **Brewer's grits**	Can be used in replacement of rice and other cereals in breweries and distilleries.
5. **Maize flakes**	Can be used to prepare various types of dishes in place of beaten rice. This can also be used in the preparation of soup and in breweries and distilleries in replacement of rice and other cereals.
6. **Maize soji** 7. **Pre-cooked Maize soji**	Can be used in the preparation of sweet and savoury dishes like Kesaribhath, Kharabhath, Idli, Dosa, Vermicelli, etc. Pre-cooked Maize Soji can be used in the manufacture of Balahar and snack foods.
8. **Maize maida**	Can be used in the preparation of Bread, Biscuit, Vermicelli, Nippottu, Obbattu, Bajji, Pakoda, Kodubale, etc. This can also be used by mixing with Wheat, Maida and Bengal gram flour for preparing the above said dishes. Also used in gum manufacturing industry.
9. **Maize flour** 10. **Pre-cooked Maize flour**	Can be used in the preparation of Ragi balls by mixing with ragi flour. Can also be used in the preparation of sweet and savoury dishes like Pakoda, Bajji, Kodubale, Chapaties, etc. As raw materials in the manufacture of binders (Gum) for being used in the foundry and paper industry. Pre-cooked flour can be used in the preparation of Soup, Curry, Sambar, Majjigehuli (khadi) and in the manufacture of cereal and other foods for babies.
11. **Maize oil**	Used as edible oil. This oil has got certain advantages like easy blood circulation, reducing body fat, etc. This can also be used in soap manufacturing industry.
12. **Maize cake** 13. **Animal meal** 14. **Bran**	Can be used in Cattle and Poultry feed industry.

Other uses. However, due to low gluten content, it does not form dough with elastic properties, but dough with good elastic properties can be made from flour made from dehulled grain. Maize starch is extensively used as a sizing material in the textiles and paper industries. In the food industry it is used in the preparation of pies, puddings, salad dressings and confections. Maize starch is used for the production of dextrose and corn syrup; also employed as a diluent for pharmaceutical preparations, dusting material to prevent articles like surgeons gloves, from sticking together, ingredient of oil-well drilling muds, and as a depressant in ore-floatation process. In cosmetics, maize starch form an ingredient of various forms of toilet powders. Dried germs yield a semi-drying oil, known as maize oil or corn oil used as salad or cooking oil; it may also be used with linseed oil for paints. Zein, recovered from maize gluten used as a binder for cork particles in forming composition cork. A textile fibre has been produced from zein under the trade name *Vicara*; it combines the virtues of cotton and wool. Cobs are rich in pentosans and used for furfural production. They may also be used for making building-boards which are water and fire-resistant. Maize silk (styles) is astringent, diuretic and chloretic. Some of the maize products include dextrose, maize starch, syrup, corn flakes and popcorns.

VEGETABLES

The term vegetable is usually applied to edible plants which store up reserve food in roots, stems, leaves and fruits and which are eaten cooked, or raw as salad. The vegetables rank next to cereals as sources of carbohydrate food. The nutritive value of vegetables is tremendous, because of the presence of indispensable mineral salts and vitamins. India grows a large variety of vegetables belonging to the tropical, sub-tropical and temperate groups. However their present availability is only 1.3 ounces per adult per day. On the other hand a balanced diet requires ten ounces of vegetables per adult per day. A good number of the vegetables in India are introductions from foreign countries. For convenience the vegetables may be classified in three categories (*i*) underground vegetables, (*ii*) herbage vegetables, and (*iii*) fruit vegetables.

UNDERGROUND VEGETABLES

In these vegetables the food is stored in underground parts. The storage organs may be true roots or modified stems, such as rootstock, tubers, corms and bulbs. From earliest time roots and tubers have furnished food for man. The underground vegetables may be classified in two groups— (*i*) roots and (*ii*) underground stems. Underground stem vegetable **potato** is described.

UNDERGROUND STEM VEGETABLE

POTATO

Solanum tuberosum Linn.; Eng. Potato; Hindi—*Alu*; Family—Solanaceae.

Bengali and Hindi—*Alu*; Marathi and Gujarati—*Batata*; Telugu—*Bangaladumpa, uralagadda*; Tamil—*Uralakilangu, wallaraikilangu*; Kannada—*Batate, alu-gidde*; Malayalam—*Urulan kizhangu*; Punjab, Kumaon, Bihar, Orissa and Assam—*Alu*.

Uses. The tubers are used as vegetable. In European countries they make a universal table food. Small tubers are utilized for the production of starch and industrial alcohol. The potatoes are also fed to livestock.

Potato chips made from fresh potatoes are famous in the South while "*katri* and *patri*" are quite common in Maharashtra and Gujarat.

Katri and patri. The fresh potatoes are made into potato chips and shavings after boiling the potatoes. These are dried in the sun. These dried chips are deep fried as and when required.

Surplus and cull potatoes are used as feed for livestock and also as raw material for manufacture of starch, ethyl alcohol, and some other industrial products. Potato is among richest foods in potassium. Biological value of potato protein is 68 and protein efficiency ratio 1.9 and it decreases on storage, more so at room temperature than at 4°C. Cooking improves digestibility of potato protein. Tuberin has a high nutritive value, being superior to wheat protein. Potatoes contain phosphorylase, amylase and several other enzymes including proteolytic enzymes. Potato flesh, even at its natural high moisture content, is superior to 72 per cent extraction of wheat flour as a source of vitamin B1, riboflavin and nicotinic acid. Concentration of thiamine is lower and that of riboflavin and folic acid is higher at the periphery than in the interior of tuber. Potato leaf haulms are useful source of a-cellulose. Potatoes are used as antiscorbutic, aperient, diuretic, and galactagogue. Extract of leaves is used as antispasmodic in cough. Tuber is ground and made into a paste for application to burns with much benefit.

Potato products include potato chips, frozen French fries, potato granules, potato flakes, potato flour, spaghetti-like potato, canned potatoes, potato starch and fermentation products.

Potatoes are used for the preparation of nutrient media, *e.g.*, potato dextrose agar media (PDA), for culture of microorganism and for potato broth, used in microbiological work.

SUGAR
SUGARCANE

Saccharum officinarum Linn.; Eng. Sugarcane; Hindi—*Ganna, Ikh*; Sanskrit—*Ikshu, khanda, sarkara* ; Bengali—*Paunda, Pundia* ; Telugu—*Cheruku* ; Tamil—*Poovan karumbu* ; Kannada—*Patta patti kabbu* ; Malayalam—*Karimbu*; Family—Gramineae/Poaceae.

Table 10.2. Common Edible Fruits

English name	Botanical name and family	Type of fruit	Edible part
Apple	*Malus sylvestris* Rosaceae	pome	thalamus
Banana	*Musa pardisiaca* Musaceae	berry	mesocarp and endocarp
Cashew-nut	*Anacardium occidental* Anacardiaceae	nut	peduncle and cotyledons
Coconut	*Cocos nucifera* Palmaceae	fibrous drupe	endosperm
Cucumber	*Cucumis sativus* Cucurbitaceae	pepo	mesocarp, endocarp and placentae
Custard apple	*Annona squamosa* Annonaceae	etaerio of berries	fleshy pericarp of individual berries
Date palm	*Phoenix sylvestris* Palmaceae	one seeded berry	pericarp
Fig	*Ficus carica* Moraceae	syconus	fleshy receptacle
Jack fruit	*Artocarpus heterophyllus* Moraceae	sorosis	bracts, perianth and seeds
Grape	*Vitis vinifera* Vitaceae	berry	pericarp and placentae
Guava	*Psidium guava* Myrtaceae	berry	thalamus and pericarp
Indian plum	*Zizyphus jujuba* Rhamnaceae	drupe	mesocarp and epicarp
Litchi	*Litchi chinensis* Sapindaceae	one-seeded nut	fleshy aril
Wheat and other cereals	*Triticum aestivum* Poaceae	caryopsis	starchy endosperm
Mango	*Mangifera indica* Ancardiaceae	drupe	mesocarp
Melon	*Cucumis melo* Cucurbitaceae	pepo	mesocarp
Orange	*Citrus aurantium* Rutaceae	Hesperidium	juicy placental hairs
Papaw	*Carica papaya* Caricaceae	berry	mesocarp
Pea	*Pisum sativum* Papilionaceae	legume	cotyledons
Pear	*Pyrus communis* Rosaceae	pome	fleshy thalamus
Pine-apple	*Ananas comosus* Bromeliaceae	sorosis	outer portion of receptacle bracts and perianth
Pomegranate	*Punica granatum* Punicaceae	special (balusta)	juicy testa
Strawberry	*Fragaria vesca* Rosaceae	etaerio of achenes or nuts	succulent thalamus
Tomato	*Lycopersicon esculentum* Solanaceae	berry	pericarp and placentae
Wood apple	*Aegle marmelos* Rutaceae	berry	mesocarp, endocarp and placentae

Uses of sugar. The sugar is used as an article of food and as sweetening agent in sweets and drinks. It is used in food preservation and in the preparation of oxalic acids in the laboratory. It is used also for the manufacture of octa-acetate.

Sugarcane juice is used mainly for three products used in foods and beverages, for sweetening purposes, *viz., Gur* and jaggery, vacuum pan sugar, and open pan sugar or *khandsari*. A good quantity of sugar is also used for chewing. Byproducts obtained during the manufacture of *gur* and sugar are molasses. *Gur* is used for direct consumption by human beings and livestock. Sugar is used for sweetening milk, tea and coffee, and for making sweets.

By-Products. There are three by-products of sugar industry, *viz.*, bagasse, molasses and press-mud. Bagasse was being used mainly as fuel for steam raising. Now it is used also for the manufacture of paper pulp, cardboard and insulation board. Molasses has demand in the preparation of acetic acid, aconitic acid, power alcohol, chemicals, chloroform, plastics, etc. Pressmud finds use in the manufacture of carbon paper and polish.

CHAPTER 11

Fibres and Fibre Yielding Plants

It goes without saying that the fibre yielding plants rank second only to food plants in their usefulness to humankind. The utilization of fibres is directly related to the advancement of civilization. From the earliest times the man required three things for his living—food, clothing and shelter. Though other things were at hand to fulfil these demands yet they were insufficient and incomplete too without the genuine aid of the plants. As far as the clothing was concerned the skins and hides were not sufficient. He needed somewhat more and that gap was fulfilled by the plant fibre. As there was advancement of civilization the needs of man multiplied several fold and the use of the plant fibres increased greatly. Till now more than two thousand species of plants have been worked out which yield fibres. However, the commercial fibre yielding plants are few in number. The fibres from other plants are used by primitive tribal people of the world.

Economically the fibres may be grouped as follows:

Textile fibres. Fibres utilized for the manufacture of fabrics, netting and cordage, etc.

Brush fibres. Fibres utilized in the manufacture of brushes and brooms.

Rough weaving fibres. Fibres utilized in making baskets, chairs, mats, etc.

Filling fibres. Fibres used for stuffing mattresses, cushions, pillows, etc.

Natural fibres. Natural fibres used as cloth without weaving.

Paper-making fibres. Wood fibres, etc., utilized for paper-making.

As regards their structure, the sclerenchyma cells are grouped into fibres. Fibres are described as long cells with thick walls, correspondingly small cavities, and usually pointed ends. The walls of fibres usually consist of lining as well as cellulose. The fibres may occur singly or in small groups. The fibres may be found in any part of the plant—stems, leaves, roots, fruits and even seeds.

The plants belonging to several families of angiosperms yield fibres. They are chiefly tropical plants. The important families of the fibre yielding plants are—Malvaceae, Linaceae, Tiliaceae, Gramineae, Musaceae, Bombacaceae, Leguminosae, Palmae, Liliaceae, Urticaceae, Amaryllidaceae, Moraceae, Asclepiadaceae, and Bromeliaceae.

TEXTILE FIBRES

These fibres are supposed to be most important because they are connected with the textile industry. This industry is concerned with the manufacture of fabrics, netting and cordage. For making fabrics and netting, the flexible fibres are twisted together into yarn and thereafter woven, spun and knitted. For making cordage the individual fibres are twisted together rather than woven. The textile fibres are always long and possess high tensile strength, together with cohesiveness and pliability. They possess a fine, uniform, lustrous staple. The chief textiles are included in three categories—(*i*) surface fibres, (*ii*) soft fibres and (*iii*) hard fibres.

Surface fibres, *e.g.*, Cottons.

Soft fibres, *e.g.*, Flax, hemp, jute and ramie.

Hard fibres, *e.g.*, Sisal, coconut, pineapple, abaca, etc.

SURFACE FIBRES

COTTON

Gossypium Linn.; Eng.—Cotton; Hindi—*Kapas*; Bengali, Hindi, Gujarati, Punjabi and Marathi—*Kapas, rui, tula*; Kannada—*Hathi*; Telugu—*Patti, karpasamu*; Tamil and Malayalam—*Paruthi, panji*; Oriya—*Karpaso, kopa*; Family—Malvaceae.

USES OF COTTON

The bulk of cotton production is consumed in the manufacture of woven goods, alone or in combination with other fibres. The principal types of woven fabrics are—print cloth, yarn fabrics, sheetings, fine cotton goods, napped fabrics, duck, tyre fabrics and towels. Products in the form of yarn and cord include unwoven tyre cord, thread, cordage and twine and crochet yarns. Unspun cotton finds use in mattresses, pads and upholsteries. Cotton constitutes one of the basic raw materials for cellulose industries including plastics, rayon and explosives. Sterilized absorbent cotton finds use in medical and surgical practice.

Yarns of varying size and fineness are needed in the production of fabrics. Coarse yarns are spun from short staple cottons and fine one from medium and long staple types. Long and uniform staples are utilized for yarns of high counts required for fine fabrics.

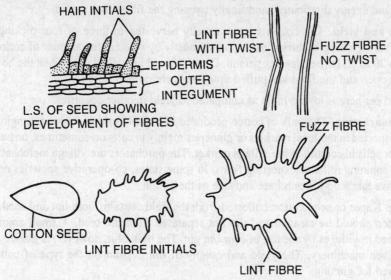

Fig. 11.1. Development of fibre in cotton.

Cotton waste is a by-product of the spinning and weaving mills and consists principally of short fibres rejected by combing and carding machines, floor sweepings, odds and ends from weaving and various scraps. The amount of waste given by cotton is an important factor in its quality evaluation.

Cotton waste of good grade is employed in making cotton blankets, sheets, towels and flannelettes. Cylindrical strips from carding machine, which are constituted of fibres of good strength, are used for warps, twines, ropes and nets; they are also useful for wadding, padding for upholstery, bed quilts, etc. Strips from Egyptian cottons are mixed with wool for making mixed woollen goods. Floor sweeping and fibres unfit for spinning are bleached and used for gun-cotton, cellulose and artificial silk. Short remnants and thread waste that can not be respun are used as wiping and polishing material.

The *stalks* of plant contain a fibre that can be used in paper making or for fuel, and the *roots* possess a crude drug. The seeds are of the greatest importance and every portion is utilized. The *hulls* are used for stock feed; as fertilizer; for lining oil wells; as a source of xylose, a sugar that can be converted into alcohol and for many other purposes. The *kernels* yield one of the most important fatty oils, cottonseed oil and an oil cake and meal which are used for fertilizer, stock feed, flour, and as a dyestuff.

DEVELOPMENT OF FIBRE IN COTTON

A cotton fibre is a delicate tubular prolongation of the peripheral wall of the seed. The fibres are formed by the outer epidermis of the outer integuments. These hairs are single celled and thick walled and attain a length of up to 45 mm These fibres also show characteristic twists and are called *lint fibres*. Intermingled with the lint hairs are some *fuzz hairs*. The maximum length attained by the latter is 10 mm They are thick walled with the narrow lumen and lack the twists.

THE COTTON INDUSTRY

Several operations are necessary in order to prepare the raw cotton fibre, as it comes from the field, for use in the textile industry. In brief these operations are as follows—ginning; baling; transporting to the mills; picking, a process in which a machine removes any foreign matter and delivers the cotton in a uniform layer; lapping, an operation whereby three layers are combined into one; carding, combing, and drawing during which the short fibres are extracted and the others are straightened and evenly distributed; and finally twisting the fibres into thread.

Harvest and yield. The cotton crop is usually harvested in three or four pickings, taken at suitable intervals. Picking is carried out by hand, mostly by women, the amount of cotton collected ranging from 20 to 50 lb. per day per person. Cotton should be picked only when the bolls are fully mature, fully open and the floss has puffed up consequent on exposure to sun.

The yield per acre is low in India as compared to yield in other countries.

Cotton marketing. The bulk of cotton produced in India is sold as *Kapas* or unginned cotton. *Kapas* is transported to the local markets or ginneries mainly in carts or, sometimes, on pack animals. The cultivator sells his cotton in the village market. The purchasers are village merchants, or agents of ginneries, spinning mills or exporting firms. In some states, co-operative societies organized by cultivators have taken up the purchase and sale of the cotton.

Ginning. Kapas or seed cotton collected from the field contains both lint and seed. For use in industry, cotton should be cleaned and the lint separated from the seed. A small amount of seed cotton is ginned in villages by the use of *charkha* gin. The bulk of it, however, is ginned in factories by power-driven machinery. The yield and quality of lint depend on the type of cotton and the machinery used for ginning.

Baling. Cotton is packed for trade purposes both in loose and compressed bales. Loose packing is adopted for inland transit of ginned cotton to a pressing factory, while compressed packing is adopted for transporting ginned cotton to the market and for storing in the godowns. Each loose bale contains 200 to 300 lb. of cotton. The usual weight of compressed bale is 392 lb. net with density of 40 lb. per cubic foot.

SOFT OR BAST FIBRES

JUTE

Corchorus Linn.; Eng. Jute; Hindi—*Patsan*; Sanskrit—*Kalasaka*; Hindi—*Narcha*; Bengali—*Chinalitapat, narcha, nalita, titapat*; Assam—*Titamara*; Family—Tiliaceae.

Utilization. Jute is used chiefly for rough weaving. The thick cloth made from jute fibre is used for making gunny-bags. Another type of fine cloth prepared from jute fibre is chiefly used as a cloth to sleep on. Another type of coarse cloth is largely used for making the sails of country boats, and also for bags to hold large seeds or fruits.

Jute is extensively used in the manufacture of carpets, curtains, shirtings, and is also mixed with silk or used for imitating silk fabrics. The fibre is also used for making twine and ropes. Short fibres and pieces from the lower ends of the stalks constitute jute butts, which are used to some extent in paper making.

India not only grows most of the jute, but it is the largest manufacturer and exporter of jute products.

COIR

Cocos nucifera Linn.; Eng. Coir; Sanskrit—*Narikela*; Hindi—*Nariyal*; Bengali—*Dab, narikel*; Marathi—*Narel, narel*; Telugu—*Kobbarichettu, narikelamu, tenkaya*; Tamil—*Tennaimaram, tenkai*; Kannada—*Tengu*; Malayalam—*Thenna, thenga, narikelam*; Family—Palmaceae/Arecaceae.

A tall palm, cultivated chiefly in Kerala, Tamil Nadu and Karnataka. Coir is the term applied to the short, coarse rough fibres which make up the greater part of the husk of the fruits of coconut palm. The husks of coconuts are soaked in salt water for several months to loosen the fibres. They are then beaten to separate the fibres, which are then washed and dried. The coconut fibres are very light and elastic, and exceedingly resistant to water. The coir extracted from the husks of coconuts, is dried in the sun and spun into coir yarn either by hand or machine.

CHAPTER 12

Vegetable and Fatty Oils

The fatty oils are liquid at ordinary temperatures and usually contain oleic acid. They are sometimes called 'fixed oils' because, unlike the essential oils they do not evaporate. Chemically, the fatty oils consist of glycerine in combination with a fatty acid.

However, the fats are solid at ordinary temperatures and contain stearic or palmitic acid. When a fat is boiled with an alkali, it decomposes and the fatty acid unites with alkali to form soap.

Usually the fatty oils are stored up in seeds of the plants belonging to many families. Sometimes, to a less extent they are also stored in fruits, stems and other plant organs. Several fatty oils are edible and used as cooking media. The edible oils contain both solid and liquid fats.

Extraction of fatty oils. The seed coats are removed and the material is being converted into a fine meal. The oils may be removed by solvents or by hydraulic pressure. The hydraulic pressure method is commonly used for extracting the edible oils. The residue or oil cake is rich in protein and makes a good cattle feed. The pressure causes the cell walls to break and the fatty oils escape. These oils are filtered and purified. The refined oil is used for food purpose, and the lower grades of oil are used in industries.

Classification of fatty oils. There are three categories of fatty oils–(1) drying and semi-drying oils, (2) nondrying oils, and (3) vegetable fats. The refined grades of drying and semi-drying oils are used as edible oils, whereas the inferior grades are used in making soaps, varnishes, paints, candles and other such articles. The nondrying oils are edible and can be used for soap and lubricants. The fats are solid or semisolid at ordinary temperatures. They are edible and are also used in the soap and candle industries.

DRYING AND SEMI-DRYING OILS

SARSON OIL

Brassica campestris Linn.; var. *sarson* Prain; Eng. Yellow sarson, Indian colza; Hindi—*Sarson*; Family—Cruciferae (Brassicaceae).

A herb. It is grown as an oil-seed crop mainly in Uttar Pradesh, the Punjab, Bihar and Assam. The oil content is 30 to 45 percent, and the oil is extracted by expression or solvents.

Uses. The oil is used for cooking and burning purposes. The oil-cake is used as cattle feed.

NUTS WITH HIGH FAT CONTENT
COCONUT

Cocos nucifera Linn.; Family—Palmae/Palmacea/Arecaceae; Eng.—Coconut; Hindi—*Nariyal*; Sanskrit—*Narikela*; Bengali—*Dab, narikel*; Marathi—*Narel, naral*; Telugu—*Kobbarichettu, narikelamu, tenkaya*; Tamil—*Tennaimaram, tenaki*; Kannada—*Tengu*; Malayalam—*Thenna, thenga, marikelam*.

Uses. The tender nuts are in demand for their liquid which provides a very refreshing and delicious drink. It is said to have laxative and diuretic properties. The soft kernel inside the tender nut is also scraped and eaten. The mature nuts are used mainly to make copra (dried meat or kernel) and for edible purposes as fresh kernel in food preparations.

The copra is crushed to obtain coconut oil which is in great demand for edible purposes. It is used as an adjunct for milk-fat, as a filler and thickener for milk and as an ingredient of artificial milk for infants. The cake left after the extraction of oil is largely used to feed cattle and poultry. It is occasionally used as food by poor people. The coconut cake helps to increase the milk content when fed to cows and the butter made from such milk has a firmer texture and better flavour than when other cakes are used.

GROUNDNUT

Arachis hypogaea Linn,: Eng. Peanut, groundnut, Hindi—*Mungphali*; Family—Leguminosae (Papilionaceae).

Bengali—*Chini badam*; Marathi—*Bhui mug*; Telugu—*Verusenagalu*; Tamil—*Verkadalai*; Kannada—*Nela-gadale*; Malayalam—*Nelakadala*.

Uses. The peanuts (seeds) are used for roasting or salting and for the preparation of peanut butter. Peanuts are a very nutritious food. One lb. of peanuts yields 2700 cal. The filtered refined oil is used for cooking and in making margarine. Peanut oil is an important food oil. The oilcake is used as fodder. The protein in peanuts is used in the manufacture of ardil, a synthetic fibre. The vegetable *ghee* is made from the peanut oil after hydrogenation.

The kernels are also used in various foods and confectionery. They are ground and made into peanut butter. Peanut flour is prepared by grinding the finest grades of peanut cake; it is used for supplementing the white flour. Cake is used as feed for cattle and other farm animals; also used as manure. Cake has high nutritive value. Seedcoats are mixed with groundnut husk and the product is called groundnut bran. Some commercial products are groundnut milk, peanut ice-cream and peanut massage oil for infantile paralysis. Hulls are used as filler for fertilizers, or ground into meal for insulation blocks, floor sweeping compounds, bedding the stables, etc. Peanut oil also finds some use as a lubricant, and blends with mineral oil have been developed.

LINSEED OIL

Linseed oil. Alsi Ka Tel. Oil is extracted from the seeds of *Linum usitatissimum* belonging to the family Linaceae.

Oil. It **is a drying oil** as it may absorb oxygen and also gets dried on exposure in the form of a thin elastic film. The seed contains 32 to 43 per cent oil. Usually it is extracted by pressure with heat or by the use of solvents. The colour of oil is yellow to brownish and has acrid taste and smell.

Uses. (1) It is used chiefly in making paints, varnishes, linoleum, soft soap and printer's ink.

(2) Oil cake is used as cattle feed.

(3) Also used as food purposes when obtained by cold process.

(*ii*) **Soybean oil.** Oil is extracted from the seeds of *Glycine max* belonging to the family Papilionaceae.

Oil. It **is a drying oil** as it may absorb oxygen and also gets dried on exposure in the form of a thin elastic film. The seed contains 19—22 per cent oil. Usually it is extracted by hydraulic or expeller process. The colour of oil is yellow to light brown.

Uses. (1) Over 50 different food products have been made from it, principally margarine.

(2) It can be used as a cooking oil after refining.

(3) A number of commercial products are made from this oil as candles, soaps, linolium, paints, greases, rubber substitutes, etc.

(4) Oil cake has 40 to 48 per cent protein so it is a valuable cattle feed and also a source of soya flour.

(5) It is also used in making adhesives, plastics, spreaders, fertilizers, a synthetic textile fibre and many other products.

COTTON SEED OIL

Cotton seed oil. Oil is extracted from the seeds of *Gossypium* species belonging to the family Malvaceae.

Oil. It is a **semidrying oil** as it absorbs oxygen very slowly and in limiting amount and forms a soft film only after long exposure. The seeds contain 30—40 per cent oil. Oil is extracted through hydraulic or expeller process.

Uses. (1) It is used for salad or cooking purpose.

(2) Oleomargarine and lard substitute (fat of pig) are made from it.

(3) The raw oil is used for making soap, artificial leather, insulating materials, washing powders, oil cloth, etc.

(4) Oil cake is used as a livestock feed and also as a manure.

SESAME OIL

Sesame oil (Til Ka Tel). Oil is extracted from the seeds of *Sesamum indicum* belonging to the family Pedaliaceae.

Oil. It **is a semidrying oil** as it absorbs oxygen very slowly and in limiting amount and forms a soft film only after long exposure, the seeds contain 50 to 57 per cent oil. The clean oil is clear yellow coloured with a characteristic smell.

Uses. (1) The refined oil is used for cooking.

(2) The raw oil is used in making soap, cosmetics, medicinal purposes, etc.

(3) Also used as an illuminant.

(4) Oil cake is used as cattle feed and as fertilizer.

SUNFLOWER OIL

Sunflower oil. Oil is extracted from the seeds of *Helianthus annuus* belonging to the family Compositae.

Oil. It is a drying oil as it may absorb oxygen and also gets dried on exposure in the form of a thin elastic film. The seeds contain 32-45 per cent oil. The oil is extracted by expression method. Oil is pale yellow in colour. *Uses.* (1) The oil is used as a cooking medium.

(2) It is used in the manufacture of paints, soaps and cosmetics.

(3) Oil cake is an excellent cattle feed.

(4) Margarines and lard substitutes are also made from it.

OLIVE OIL

Olive oil (Jaitun Ka Tel). Oil is extracted from the fruits of *Olea europaea* belonging to the family Oleaceae.

Oil. It **is a non-drying oil** at ordinary temperature, it remains liquid and do not form a film. The colour of oil is golden yellow and is clear and odourless.

Uses. (1) The oil is used as a cooking medium.

(2) It is widely used as a medicine.

(3) Inferior grades have a greenish tinge and are used for soap making and as lubricants.

(4) Olive oil is used greatly as a food oil.

(5) Oil cake is a cattle feed and fertilizer.

COCONUT OIL

Coconut oil (Nariyal Ka Tel). Oil is extracted from the endosperm of the fruits of *Cocos nucifera* belonging to family Palmae.

Oil. **It is a vegetable fat** Here the yield is 65 to 70 per cent. The oil is pale yellow or colourless, and solidifies below 74° F.

Uses. (1) Refined oil is edible. Margarine, candy bars and similar type of confectionery are made from it.

(2) Best kind of soaps, shaving creams, cosmetics, shampoo, etc., are made by it.

(3) It is only oil used in marine soaps.

(4) Oil cake is used as cattle feed and fertilizer.

CASTOR OIL

Castor Oil. Oil is extracted from the seeds of *Ricinus communis* belonging to family Euphorbiaceae.

Oil. **It is a non-drying oil** as at ordinary temperature they remain liquid and do not form a film. The characteristically marked seeds contain 35—55% oil. Oil is colourless or greenish.

Uses. (1) It is vastly used as a medicine in the form of a purgative.

(2) It is an excellent lubricant for aeroplanes.

(3) It is water resistant so also used in coating fabrics and as protective covering for aeroplanes.

(4) It is used for making soaps, links, plastic, etc.

(5) It is used as an illuminant.

(6) Oil cake is used as a fertilizer.

(7) When hydrated, it gets converted into drying oil and used in paint and varnish.

13

CHAPTER

Wood and Cork

From the time immemorial food, clothing and shelter have been the three great necessities of mankind. The wood is the most familiar and most important forest products. The wood has contributed a lot to the advancement of civilization. Today the wood is the most widely used commodity other than food and clothing. It is one of the most important and versatile of the raw materials of the industry. It has so many advantages over the metals.

It is cheap, light and may easily be worked with tools. It is very strong for its weight and it is embodiment of strength, toughness and elasticity. It is a bad conductor of heat and electricity. Wood is also used in the form of thin sheets or veneers. The wood is definitely superior to metals in several respects.

DIAGNOSTIC FEATURES OF WOODS

On the basis of several important diagnostic features the commercial woods may be identified to some extent. The more important diagnostic features are mentioned here:

Porous and nonporous woods. The presence or absence, and the nature and arrangement of pores, serve as a ready means of classifying woods. The coniferous woods do not possess pores, and are known as *nonporous* woods, whereas the angiospermic woods possess numerous pores and are termed as *porous* woods. On the basis of the distribution of pores, the woods may be of two types— *ring porous* and *diffuse porous* woods. In ring porous woods (*e.g.*, ash, elm, oak, etc.) the pores are found to be arranged in concentric circles, the outer and inner portions of which differ with regard to the number and size of the pores. In diffuse porous woods (*e.g.*, beech maple, walnut, etc.) the pores are small and nearly of the same size and are found to be scattered uniformly throughout the wood.

Early wood and late wood. In temperate regions, every year new wood is formed in a limited growing season, with the result definite growth layers develop, which show two distinct areas within each layer. The wood thus formed in the spring is called the *spring wood* or early wood, and that formed in winter is called the *autumn wood* or late wood. There is a sharp contrast between the late autumn wood and the early spring wood, and this makes the successive rings distinct. The growth ring of a single year is called an annual ring and the number of these annual rings gives an indication of the age of tree. Annual rings of successive years may vary greatly in width. Wide rings are formed under favourable conditions of growth of the tree, and narrow ones are formed when conditions are unfavourable.

Sapwood and heartwood. The outer region of the wood which is of lighter colour is known as the *sapwood*, and this alone is used for conduction of water and salt solutions. The cells of this region are alive and physiologically active. In old trees the central region of the secondary wood is filled up with tannin and other substances which make it hard and durable. This region is known as the *heartwood*. It looks black owing to the presence of tannins, oils, gums, resins, etc., in it. The vessels often become plugged with tyloses. The function of the heartwood is no longer conduction of water, but it simply gives mechanical support to the stem. The heartwood usually takes good polish and is used for cabinet work, furniture and other high grade wood-working industries.

Texture, grain and figure. *Texture* refers to the relative size and quality of the various woods, while *grain* refers to their structural arrangement. *Figure* is applied to the design or pattern which appears on the surface of wood.

Rays. The rays are made of parenchyma cells that are oriented at right angles to the main axis of the stem. They vary greatly in width, height and arrangement.

MECHANICAL PROPERTIES OF WOOD

Wood possesses some important mechanical properties which either alone or in combination, determine its usefulness and suitability for various purposes. These properties may differ in different species. The mechanical properties enable the wood to resist various external forces which tend to change its shape and size and produce deformations. The important mechanical properties of wood are mentioned here.

Strength

The strength is restricted to the ability to resist certain definite forces which may be termed— crushing strength, tensile strength, shearing strength and cross-breaking strength. They are as follows:

Crushing strength. It is the resistance offered to forces that tend to crush wood.

Tensile strength. It is the resistance to forces that tend to pull wood apart.

Shearing strength. It is resistance to those forces which tend to make the fibres slide past one another.

Cross-breaking strength. This is the resistance to forces which cause the beams to break, and all the above-mentioned forces are involved.

Stiffness. It is the measure of the ability of wood to resist forces that tend to change its shape.

Toughness. It is referred to the ability of wood to absorb a large amount of energy, and so resist repeated, sudden sharp blows or shock.

Hardness. It is the measure of the power of wood to resist indentations, abrasion and wear.

Cleavability. It is an expression of the ease with which wood can be split.

STRENGTH AND OTHER PROPERTIES OF WOOD

The strength of wood is the most important property in determining the value of any species for structural purposes. It is a very variable property, and is influenced by the density of the wood, the moisture content, the presence of defects and many other factors. Suitability figures for eight different properties have been calculated by taking into consideration the various strength functions of both green and seasoned timber as shown in the table.

Suitability	Strength and other properties of wood
1. **Weight**	Specific gravity based on weight oven dry and the volume of seasoned timber (approximately 12%) moisture content.
2. **Strength as a beam**	Modulus of rupture and fibre stress as the elastic limit in static bending. Fibre stress at the elastic limit in impact bending.
3. **Stiffiness as a beam**	Modulus of elasticity in static bending. Modulus of elasticity in impact bending.
4. **Suitability as a post**	Maximum crushing strength and strength at the elastic limit in compression parallel to grain. Modulus of elasticity in static bending.
5. **Shock-resisting ability**	Work to maximum load and total work in static bending.
6. **Retention of shape**	Shrinkage green to oven dry in volume and in the radial and tangential directions.
7. **Shear**	Shearing strength in the radial and tangential directions.
8. **Hardness**	Fibre stress at the elastic limit in compression perpendicular to the grain. Radial, tangential and end hardness.

SEASONING OF WOOD

Wood always contains moisture, the amount of which varies from 40 per cent to 100 per cent or more of the dry weight. The water found within the wood is known as *hygroscopic water*. The amount of hygroscopic water constitutes from 20 to 35 per cent of dry weight. This property of wood is known as *hygroscopicity*. The moisture content of wood has an important bearing on its weight, density, and often on its strength. It is only the loss of hygroscopic water which is responsible for the increase in strength, that accompanies seasoning, as the drying out of wood is called. The loss of hygroscopic water causes the shrinkage of wood. This tendency of wood to shrink as it dries is one of the great drawbacks to its use. As the result of uneven shrinkage, warping and other defects may develop, which tend to counteract any increase in strength. However, dried or seasoned wood is for the most part stronger, harder, stiffer and more durable than unseasoned wood. Artificial methods, of wood seasoning are employed. There are two chief types of artificial wood seasoning—1. *air seasoning* and 2. *kiln drying*.

Air seasoning. Here, the moisture is removed by exposure to air without resorting to artificial heat. It is carried out in open until the wood ceases to lose weight. The ultimate water content varies from 12 to 30 per cent. The main objects of air-seasoning are to reduce weight, the amount of shrinkage and other defects. This is a long-time process.

Kiln drying. Here, heat is applied to wood in an enclosed space. In this process, the moisture is removed more rapidly and more completely. The final moisture content varies from 4 to 12 percent. If green wood is kiln-dried, warping and other defects may be prevented. This process is completed in short duration.

PRINCIPAL WOODS OF INDIA

Babul

Acacia nilotica (Linn.) Del.; Syn. *A. arabica* Willd.; Trade name—Babul; Hindi—*Babul, kikar*; Bengali—*Babul*; Hindi—Punjab and Uttar Pradesh—*Kikar*; Gujarati—*Baval*; Telugu—*Nallatumma*; Tamil—*Karuvelei*; Kannada—*Jaali, gobbli*; Malayalam—*Karivelan*; Family—Mimosaceae.

The sapwood is yellowish-white and usually wide. The heart-wood when freshly cut, is a pinkish or old rose colour, but it darkens on exposure to a dull red or reddish brown. It is often mottled with darker streaks. The wood is dull and without taste or smell, hard, fairly close-textured and with straight or slightly twisted grain.

There are several varieties of *babul*. The two best known are the *telia* and *kauria* varieties, the wood of the former having a better reputation than the latter.

Seasoning. Babul is a wood which can be air-seasoned with fairly good results if care is taken. One year is sufficient to air-season babul boards up to 2 in. in thickness. It can be kiln-seasoned without difficulty.

Strength. Babul is an extremely strong, hard and tough wood. It is nearly twice as hard as teak and has a very good shock resisting ability.

Durability. The sapwood is not durable. The heartwood is durable in most situations but not to the same degree as teak and sal.

Working qualities. An easy wood to convert and to saw when green, but it becomes harder and tougher when seasoned. It works well by hand, and machines and finishes to a good surface. It takes a fair polish but requires careful filling.

Uses. It is popular for parts of carts (body work, spokes, naves, axles, felloes, yokes and shafts), and for agricultural implements such as ploughs, harrows and clod-crushers. It is a useful tool handle wood but not for all types of handle, and it can be used for tent pegs. It can be described as one of the best Indian utility woods where hardness and toughness are required. It is a good turnery wood.

Sources of supply. Babul is usually available in small logs only, but in some districts larger logs are available. It is found throughout the drier regions of North, Central and South India.

Simul

Bombax ceiba L.; Syn. *Salmalia insiginis* (Wall.) Schott & Endl.; Hindi—*Semul*; Sanskrit—*Salmali, rakta-pushpa*; Bengali—*Simul, roktosimul*; Marathi—*Saur, simlo*; Gujarati—*Sawar, simalo*; Telugu—*Booruga, konda-buruga*; Tamil—*Mullialava*; Kannada—*Booruga*; Malayalam—*Pula-maram*; Oriya—*Bour*; Garo—*Panchu*; Mundari—*Edelsong*; Family—Bombacaceae.

A large tree found in the Western Ghats, Assam and the Andaman Islands. The wood is very soft creamy white or pale pink timber, very light in weight and with large open pores.

Seasoning. Quick drying can be achieved by exposing freshly converted timber directly to the drying action of the sun and wind or by kiln-seasoning. If air-seasoning is to be done, the best method is to stack the freshly sawn stock in a vertical position against a building or railing with the planks facing the sun. The boards should be turned from time to time so that both surfaces are exposed, kiln-seasoning is the surest and best method of drying *simul*.

Uses. The wood is used for matches, packing cases, penholders, veneers and ply-wood.

Wood is most widely used in match industry, especially for match boxes. Suitable for shingles, canoes, toys, scabbards, cooperage, bush handles, tea-chest plywood and picture frames. Also used for cushioning mine-props and for inside portions of opium chests. Floss used for stuffing life belts, mattresses, cushions and pillows, upholstry and quilts. Tree yields a gum called *mocharus*.

Albizia

There are several common commercial *Albizia* woods. The best known is perhaps *Albizia lebbeck* (Linn.) Benth.; the others *A. odoratissima, A. procera*, and *A. stipulata*.

Red Cedar

Toona ciliata Roem.; Eng. Cedrela tree, Red cedar; Hindi—*Toon*; Sanskrit—*Nandivriksha, tunna*; Hindi and Bengali—*Tun, mahanim*; Marathi—*Kuruk*; Tamil—*Santhanavembu, tunumaram*; Telugu—*Nandichettu*; Kannada—*Mandurike*; Malayalam—*Malarveppu*; Assam—*Poma*; Family—Meliaceae.

A tree cultivated in the Punjab, Assam, Bihar, the Western Ghats, Maharashtra, Madhya Pradesh and the Nilgiris.

Description of wood. The wood is a pinkish brick red, when freshly cut, toning to a light brownish red on exposure. The wood is a light weight, and usually straight grained timber. The wood has a distinct cedar like smell.

Seasoning. *Toon* is a fairly easy wood to air-season if care is taken with the stacking. Kiln-seasoning can also be done.

Strength. *Toon* is a timber of only moderate strength qualities. Hill *toon* is strongest and has about 80% the strength of teak.

Working qualities. *Toon* is one of the easiest of Indian woods to saw and work. If properly finished and filled, it takes a very good polish. It makes up into a good type of plywood. It makes high quality congealated wood.

Uses. The wood is used for furniture, tea-chests, shuttles and picking sticks which are used in the textile industry, and cigar boxes.

Walnut

Juglans regia Linn.; Eng. English walnut, Persian walnut; Hindi—*Akhrot*; Family—Juglandaceae. Found in Kashmir, Himachal Pradesh, the Khasia hills and in the hills of Uttar Pradesh.

Indian walnut varies considerably in colour, sometimes being a dull grey, while other wood may be a dark brown with even darker markings. It is relatively light wood for its strength and it works very easily and finishes to a fine surface. Its most important quality, however, is that, when once dried it does not shrink, swell or split. This, combined with its lightness, strength and good working qualities gives it pre-eminence as a wood for rifle parts, gun stocks, high class cabinet making, and delicate carvings.

Seasoning. Walnut wood seasons slowly and springs considerably while drying out, but apart from this, it is a model wood in so far as seasoning is concerned, both in air-drying and kiln-drying. Green conversion, followed by stacking under cover with a good air circulation is the method of seasoning recommended.

Strength. For its weight, walnut is a relatively strong wood. It is about 85% the weight of teak and in shock resistance is about equal to teak.

Working qualities. An extremely easy and pleasant wood to saw and work to a fine finish. It takes an excellent polish and needs very little filling.

Uses. The wood is used for musical instruments and cabinet work. Used extensively in Kashmir and North India for carving. Well known as an excellent veneer and plywood timber. It is also used for gun stocks.

White Willow

Salix alba Linn.; Eng. White willow; Hindi—*Bis*; Kashmir—*Vivir*; Punjab—*Bis, madnu, bhushan*; Family—Salicaceae.

A small tree, found in the North-Western Himalayas and in the valley of Kashmir. The twigs are used for making baskets. Cricket bats are made of the wood.

Used also for house building, match-boxes and splints, shoes, tool-handles, agricultural implements, boats, boxes, combs and toothpicks; suitable for paper pulp and charcoal making.

Mulberry

Morus alba, Linn; Eng. White mulberry; Hindi—*Tut*; Family—Moraceae. A tree, native of China. In India, it is grown in Punjab, Uttar Pradesh, Kashmir and the North-Western Himalayas. It is also cultivated in Karnataka state for silk worm cultivation.

Description of the wood. The sapwood is white and sharply delimited from the heartwood, which is a bright yellowish brown when freshly cut. No odour or taste. Straight-grained and of rather open medium coarse texture.

Seasoning. The best results have been obtained by storing the logs for some months before final conversion. The wood can be kiln-seasoned without difficulty. In practice, the most of the mulberry used in Punjab is used in a green state by the sports goods manufacturers. The timber is converted green, steam bent, and the dried out in a bent form tightly held in a clamp.

Strength. It is approximately the same in weight as teak, and in shock resistance, shear and hardness it is considerably higher than teak.

Uses. The primary use is for sports goods, for which purpose it is eminently suitable. It is used mainly for the manufacture of hockey sticks. It is also used for tennis rackets, badminton and squash rackets, presses, cricket stumps, etc.

Also suitable for house-building, agricultural implements, furniture, spokes, poles, shafts, bent parts of carriages and carts and for turnery. Bark is used for paper making; also yields a textile fibre.

Deodar

Cedrus deodara Loud.; Eng. Deodar; Hindi—*Deodar, Diar*; Family—Pinaceae.

A tall evergreen tree found in the North-Western Himalayas from Kashmir to Garhwal.

Description of the wood. It is of light yellow-brown colour and possesses distinctive odour. It is a medium weight wood which is very sturdy in use and durable. It is usually even-grained and of medium to fine texture, but the presence of large knots is a common feature.

Seasoning. It is an easy wood to air-season. It can also be kiln-seasoned.

Strength. Deodar is the strongest of the Indian conifers. Its weight is 20% less than teak and its strength is also about 20% less.

Working qualities. It is an easy timber to saw and work to a smooth finish.

Uses. The timber is used for construction work and for railway sleepers. It is also suitable for beams, floor boards, ports, window frames, light furniture and shingles.

This is strongest of Indian coniferous woods, also used for doors, furniture, packing cases, masts, spars and also for wooden bridges. Wood yields an oleoresin and a dark coloured oil used for ulcers and skin diseases.

Himalayan Spruce

Picea smithiana (Wall.) Boiss. ; Eng. Himalayan spruce; Hindi— *Bajur*; North West Himalayan region—*Rai, rau, re, kachal, salla, tos*; Jaunsar, Garhwal and Kumaon— *Roi, rhai, ragha, morinda*; Trade— Spruce; Family—Pinaceae.

A tree commonly found in the Western Himalayas. The wood is used for construction work, railway sleepers, cabinet making, packing cases and wood pulp.

One of the most useful timber trees of the Western Himalayas. Wood is used for planking, general fittings and joinery, rough furniture, tea-boxes and packing cases. This is one of the best light boxwood of India. Wood is suitable also for match boxes, battery separators, for fence posts, transmission poles, piles and newsprint manufacture.

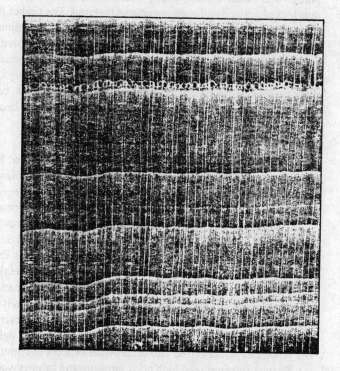

Fig. 13.1. Deodar wood (non-porous), sectional view of micrograph X 10.

Pine Wood

Pinus roxburghii Sar.; Eng. Long-leaved pine; Hindi—*Chir, Salla*; Family—Pinaceae.

An evergreen coniferous tree. It is found in the Western and Eastern Himalayas. The wood is used for construction work, railway sleepers, packing cases, furniture and in match industry.

Pinus merkusii Jungh & de Vries. A tree. The wood is very resinous with reddish-brown heartwood and yellow sapwood. It is used for building purposes and general carpentry.

Pinus wallichiana A. B. Jackson; Eng. Indian blue-pine; Hindi—*Kail, Chil*. A coniferous tree. The wood is used for pencils, penholders, splints, match boxes, construction work, railway sleepers, and furniture. Also used for shingles, packing cases, constructional work and house fitments. It is a good wood for pattern making, cores for laminboards, drawing boards, and planetables.

Indian Rosewood

Dalbergia latifolia Roxb.; Eng. Indian rosewood; Verna. *Kali Shisham*; Sanskrit—*Shishapa*; Bengali—*Sitsal, swetasal*; Marathi—*Shisham, siswa*; Gujarati—*Shissam, kalaruk*; Telugu—*Cittegi, irgudu*; Tamil—*Itti, karundorviral*; Kannada—*Bite, todagatti*; Malayalam—*Itti, colavitti*; Oriya—*Sisua*; Trade—Indian Rosewood; Family—Papilionaceae.

A large deciduous or nearly evergreen tree with cylindrical, fairly straight bole and full rounded crown, found in the Sub-Himalayan tract of Eastern Uttar Pradesh, Bihar, Orissa and central, western and southern India. It attains its maximum development in the southern region of western ghats, where trees 130 ft. high up to 20 ft. in girth and 70 ft. clear bole are sometimes found. The minimum exploitable size is 6 ft. girth.

The sapwood is narrow and pale yellowish white in colour, often with a purple tinge. The heartwood ranges in colour from golden brown through shades of light rose, purple with darker streaks, to deep purple with rather distant, nearly black lines, darkening with age. It is fragrant, heavy, narrowly interlocked grained and medium coarse-textured. The timber is stronger and much harder than teak.

Indian rosewood ranks among the first wood for furniture and cabinet work. It is a valuable decorative wood suitable for carving and ornamental ply-boards and veneers. It is specially useful for pattern-making, calico printing blocks, mathematical instruments and screws. It is also used for gun carriage wheels, ammunition boxes and army wagons, pulleys, handles, shelves, decorative carriage parts, temple chariots, boat knees, agricultural implements, combs, razor handles and brush backs. Carefully selected and manufactured Indian rosewood ply-boards satisfy aircraft specifications.

Sissoo

Dalbergia sissoo Roxb.; Eng. Sissoo; Verna. *Shisham*; Sanskrit—*Shinshapa, aguru*; Hindi—*Shisham, sissu, sissai*; Bengali—*Shisu*; Gujarati—*Sisam, tanach*; Telugu—*Errasissu, sinsupa*; Tamil—*Sisu itti*; Kannada—*Agaru, biridi*; Malayalam—*Iruvil*; Oriya—*Sisu, simsapa*; Punjab—*Tali, shisham*; Marathi—*Sissu*; Trade—Sissoo, Shisham; Family—Papilionaceae.

A deciduous tree, often with crooked trunk and light crown. Normally the tree attains a height of about 100 ft., a girth up to 8 ft. and a clear bole up to 35 ft. It occurs throughout the sub-Himalayan tract from Ravi to Assam, ascending up to 5,000 ft. It is extensively cultivated in Punjab. Uttar Pradesh, Bengal and Assam. No other timber tree, except teak is cultivated to a greater extent.

The sapwood is white to pale brownish white in colour and the heartwood, golden brown to dark brown with deep brown streaks becoming dull on exposure. It is heavy, narrowly interlocked grained and medium textured. It can be air or kiln-seasoned. However, kiln-seasoning enhances the value of timber as the colour darkness and the difference between lighter and darker bands gets intensified. The wood can be converted into ornamental veneers or commercial plywood of good quality.

Sissoo (*Shisham*), is a high class furniture and cabinet wood widely used throughout north India. On account of its great strength, elasticity and durability, it is highly valued as constructional and general utility timber and is used for all the purposes for which Indian rosewood is employed in the south. It is esteemed also for railway sleepers, musical instruments, *Charpai* legs, hammer handles, shoe heels, *hookah* tubes and tobacco pipes. Carefully selected and manufactured plywood logs satisfy the specifications prescribed for aircraft, and for this purpose, the wood from trees, growing on canal banks and in plantations is considered to be the best. Sissoo wood is suitable for making laminated skiis. It can be worked into decorative ornamental carvings.

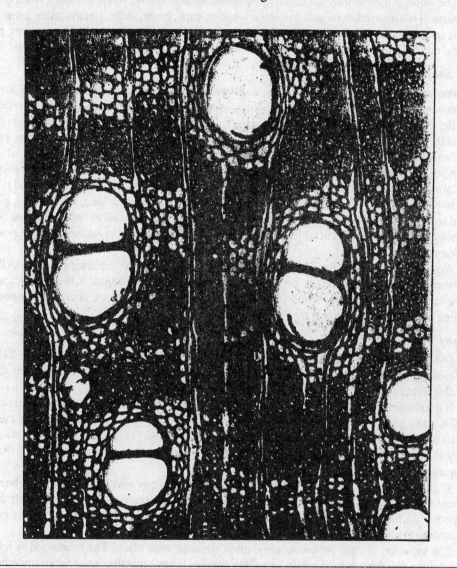

Fig. 13.2. *Dalbergia sissoo* (porous wood) micrograph of wood x 110.

Andaman Redwood

Pterocarpus indicus Wild; Eng. Andaman redwood; Verna. *Padauk*. It is a large and lofty tree found in the Andaman islands. Sapwood is small. Heartwood is dark-red, close-grained, moderately hard with a slight aromatic scent. It is durable and not attacked by white ants. When thoroughly seasoned it is unaffected by alternate dryness and moisture of the atmosphere. It seasons well, works well and takes a very fine polish. It is used for furniture, carts, gun carriages, and other purposes, and is said to be the most useful wood in the Andamans, and where it grows to an enormous size.

Indian Kino Tree

Pterocarpus marsupium Roxb. Sanskrit—*Pitasara*; Hindi—*Bijasal*; Bengali—*Pitshal*; Marathi—*Asan, bibla*; Gujarati—*Biyo*; Telugu—*Yegi, peddagi*; Tamil—*Vengai*; Kannada—*Honne, bange*; Malayalam—*Venga*; Oriya—*Byasa*; Trade—Bijasal; Family—*Leguminosae*.

The wood is used chiefly for building purposes, such as doors, window frames, rafters, beams and posts. It is also used in railway carriages, wagons, carts, boats, ships, electric poles, pit-props in mines, agricultural implements, drums, tool handles, camp furniture, mathematical instruments, picture frames, combs, and parts of textile looms. It is a very important timber in peninsular India.

Red Sandalwood

Pterocarpus santalinus Linn.; Eng. Red sandalwood; Verna. *Rukhto-chandan*; Sanskrit—*Raktachandana*; Hindi and Bengali—*Raktachandan, lalchandan*; Marathi—*Tambada chandana*; Gujarati—*Ratanjali*; Telugu—*Agarugandhamu, raktagandhamu*; Tamil—*Atti, sivappu chandanam*; Kannada—*Agaru, honne, kempugandha*; Malayalam—*Patrangam*; Oriya—*Raktachandan*; Trade—Red Sanders.

A small tree of South India, chiefly found in Cuddapah, North Arcot, and the southern portion of the Karnul district. It favours a dry, rather rocky soil, and a hot fairly dry climate. Sapwood is white. Heartwood is purplish-black dark orange-red when fresh cut, extremely hard, the shavings giving a blood red-orange colour. It is used for building and for turning, and is said to be much prized because it is not subject to the attacks of white ants. It is much used for carvings in Andhra Pradesh especially at Tirupati.

Wood is highly prized for house posts; also used for agricultural implements, poles, shafts and bent rims of carts, picture frames, boxes and other joinery work. In Japan, it is used for a musical instrument called **Shamisen**. Wood is ground and used for dyeing wool, cotton and leather, and staining other woods; *santalin* is the colouring principle.

Ebony

Diospyros ebenum Koenig.; Eng. Ebony; Verna. *Abnus*; Hindi—*Ebans, abnus*; Telugu—*Nallavalludu*; Tamil—*Tumbi, karunkali*; Kannada—*Karemara*; Malayalam—*Karu, vauari*; Oriya—*Kendhu*; Trade—Ebony.

It is a moderate to large sized evergreen tree with a dense crown, sometimes attaining a height up to 80 ft. and a girth of 7 ft. The girth of heartwood is not more than 4 ft. It is found in the dry evergreen forests of Deccan, Karnataka, Coimbatore, Malabar, Cochin and Travancore. It prefers well-drained rocky soil and grows well on sandy loam. It is found sparsely scattered in the forests in mixture with other trees.

This is perhaps the best ebony yielding tree and the only one which yields jet black heartwood without streaks or markings, the true ebony of commerce, *D. ebenum* is not very commonly found in India, nor do the trees, where they occur, attain any large size. Only limited supply of ebony is available in the area of its occurrence.

The sapwood is light yellowish grey, often streaked with black. The heartwood is jet black, rarely with a few dark or light brown or golden streaks. It has a metallic lustre when smoothed. It is heavy, straight-grained or somewhat irregular or wavy-grained, fine and even-textured.

Ebony is difficult to season. It is best to convert the green logs to the smallest size permissible and to store them under cover, well protected from hot winds.

The heartwood is resistant to attack by insects and fungi. It is very durable. The value of this wood depends on its intense blackness, working quality and the high finish it takes. It is difficult to work, especially when dry, but finishes to a glossy surface. It requires little hand finishing and takes a high lasting polish. It is one of the most valuable woods in the fancy wood market. It is used for ornamental carving and turnery, and for special purposes in decoration. It is used for veneers, in laying, musical instruments, sports goods, mathematical instruments, piano keys and caskets.

Diospyros virginianum Linn. is widely used for weaving shuttles and is the standard wood for the heads of golf clubs.

Saffron Teak

Adina cordifolia Hook. f.; Eng. Saffron teak; Verna, *Haldu*, Hindi—*Haldu*; Bengali—*Petpuria, dakom*; Marathi—*Heddi*; Telugu—*Pasupukadamba*; Tamil and Malayalam— *Manjakadamba*; Kannada—*Arsintega, yettega*; Trade—Haldu; Family—Rubiaceae;

This makes an important Indian timber, used for a great variety of purposes; Pearson and Brown (1932) state that it is one of the best turnery wood in India and that selected pieces are attractively figured. The wood is commonly used for carvings, construction work, flooring and for railway carriages.

Timber is easy to saw, seasons well and takes good polish; durable under cover, resistant against subterranean termites, but highly susceptible to drywood termites. Haldu is accepted as grade I commercial and moisture-proof plywood timber.

Wrapping, writing and printing paper is manufactured from the wood pulp.

Teak

Tectona grandis Linn.; Eng. Teak; Hindi—*Sagaun*; Sanskrit—*Saka*; Bengali—*Segun*; Marathi—*Sag, sagwan*; Gujarati—*Saga*; Telugu—*Adaviteeku, teeku*; Tamil—*Tekkumaram, tekku*; Kannada—*Jadi, sagwani*; Malayalam—*Thekku, tekha*; Oriya—*Singuru*; Assam—*Chingjagu*; Lepcha—*Ripnyok*; Family—Verbenaceae.

A large, deciduous tree, indigenous to both peninsulas of India. In Western India it does not extend far beyond the Mhye. In Central India it attains its northern most point in the Jhansi district, and from that point the line of its northern limit continues in a south-east direction to the Mahanadi river in Orissa. It is found wild in Assam. It is, however, cultivated throughout Bengal, Assam and Sikkim, and in North-West India without difficulty as far as Saharanpur. The forests richest in large timber on the west side of the Peninsula are the Travancore, Anamally, Wynad, South-west Karnataka and North Kanara forests. In the centre of the Peninsula the Godavary forests are most compact and valuable.

Structure and utility of wood. Sapwood white and small; the heartwood when cut green, has a pleasant and strong aromatic fragrance and a beautiful dark golden yellow colour, which on seasoning soon darkens into brown, mottled with darker streaks. The timber retains its fragrance to a great age, the characteristic odour being apparent whenever a fresh cut is made. It is moderately hard, exceedingly durable and strong, does not split, crack, warp, shrink or alter its shape when once seasoned; it works easily, takes a good polish. Teak owes its chief value to its great durability, which is ascribed, probably with justice, to the circumstance that it contains a large quantity of fluid resinous matter which fills up the pores and resists the action of water. (At the Karli caves near Poona the teak-wood-work, two thousand years old, seems perfectly good at the present day).

The many uses of teak are well known. In India it is highly prized for construction, ship building, and for making sleepers and furniture.

Wood is very durable and resistant to fungi. It is used for poles, beams, trusses, columns, roofs, doors, window frames, flooring, planking, panelling, stair cases, and other constructional work. It is one of the best timbers for furniture and cabinet making, wagons and railway carriages. Due to its better shape-retention ability, teak is popular in marine constructions and is a class by itself for boat and ship–building, particularly for decking. On account of its resistance to chemicals, teak articles are used in chemical industries and for making laboratory bench-tops; suitable for casks and vats for shipping corrosive liquids and for storing vegetable oils, fruit syrups, chutneys, etc. Teak is employed for sound-boards of musical instruments, keys, etc., and for different grades of plywood. Wood waste in the form of wood-shavings and sawdust is used for chip-boards, fibre-boards and plastic-boards.

Sal

Shorea robusta; Eng. Sal tree; Hindi—*Sal*; Bengali and Hindi—*Sal, sakhu*; Marathi and Gujarati—*Ral*; Telugu—*Gugal*; Tamil—*Kungiliyam*; Kannada—*Kabba*; Malayalam—*Maramaram*; Oriya—*Sal, sagua*; Punjab and Haryana—*Sal*; Lepcha—*Taksal–Kung*; Assam—*Sal, bolsal*; Trade—Sal; Family—Dipterocarpaceae.

A large gregarious tree, often covering certain interrupted tracts without the existence of connecting patches. It occurs along the base of Tropical Himalayas from the Sutlej to Assam, in the eastern districts of Central India, and on the Western Bengal Hills.

Structure and utility of wood. The *sal*, one of the most valuable timber trees in India, has a distinct sapwood which is small in amount, whitish and not durable. The heartwood is brown in colour, finely streaked with darker lines, coarse grained, hard, strong and tough, with a remarkably fibrous and cross-grained, structure. The fibres of successive concentric strata do not run parallel, but at oblique angles, to each other, so that when the wood is dressed the fibres appear interlaced. It does not season well, but warps and splits in drying, and even when thoroughly seasoned, absorbs moisture with avidity in wet weather. During the process of seasoning, it dries when first cut, and evaporation goes on afterwards with extreme slowness. *Sal*, when once thoroughly seasoned, stands almost without a rival, as a timber, for strength, elasticity, and durability, which qualities it retains without being sensibly affected, for an immense length of time. Average weight of the seasoned *sal* about 35 lb. per cubic foot (Brandis; Gamble).

The timber is the one most extensively used in Northern India. It is in constant request for piles, beams, planking and railing of bridges, doors, and window posts of houses, for the bodies of carts, and above all, for railway sleepers. In Assam it is favourite wood for boat-building, and in the hills of Northern Bengal where it is found, perhaps, of the largest size available, the trunks are hollowed out into canoes. Owing to the fact that when unseasoned it is not floatable, difficulty is experienced in most sal forests in getting the timber out of the forests in log. This is, however, overcome by floating the logs either with the assistance of the boats or with floats of light wood or bamboos (Gamble).

Sal wood ranks with teak and deodar as one of the best sleeper woods in India; also used in form of bellies and poles. After treatment, the poles are suitable for overhead electric, telegraph and telephone lines. As domestic timber it is used for beams, scantlings, rafters and floors; also used for piles, mine work and pit props, bridges, dug-out boats, carriages and wagon building, spokes, fellows and hubs of wheels, agricultural implements, tool-handles, tent pegs, liquid storage vats, and beer and oil casks.

VENEERS

The veneers are thin slices or sheets of wood of uniform thickness. The common thickness is about 1/20 in. to 3/8 in. In making veneers or logs pieces of woods are peeled and boiled and then cut with sharp knife. Usually the veneers are cut by **rotary process** which involves turning a log on a lathe against a stationary knife, with the formation of a continuous sheet of veneer. The other process is known as **slicing process**. Here the logs are quartersawed and therefore show a more attractive figure. The logs are first quartered and thereafter sliced with a stationary knife, resulting in the formation of separate sheets. Freshly cut veneers are usually wet and must be thoroughly dried.

Uses. The veneers are used in the manufacture of boxes, baskets, door panels, cooperage, trunks, mirrors, musical instruments and several other articles.

PLYWOOD

To overcome some of the natural defects in wood is the manufacture of so-called "*built up*" stock or plywood. The plywood is made by gluing together from three to nine thin veneers. The grain of each successive layer is at an angle to the next, so that the strength is redistributed. With the result the finished product becomes very strong and stable and does not warp or twist like ordinary wood. The plywood does not split when the nails and screws are driven close to its edge.

The manufacture of a five-ply plywood panel consists of preparing the face, back, cross band, and core sheets; applying the adhesive; pressing the glued stock into a panel; and drying and finishing the product. The soft woods are generally used for the purpose, as they can be glued more easily. Several resins and gums are used in the manufacture of plywood.

Uses. The plywood is extensively used in the home for doors, walls, flooring, cabinets, shelves, partitions, furniture and interior trim. A large quantity of plywood is utilized in making concrete forms, boats, prefabricated houses, airplanes, railroad cars and the body making of station wagons.

LAMINBOARDS

Laminboards are usually made up with cheap inferior woods for the cores, and better quality decorative good for the faces. Such timber as pine, spruce, fir, *Bombax ceiba, Ailanthus grandis, Tetrameles nudiflora* and *Kydia calycina* are very suitable for core work, while better class timbers such as teak, rosewood, sissoo and toon make excellent face veneers. Face veneers are usually sliced.

Uses. The laminboards are commonly used for making doors and cabinets.

CORK

Most commercial cork is obtained from the cork oak (*Quercus suber*). Cork or "corkwood" consists of the outer bark of the tree. This can be removed without injury to the tree. At the age of about 20 years, when the tree is about 40 cm in circumference, this outer layer, known as virgin cork, is removed by stripping. The operation consists of making vertical and horizontal cuts with knives or saws, and then prying off large pieces of the bark. The underlying exposed phelloderm and cortical cells die, and a new cork cambium layer is formed several millimetres deeper in the cortex. By this cork cambium (*phellogen*) new cork is formed more rapidly than by the first layer, and after 9 to 10 years the new cork layer has attained sufficient thickness to be commercially valuable and is in turn removed. This cork is of better quality than the nearly useless virgin cork, but is not so good as that obtained at the third and subsequent stripings which take place at intervals of about 9 or 10 years until the tree is 150 years old. Usually the trees live for 100 to 500 years, and have an average yield of 40 to 500 lb. per tree. After stripping the pieces of cork are dried for several days. They are first boiled in large copper vats. This process removes the sap and tannic acid, increases the volume and elasticity and flattens pieces. The rough edges are then trimmed off and the flat pieces are sorted and baled.

Cork is exceedingly buoyant due to its composition of dead watertight cells. It is highly compressible. It is durable, a bad conductor of heat and electricity, and is resistant to passage of moisture and liquids. It absorbs sound and vibrations and also possesses some frictional characteristics.

Uses of Cork

It is used for many purposes and for the manufacture of several products. In some cases the natural cork is used whereas in other cases composition cork, made of finely ground pieces treated with adhesives and molded.

The natural cork is used to make stoppers, hats, helmets, cigarette tips, handles of golf clubs, penholders, fishing rods, floats, life preservers, life jackets, base balls, mats, tiles and several other such products. Cork board is used as an insulating material for cold storage plants, houses and refrigerators.

Composition cork is utilized for the lining of crown caps, the metal tops for sealing bottles; gaskets; toes, counters and innersoles for shoes.

LINOLEUM

A type of floor covering is made from cork or wood flour, linseed oil, resins, such as rosin or kauri gum, pigments and burlap. The oil is boiled and allowed to solidify by dripping on pieces of cloth. The solidified oil is ground up and melted with the resins. This mixture is cooled and hardened, and after 'curing' for several days it is mixed with the cork, which has been ground as fine dust, and with the dry colour pigments. It is then pressed into burlap cloth with hydraulic presses. It is then seasoned in ovens and finished by giving it a protective surface of nitrocellulose lacquer. The tiles, known as linotiles are made from ground cork and linseed oil, but thicker than linoleum.

FUELWOOD

Fuel is one of the great necessities of modern life and it is indispensable, both in the home and in industry, as a source of heat and power. Any material that burns readily in air can be utilised, and a great variety of plant products are so used. The most important of these are wood and coal.

Though much less wood is used for fuel at the present time than formerly, the total consumption is probably greater than for any other purpose. However, the extensive use of wood for fuel does not represent a proportional drain on the forest resources, for much waste material is used as well as wood unfit for other purposes.

Wood is 99 per cent combustible when perfectly dry, and thus makes an excellent fuel. It is also a flaming fuel and well adapted for heating large surfaces. Hard woods have the greatest fuel value. The woods of *Fagus, Betula, Pinus, Acacia, Mangifera, Quercus*, etc., are of much value for fuel purposes.

Coal comprises the fossilized remains of plants that lived in former geological periods. The original plant tissue has been more fully decomposed and converted into carbon. Coal possesses a great heating power. Anthracite or hard coals are the oldest and contain about 95 per cent carbon.

It is generally supposed that petroleum had an organic origin and was formed under pressure from the plant and animal life of former shallow seas.

BAMBOOS IN INDIA

Bamboos are integral not only to the culture of India but that of the entire Southeast Asia. The wide range of their uses qualifies this group of species to be the one foremost associated with the mainstay of rural life and culture in our country. Its versatility has led to the coinage of such terms as "bamboo culture", "green gold", "poor man's timber", "friend of the people" and "cradle to coffin timber". In fact, bamboo can be used as a substitute of timber in many respects.

Bamboos belong to the grass family *Poaceae* (Gramineae). In India, there are 125 indigenous as well as exotic species of bamboos belonging to 23 genera. Bamboo forests occupy an area of 10.03 million ha, roughly 12.8% of the total forest area in the country.

Properties. Bamboo is considered to be the most efficient natural resource as far as strength vis-a-vis cost. Strength of the bamboo depends upon the species, climatic factors and its moisture content. Bamboo is strong, though not stronger than timbers like Sal and Teak. Seasoning is a essential pre-requisite for maintaining the appearance and strength of bamboo products and structures. Unseasoned bamboo is highly susceptible to insects and fungal attack, decay and mechanical degradation.

Seasoning of bamboos has to be done properly and carefully as rapid drying results in splitting. To prevent cracks during seasoning green bamboos may be split into halves. The bamboos are best dried by air seasoning under overhead cover for 2-3 months. Kiln drying under controlled conditions can be done successfully in about 2-3 weeks.

Bamboo can be cut and split easily with hand saw. Strips of any measurement can be made with knife. Immature bamboos are soft and pliable and can be moulded to desired shape. Bamboo takes polish and paint well.

Uses. The strength of the culms, their straightness and lightness, combined with hardness, range in size, hollowness, long fibre and easy working qualities, make the bamboos suitable for a variety of purposes. Whether it is the tender shoots, used for pickles and curries, the slivers, used for tooth picks and meat barbecues, ribs for fans or slats for sun screens, or the dried culm as the sturdy lathi and for construction of the so called bamboo houses, the versatility of bamboo is legendary. The thousand and one uses for bamboos have long been known and established. Some of the traditional uses are: Agricultural implements, anchors, arrows, back scratchers, baskets, beds, blinds, boats, bottles, bows, bridges, brooms, brushes, buildings, caps, cart-yokes, caulking material, chairs, chicks, chopsticks, coffins, combs, containers, cooking utensils, cordages, dust-pans, fans, fences, fish-traps, fishing-nets, fishing rods, flag-poles, floats for timber, flutes, flower-pots, food, food-baskets, fuel, furniture, hats, handicrafts, haystack stabilisers, hedges, hookah-pipes, joss-sticks, kites, ladders, ladles, lamps, lance staves, lanterns, lining of hats and sandals, masts, match-sticks, mats, musical instruments, nails, net floats, ornaments, props, paper, pens, polo mallets, rafts, rayon pulp, roofing, sails, scaffoldings, scoops, seed-drills, shoes, shuttles, slats, sports goods, sprayers, stools, sticks, tables, thatching, tobacco pipes, toys, tool handles, traps, trays, tubes, umbrella-handles, walking-sticks, walls, vessels and wrappers.

CHAPTER

Spices and Condiments

The spices cannot be grouped as foods, for they contain less nutritive value. However, they give a good flavour and aroma to food, and add greatly to the pleasure of eating. They stimulate the appetite and increase the secretion and flow of gastric juices. For this reason they are commonly known as "*food adjuncts*". The aromatic value of the spices is due to the presence of the essential oils.

In general, all aromatic vegetable products that are used for flavouring foods and drinks are known as spices. Sometimes the term "*spice*" is restricted to hard or hardened parts of plants, which are generally used in a pulverized state. *Condiments* are spices or other flavouring substances which possess a sharp taste, and are commonly added to food after it has been cooked.

India is one of the largest suppliers of spices and condiments. India alone contributes 25-30 per cent of the total world trade.

Most of the important spices are grown in India. The classification of *spices* and *condiments* in the present text is based on the morphology of the plant organ which is used for the purpose. The general categories of the plants yielding *spices* and *condiments* are as follows:

SPICES AND CONDIMENTS OBTAINED FROM ROOTS

Asafetida

Ferula Linn.; English—Asafetida; Hindi—*Hing*; Kashmiri—*Anjudan*; Gujarati—*Hing*; Mumbai—*Hing*; Tamil—*Kyam*, *perungayam*; Sanskrit—*Hingu*; Family—Umbelliferae (Apiaceae).

This is a genus of perennial herbs commonly distributed from the Mediterranean region to central Asia. Some of the species are important as sources of oleogum - resins, used as condiment and in medicine. Three species are found in India. The main bulk of asafetida and other ferula gum - resins are being imported in India from Afghanistan.

Asafetida is the dried latex obtained mainly from living rootstocks or taproots of several species of *Ferula*, such as : *F. foetida* Regel, *F. alliacea* Boiss., *F. rubricaulis* Boiss., *F. assafoetida* Linn. and *F. narthex* Boiss., found in Central Asia. *F. narthex* and *F. assafoetida* are found in Himachal Pradesh and Kashmir.

Uses. Asafetida is bitter and acrid in taste and emits a strong and peculiar odour. In India, it is used for flavouring curries, sauces and pickles. It is also used in Ayurvedic medicines. It stimulates the intestinal and respiratory tracts and the nervous system. It is useful in asthma, whooping cough and chronic bronchitis. It is used as an enema for intestinal flatulence. It is also used in epileptic and hysterical affections and in cholera. It is also used in veterinary medicine.

Lovage

Levisticum officinale Koth., English—Lovage; Family—Umbelliferae (Apiaceae).

This is a perennial plant, introduced from Europe. It is grown as a garden plant. It thrives best in well-drained soil. It is propagated either by seeds or roots. The roots are dug out in October of second or third year after setting the plants. The freshly dug roots are washed, cut into slices and dried.

Uses. Generally the roots are used for flavouring foods. Sometimes the seeds are used for flavouring confectionery. The leaves and stems are also eaten as salad. The dried roots; on steam distillation yield volatile oil known as 'lovage oil'. The oil is used for flavouring foods.

SPICES AND CONDIMENTS OBTAINED FROM UNDERGROUND STEMS

Onion

Allium cepa Linn.; English—Onion; Hindi—*Piyaz*; Tamil—*Vella-vengayam, irulli*; Telugu—*Vulli-gaddalu*; Kannada—*Vengayam, nirulli*; Malayalam—*Bawang*. They are cultivated all over India. Onion seed will not keep for certain more than one year. The selected bulbs be planted, and seed obtained from these. If planted in the cold season, they will produce seed in the beginning of the hot season, and if carefully preserved, after being well ripened and dry, the seed obtained in this way will be found to yield a good crop in the following cold season, from October to February.

Uses. The bulbs are used as food and condiment.

Garlic

Allium sativum Linn.; English—Garlic; Hindi—*Lasan, lahsun*; Bengali—*Lashan*; Sanskrit—*Maha-ushadha*; Tamil—*Vallaipundu*; Telugu—*Vellulli fella-gadda*; Kannada—*Belluli*; Family—Liliaceae. Cultivated all over the country. It is propagated by planting out the cloves singly, in October, in drills about 6-7 inches apart and 2-3 inches deep. The crop is taken up in the hot weather, and after being dried in the sun the bulbs are stored for further use.

Numerous bulbs remain enclosed in a common membranous covering. Stem simple, about 2 feet high; scape is smooth and shining, solid terminated by a membranous pointed spathe enclosing a mass of flowers and solid bulbils prolonged into leafy points; leaves long, flat, acute, sheathing the lower half of the stem; flowers small, white.

Uses. The bulbs (rhizomes) are used as a condiment and flavouring substance. Garlic powder is used as a condiment. It is a carminative, diuretic, stomachic, alterative, emmenagogue, and tonic.

Turmeric

Curcuma domestica Valet; Syn. *C. longa* Auct. non Linn.; English—Turmeric; Hindi—*Haldi*; Bengali—*Halud*; Punjabi—*Haldar, halja*; Tamil—*Manjal*; Telugu—*Pasupu*; Malayalam—*Mannal, marinalu*; Kannada—*Arishina*; Marathi—*Halede*; Gujarati—*Halada*; Sanskrit—*Haridra, nisa*; Persian—*Zard-chobah, dar-zard*; Family—Zingiberaceae.

The plant of turmeric is a robust perennial with a short stem and tufted leaves. The pale-yellow flowers are found in dense spikes, topped by a tuft of pinkish bracts. The rhizomes, which yield the colourful condiment, are short and thick with blunt tubers. They are cleaned, washed and dried in the sun, it is very aromatic, with a musky odour and yellow colour. It has a pungent bitter taste.

Uses. It is used as a condiment. It is used to flavour and colour pickles, and foodstuffs. It is one of the principal ingredients of curry.

Ginger

Zingiber officinale Rosc.; English—Ginger; Hindi—Plant = *adrak*, Dried rhizome = *sonth*, fresh rhizome = *adrak*; Bengali—Plant = *ada*, dried rhizome = *sont*, fresh root = *adrak, ada*; Assamese—Plant = *ada*; Nepalese—Dried rhizome = *sunt*; Oriya—Plant = *ada*; Punjabi—Plant = *ada, adrak*, dried rhizome = *zangzabil, sunt*, fresh rhizome = *zunjbel, adrak*; Marathi—Plant = *ale*, Gujarati—

Dried rhizome = *sunt*, fresh rhizomes *adu, adhu*; Tamil—Dried rhizome = *shukku*, fresh rhizome = *inji*; Telugu—Plant = *allam*, dried rhizome = *sonti, sonthi, allam*, fresh rhizomes = *allam*; Kannanda— Dried rhizomes = *vana sunthi*, fresh rhizome = *hasisunthi*; Malayalam—Dried rhizome = *Chukka*, fresh rhizome = *inchi*; Sanskrit—Plant = *adraka, sringavera*, dried rhizome = *vishva-bhishagam, nagara, sunti, mahaushadha*, fresh rhizome = *ardrakam*; Persian—Dried rhizome = *zanjabile-khushk*, fresh rhizome = *zanjabile-tar*; Family—Zingiberaceae.

Ginger of commerce is a dry product prepared from the green underground stems or rhizomes.

After digging out, the rhizomes are thoroughly washed with water to remove the soil and dirt sticking to them. These underground stems are kept in the sun for a day or so, and then taken to the market for sale as green ginger (*adrak*). The preparation of dry ginger (*sonth*) is a local craft of Kerala State. For purpose of export only dry ginger is used.

In India, about 48,000 acres are under the crop, and the estimated production of cured ginger is 24,000 tonnes of which about 18,000 tonnes are produced on the west coast alone. About 25 per cent of the produce on the west coast is sold as the green ginger (*adrak*) and (*sonth*) and exported to other countries. The chief countries which import ginger from India are the U.K., U.S.A., France, Germany and Arabia.

Chemical composition. Moisture 10.5%; volatile oil 1.8%; oleoresin 6.5%; water extract 19.6%; cold alcohol extract 6.0%; starch 53.0%; crude fibre 7.17%; crude protein 12.4%; total ash 6.64%.

Uses. Ginger is used more as a condiment than as a spice. The aroma of ginger is due to essential oil, whereas the pungent taste is due to the presence of carminative and digestive stimulant. The essential oil, obtained from the rhizomes, is used for flavouring food stuffs. Ginger is exceedingly popular for flavouring beverages, such as ginger bear and ginger malt.

Zerumbet Ginger

Zingiber zerumbet (Linn.) Rosc. ex Smith; English—Zerumbet ginger; Hindi—*Mahabari bach, nar kachur*; Punjabi—*Kachur, nar kachur*; Malayalam—*Kathu-inshi-kua*; Sanskrit—*Sthula granthi*; Family—Zingiberaceae.

A perennial herb. Found throughout India.

Uses. The rhizomes are used as spice and condiment. The rhizomes has a slightly aromatic odour and possesses similar properties to those of *Zingiber officinale*, but in a minor degree.

SPICES AND CONDIMENTS OBTAINED FROM BARK

Cassia China

Cinnamomum aromaticum Nees.; English—Cassia China; Family—Lauraceae.

Cassia China is obtained from *C. aromaticum* Nees cultivated in China. The bark is the regular cassia China of commerce. Because of its brittle nature, much of the bark is broken, thus yielding the '*broken grade*'. The main grades are: 1. Whole Quills or China Rolls, 2. Selected Brokens or Canton Rolls, and 3. Extra selected brokens. Trees growing at higher altitude (180-300 metres) yield better quality bark with higher volatile oil content. The bark has been known from the earliest times. The dried immature fruits constitute the well known '*Cassia buds*', known in India as *Kala Nagkesar*. This species of Cassia is not grown in India but considerable quantities of it are imported into the country.

Uses. It is used as a spice or condiment in curries and similar preparations. The important constituent of commercial importance is the volatile oil which finds numerous uses in the various culinary preparations, perfumery and cosmetics as well as pharmaceutical preparations.

Indian Cassia

Cinnamomum tamala Nees. & Eberm.; English—Indian Cassia; Hindi, Bengali and Punjabi— *Tejpat, tejput*; Gujarati—*Tamalapatra*; Marathi—*Darchini*; Sanskrit—*Tamalaka, tejpatra*; Tamil— *Talishapattiri*; Telugu—*Talishapatri*; Family—Lauraceae.

A moderate-sized evergreen tree. Distributed in tropical and subtropical Himalayas (915 to 2440 metres altitude), Khasi and Jaintia hills (915-1220 metres altitude).

The bark of the tree, known in trade as Indian Cassia or Indian Cassia Lignea, is collected from trees growing at the foot of the Sikkim Himalayas. Regular plantations of *C. tamala* are grown in Khasi and Jaintia Hills, Gara Hills, Mikir Hills, Manipur and Arunachal.

Uses. The bark is aromatic. It is coarser than the bark of true cinnamon and is one of the common adulterants of true cinnamon. The essential oil from the bark is pale yellow and contains 70–85 per cent cinnamic aldehyde.

Cinnamon

Cinnamomum zeylanicum Bl.; English—Cinnamon; Hindi—*Dalchini, qalmi-dar-chini*; Bengali—*Dalchini*; Punjabi—*Dar-chini, kirfa*; Mumbai—*Taj, dalchini, tikhi*; Marathi—*Darachini, dalchini*; Tamil—*Karruwa, lavangap-pattai*; Telugu—*Sanalinga, lavanga-patta*; Malayalam—*Lavanga-patta*; Kannada—*Lavanga-patta, dalachini*; Sanskrit—*Gudatvak*; Persian—*Tali khahe, dar-chini*; Family—Lauraceae.

Cinnamon is one of the oldest known spices. The true cinnamon, also called as Ceylon Cinnamon is the dried bark of *Cinnamomum zeylanicum* B_1.

Chemical composition. Moisture 9.9%; protein 4.6% fat 2.2%; fibre 20.3%; carbohydrates 59.9%; ash 3.5%; calcium 1.6%; phosphorus 0.05%; iron 0.004%; sodium 0.01%; potassium 0.4%; vitamin B_1 0.14 mg/100 g.; vitamin B_2 0.21 mg/100 g.; niacin 1.9 mg/100 g.; vitamin C 39.8 mg/100 g.; Vitamin A 175 I.U./100 g.; calorific value 355 calories/100 g.; cinnamon leaf oil equals clove oil in eugenol content (70-95%), root bark yields 3% oil which differs from both stem bark and leaf oils.

Uses. Cinnamon is generally used as a spice or ingredients of curry powder. It is used as a spice or condiment in curries and similar preparations. It is also used in medicine as a cordial stimulant. It is also used in bowel complaints such as dyspepsia, diarrhoea and vomiting. Powder cinnamon is a reputed remedy for diarrhoea and dysentery. The bark also yields an oil of which the chief constituent is Cinnamic aldehyde.

SPICES AND CONDIMENTS OBTAINED FROM LEAVES AND TWIGS

Indian Cassia

Cinnamomum tamala (Buch.-Ham.) T. Nees & Eberm.; English—Indian Cassia; Hindi—Leaves = *tejpat, tajpat*, bark = *taj kalami, dalchini, talispatri, silkanti*; Bengali—*Tejpat*; Nepali—*Chota sinkoli*; Assamese—*Dopatti*; Mumbai—*Darchini, tamala*; Gujarati—*Taj, tamalpatra*; Marathi—*Dalchini tiki*; Tamil—*Talisha-pattiri*; Telugu—*Tallisha-patri*; Kannada—*Lavanga patte*; Sanskrit—*Tamal, tespatra*; Arabic—*Zarnab*; Family—Lauraceae.

A moderate-sized evergreen tree, found on the Himalayas, between 3,000 and 7,000 feet, in Bengal, the Khasia hills and Assam.

A cinnamon known as Indian Cassia is obtained from this plant. It is a coarser and sold in larger pieces than the true cinnamon or bark of *C. zeylanicum* Bl., for which it is often used as an adulterant. The bark of the root is quite as good as the true cinnamon bark. In Manipur, the natives collect the root-bark instead of the stem-bark.

Cassia buds. These are the immature fruits of tree yielding Indian Cassia. They are something like cloves, and consist of the unexpanded flower-heads. They possess properties similar to those of the bark. Cassia buds were once employed in preparing the speed wine called *Hippocras*.

Cassia bark. The bark has a general resemblance to cinnamon, but is in simple quills, not inserted one within the other. The quills, are less straight, even and regular, and of dark-brown colour. It breaks with a short fracture.

Uses. The leaves are known as *tejpat*, and bark as *taj*. The bark and dried leaves are used to flavour dishes. The leaves are commonly used as a condiment. They are famous for their pungency and added in cooked rice (*pulao*) and curries.

Leaves are also used medicinally. They are stimulant, carminative, used in rheumatism, colic, diarrhoea, and in scorpion sting. Bark is aromatic and used in gonorrhoea.

Leaves yield an essential oil, which contains d–phellandrene and 78% eugenol.

Sweet Marjoram

Majorana hortensis Moench; English—Sweet marjoram; Hindi— *Murwa*; Bengali—*Murru*; Kannada— *Maruga*; Malayalam—*Maruvamu*; Tamil—*Marru*; in Kumaon it is called Bantulsi and in Dakshin Bharat Murwa; Family—Labiatae (Lamiaceae).

This is an aromatic, branched perennial, 1-2 feet high. It is native of mediterranean region, North Africa and Asia Minor. The herb is commonly grown in Indian gardens. It is well suited for hilly places in India. Leaves oblong-ovate; flowers small, whitish or purplish, in terminal clusters; seeds minute, oval, dark brown.

Sweet marjoram possesses a strong, spicy and pleasant odour and flavour. The dry herb contains - water, 7.61%; protein 14.31%; fixed oil 5.6%; volatile oil 1.72%; pentosans 7.68%; fibre 22.06%; and ash 9.69%. Tannin and ursolic acid are also present.

Steam distillation of the leaves and flowering heads yields a volatile oil, known in the trade as *Oil of Sweet Marjoram*. The oil is colourless or pale-yellow to yellow-green with a peculiar odour.

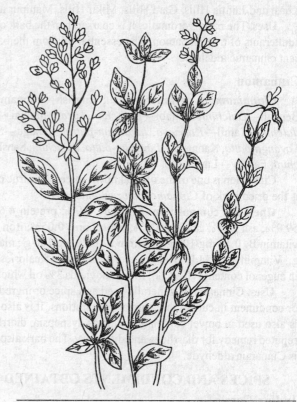

Fig. 14.1. Spices and condiments. *Majorana hortensis* Moench., Eng. Marjoram (Labiatae, Lamiaceae). The dried leaves of the herb are used as spice and flavouring agent.

Uses. The leaves of the plant are used fresh or dried and highly esteemed as a condiment for seasoning food. Fresh leaves are employed as garnish and incorporated in salad. They are used also for flavouring vinegar. The aromatic seeds are used in confectionery. It is a carminative, expectorant and tonic. Leaves and seeds are astringent. An infusion of the plant is used as stimulant, emmenagogue and gulactagogue. The oil is used in high grade flavour preparations and perfumes, and in soap and liqueur industries. It is used as an external application for sprains, bruises, paralytic limbs and toothache.

Field mint or Corn mint

Mentha arvensis Linn.; English—Field mint or corn mint; Hindi—*Podina, Pudina*; Bengali— *Mar.*; Gujarati and Telugu—*Podina, Pudina*; Kannada—*Chetni maragu*; Family—Labiatae (Lamiaceae).

An erect herb, 10-60 cm. in height found throughout temperate North Asia. Leaves 2.5-5 cm. long, shortly petioled or sessile, oblong ovate or lanceolate, serrate, cuneate at the base, hairy or glabrous; flowers in axillary, capitate whorls, borne on axils of leaves on upper stem.

Mentha arvensis grows wild in Kashmir at 1,500-3,000 m. It has also been reported from other parts of India.

Uses. The leaves are used for flavouring food stuffs. It is used as a stimulant and carminative. An infusion of leaves is a remedy for indigestion and rheumatism. A volatile oil is obtained from the plants by steam-distillation. The oil is used as a flavouring ingredient.

Mint

Mentha longifolia (Linn.) Huds.; English—Mint; Hindi—*Pudina, jungli pudina*; Punjabi—*Baburi, pudnakushma*; Mumbai—*Pudina, vartalau*; Family—Labiatae (Lamiaceae).

This is an aromatic herb, found in temperate Himalayas and in Kashmir, Garhwal, Kumaon, Punjab, Maharashtra and Uttar Pradesh.

Uses. The leaves are used as a flavouring agent. The dried leaves are used as carminative and stimulant. The essential oil obtained from the plant on steam distillation can be used as a substitute for peppermint oil to flavour confectionery.

Peppetrmint

Mentha piperita Linn.; English—Peppermint; Hindi—*Vilaiti pudina, paparaminta, gamathi phudina*; Family—Labiatae (Lamiaceae).

This is an aromatic herb. It is native of Europe. It is grown in Indian gardens and also cultivated in Kashmir, Nilgiris, Mysore, Delhi and Dehradun. *M. piperita* is considered to be hybrid between *M. spicata* and *M. aquatica*.

Uses. The leaves and flavouring tops are used for flavouring food stuffs. The herb is aromatic, stimulant, stomachic and carminative, and used medicinally. The herb yields a true peppermint oil on steam distillation. The oil is extensively used for flavouring food stuffs and in pharmacy. Peppermint oil is one of the most popular and widely used essential oils. It is employed for flavouring chewing gums, candies, ice creams, confectionery, mouth washes, pharmaceuticals, dental preparations and alcoholic liqueurs. It is widely employed for nausea, flatulence and vomiting. It has a refreshing odour and a persistent cooling taste. It may be taken with sugar or in the form of tablets or lozenges.

Spearmint

Mentha spicata Linn.; English—Spearmint; Hindi—*Pahari pudina, pudina*; Family—Labiatae (Lamiaceae).

A perennial aromatic herb, 1 to 3 feet high, with creeping rhizomes. It is native of temperate Europe and Asia. In India, it is cultivated in the Punjab, Uttar Pradesh and Maharashtra.

Uses. Both fresh and dried leaves are used for mint sauce and jelly and to flavour soups, stews, sauces and beverages. The leaves are the source of spearmint oil, which is used for flavouring food products. Spearmint oil is used in U.S.A. for flavouring chewing gums, confectionery and pharmaceuticals. In India, green leaves are used for making chutney and for flavouring culinary preparations, vinegars, jellies and iced drinks. The herb is considered stimulant and carminative. A soothing tea is brewed from the leaves.

Common Basil

Ocimum basilicum Linn.; English—Common basil, sweet basil; Hindi—*Babui-tulsi, Kali-tulsi, sabzah, marua*; Bengali—*Babui tulsi, khub kalam, debunsha*; Oriya—*Dhala tulasi*; Punjabi—*Baburi tulsi, rehan*; Marathi—*Sabza*; Tamil—*Tirmutpatchie*; Telugu—*Bhu-tulasi, rudra jada, vibudi-patri*; Kannada—*Kam-kasturi*; Malayalam—*Tiru-nitru*; Sanskrit—*Munjariki, Varvara*; Persian—*Firanj-Mushk*; Family—Labiatae (Lamiaceae).

An erect, herbaceous, glabrous or pubescent annual, 1-3 feet high, native of Central Asia and North-West Asia, growing throughout India. Leaves ovate - lanceolate, gland dotted; flowers white or pale purple. It is cultivated throughout tropical India from the Punjab to West Bengal.

Uses. Common basil or sweet basil possesses a clove like scent and a saline taste. It yields an essential oil known as oil of basil, which is used as a flavouring agent. Oil of basil is commonly used for flavouring confectionery, baked goods, sauces, ketchups, tomato pastes, pickles, vinegars, spiced meats, sausages and beverages.

Pot Marjoram

Origanum vulgare Linn.; English—Pot Marjoram or Common Marjoram; Hindi—*Sathra*; Telugu—*Mridu-maruvamu*; Kannada—*Maruga*; Punjabi—*Mirzanjosh*; Family—Labiatae (Lamiaceae).

It is native of Europe. In India, it is found in the temperate Himalayas from Kashmir to Sikkim at altitudes of 1,500-3,600 m. It is an aromatic, branched perennial herb, 1-3 feet in height. Leaves broadly ovate, entire or rarely toothed; flowers purple or pink, in corymbose cymes; nutlets smooth, brown.

It is commonly found in Shimla hills and Kashmir valley. It is grown in warm garden soils. It is propagated by seeds, cutting and root-division. It is commonly sown during October in the plains and during March and April in the hills.

It contains a volatile oil, tannin and a bitter principle. The oil possesses an aromatic spicy, basil like odour. It contains thymol (7%), carvacrol, free alcohols, esters, and bicyclic sesquiterpene.

Chemical composition of the leaves. Moisture 8.0%; protein 11.7%; fat 6.4%; crude fibre 11.0%; carbohydrates 53.9%; total ash 9.0%; calcium 1.7%; phosphorus 0.20%; iron 0.05%; sodium 0.02%; potassium 1.7%; vitamin A 1010 international units (I.U.)/100 g.; vitamin B_1 0.34 mg/100 g.; vitamin B_2 0.41 mg/100 g.; niacin 6.2 mg/100 g. and vitamin C 12 mg/100 g; calorific value 360 calories/100 g.

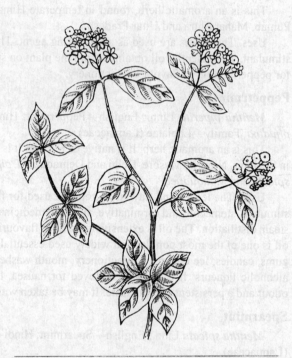

Fig. 14.2. Spices and condiments. *Origanum vulgare* Linn.; Eng. Pot marjoram (Labiatae, Lamiaceae). The dried leaves of the herb make the Origanum, Oregano, Mexican Origanum or Pot marjoram, which is used as a condiment. The taste of the herb is spicy, warm, pungent and bitter. The herb contains a volatile oil, tannin and bitter principle.

Uses. The leaves and tops of the herb cut prior to blooming are used to flavour food stuffs especially meats, egg preparations and salads. The volatile oil from herb is aromatic, carminative, stimulant, tonic, stomachic, diaphoretic, emmenagogue, rubifacient, given in colic, diarrhoea and hysteria, also applied in toothache.

Rosemary

Rosmarinus officinalis Linn.; English—*Rosemary*; Hindi—*Rusmary*; Family—*Labiatae (Lamiaceae)*.

A small shrub, native of Mediterranean region. It is found wild on dry rocky hill in the Mediterranean region. In India, it is cultivated to some extent in the temperate Himalayas and Nilgiris hills in dry to moderately moist climate.

Chemical composition of dried leaves.
Moisture 5.7%; Protein 10.2%; fat 14.1%; crude
fibre 16.0%; carbohydrates 46.3%; total ash 7.7%;
Calcium 1.8%; Phosphorus 0.09%; Iron 0.03%,
Sodium 0.01%; Potassium 1.0%; vitamin B_1 0.75
mg/100 g.; vitamin B_2 0.34 mg/100 g.; vitamin C
39.8 mg/100 g.; niacin 5.7 mg/100 g.; vitamin A
2395 International Units (I.U.)/100 g.; calorific
value 415 calories/100 g.

Thyme

Thymus vulgaris Linn.; English—Thyme;
Family—Labiatae (Lamiaceae).

A flowering plant. It is a perennial garden
plant. It is native of Mediterranean region. In India
it is found in Himalayas from Kashmir to Kumaon.

The dried leaves and tender tops make
"thyme" of commerce. A volatile oil of pleasant
odour is obtained on steam distillation of herb.

Chemical composition of dried leaves.
Moisture 7.1%; Protein 6.8%; fat 4.6%; crude
fibre 24.3%; carbohydrates 44.0%; mineral matter
13.2%; Calcium 2.1%; Phosphorus 0.20%; Iron
0.14%, Sodium 0.08%; Potassium 0.9%; vitamin
B_1 51 mg/100 g.; vitamin B_2 0.4 mg/100 g.;
vitamin C 12.0 mg/100 g.; niacin 4.9 mg/100 g.;
vitamin A 175 International Units (I.U.)/100 g.;
calorific value 340 calories/100 g.

Fig. 14.3. Spices and condiments. *Thymus vulgaris* Linn.; Eng. Thyme (Labiatae, Lamiaceae). A flowering plant. The dried leaves and tender tops of *T. vulgaris* Linn., make "thyme" of commercial value. It is a perennial garden plant.

Uses. The dried leaves are used for dressing and seasoning meat preparations, egg curries, pork
sausage, etc.

SPICES AND CONDIMENTS OBTAINED FROM FLOWER BUDS, FLOWERS AND INFLORESCENCE

Saffron

Crocus sativus Linn.; English—Saffron; Hindi—*Kesar, zafran*; Bengali—*Jafran*; Mumbai—
Safran, kessar, kecara; Marathi—*Kecara*; Gujarati—*Keshar*; Tamil—*Kungumapu*; Telugu—*Kumkum
apave*; Kashmiri—*Kong*; Sanskrit—*Kunkuma, kashmirajanma, kumkuma*; Arabic & Persian—
Zaafaran; Family—Iridaceae.

A rhizomatous herb. It is cultivated in Kashmir at Pampur near Srinagar. To a small extent it is
cultivated also at Bhersar and Chaubattia in Uttar Pradesh. The dried stigmas and tops of the styles
make the saffron of commerce. The product is obtained from the stigmas of the flowers, 4,000 of
which are required to produce 25 gms. of saffron.

Uses. The saffron is used as a spice and dyestuff. It possesses a pleasant aroma. Saffron is an
ingredient of many Indian dishes, particularly cooked rice and sweet rice (Kesaria chaval) and pulao.

Clove

Syzygium aromaticum (Linn.) Merr. & Perry; Syn. *Eugenia aromatica* O. Kuntze; *E.
caryophyllata* Thunb.; English—Clove; Hindi—*Laung*; Bengali—*Lavange, langa*; Punjabi—*Laung,
karanfal*; Kashmiri—*Raung*; Marathi & Gujarati—*Lawanga, lavinga*; Tamil—*Kiramber, ilavang
ap-pu*; Telugu—*Lavangalu*; Malayalam—*Chanki*; Sanskrit—*Lavanga*; Persian—*Mekhak*; Family
Myrtaceae.

Clove is the dried unopened flower bud of *Syzygium aromaticum*, a medium statured, cone-shaped ever-green tree belonging to the Family—Myrtaceae. Clove tree attains a height of 10 to 12 metres. The stem is usually forked near its base with two or three main branches. Smaller branches are slender, rather brittle and covered with grey bark. The leaves appearing in pairs, are lanceolate, acute at both ends and are of dark shining green colour. The aromatic nature of the leaves is due to numerous oil glands found on their under-surfaces. The flower buds are greenish when fresh and are borne on ends, which are picked green and dried in the sun till they become dark brown, form the 'clove' of commerce. The buds have slightly cylindrical base and are surmounted by the plump ball like unopened corolla which is surmounted by the four toothed calyx. If the bud is left unpicked, the flower develops after fertilization into a fleshy, purple and one-seeded oval fruit as 'Mother of clove'. The fruit is about 2.5 cm. long and 1.25 cm. in width. The seed is oblong, rather soft in texture and grooved on one side. The leaves, unripe fruit and broken clove, including the stalk are all aromatic and yield an essential oil.

Fig. 14.4. Spices and condiments. *Syzygium aromaticum* (Linn.) Merr. & Perry, syn. *Eugenia aromatica* O. Kuntze, *E. caryophyllata* Thunb; Eng. Clove (Myrtaceae). A, a flowering twig; B, dried unopened flower bud.

SPICES AND CONDIMENTS OBTAINED FROM FRUITS

Celery

Apium graveolens Linn. var. *dulce* DC.; English—Celery, celery seed, garden celery; Hindi—*Ajmud, bari-ajmud, karafs*; Bengali—*Chanu, randhuni*; Mumbai—*Bori ajamoda, ajmud*; Punjabi—*Bhut jhata*; Arabic— *Karafs*; Persian—*Karasb*; Family— Umbelliferae (Apiaceae).

It is native of England and other parts of Europe. In India, it is cultivated in the/North-Western Himalayas and in the hills of Uttar Pradesh, the Punjab and South India. In Indian plains, it is cultivated during the cold weather,

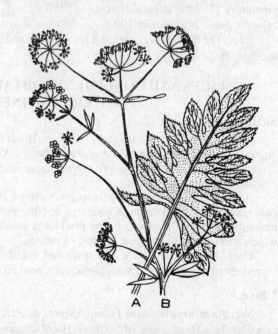

Fig. 14.5. Spices and condiments. *Apium graveolens* Linn. var. *dulce* DC.; Eng. Celery, Celery seed, Garden celery (Umbelliferae, Apiaceae). A, leaf; B, floral axis with typical umbels.

chiefly as a garden crop in the vicinity of towns. The fruits are small and dark brown with peculiar flavour.

Uses. The herb is eaten as salad, or made into soup. The seed (fruit) is eaten as spice. The seed tied into a piece of cloth are used to flavour soup. The soil extracted from the seeds is stimulant and used chiefly for flavouring soups and curries. The seeds are also cordial, tonic, carminative, diuretic, emmenagogue and antiseptic.

Chemical composition. Moisture 5.1%; protein 18.1%; fat (ether extract) 22.8%; crude fibre 2.9%; carbohydrates 40.9%; total ash 10.2%; calcium 1.8%; phosphorus 0.55%; iron 0.45%; sodium 0.17%; potassium 1.4%; iron 0.53%; vitamin B_1 (thiamine) 0.41 mg/100 g.; vitamin B_2 (riboflavin) 0.49 mg/100 g.; vitamin C (ascorbic acid) 17.2 mg/100 g.; niacin 4.4 mg/100 g.; vitamin A 650 international unit (I.U.); calorific value 450 calories/100 g.

Sweet Pepper

Capsicum annuum Linn.; English—Sweet pepper, paprika, Hungarian paprika, Spanish pimento; Family—Solanaceae.

This is a non-pungent variety of chilli. The red paprikas are famous for their brilliant red colour and mild flavour.

Uses. Paprika is used for its colouring and flavouring properties. It is used largely as a garnish for light coloured foods, such as eggs, fish, potatoes, salads and salad dressings. In food manufacturing, flavour is important, as this spice becomes a vital ingredient of sausages, soups, salad, salad dressings and many ready prepared foods.

Chemical composition. Moisture 7.9%; protein 13.8%; fat 10.4%; fibre 19.2%; carbohydrates 41.1%; total ash 7.6%; calcium 0.2%; phosphorus 0.3%; iron 0.23%; sodium 0.02%; potassium 2.4%; vitamin B_1 (thiamine) 0.60 mg/100 g.; vitamin B_2 (riboflavin) 1.36 mg/100 g.; vitamin C (ascorbic acid) 58.8 mg/100 g.; niacin 15.3 mg/100 g.; vitamin A 4915 International Units (I.U.)/100 g.; calorific value 390 calories/100 g.

Fig. 14.6. Spices and condiments. *Capsicum annuum* Linn.; Eng. Paprika, Hungarian Paprika, Sweet pepper, Spanish pimento (Solanaceae). A flowering twig. This is a mild or non-pungent variety of chilli.

Red Pepper, Chillies

Capsicum frutescens Linn.; Syn. *C. annuum* Linn.; English—Red pepper; chillies; Hindi & Punjabi—*Lal mirch, marcha, mirch, gachmirch, mattisa, wangru*; Bengali—*Lal-mirch, lanka-marich, gach-marich*; Kumaon—*Matisa-wangru*; Kashmiri—*Mirtz-a-vangun, mirch-wangum*; Gujarati—*Lal-mirch, marchu*; Marathi—*Mirsinga*; Tamil—*Milagay, mollagu*; Telugu—*Mirapakaya*; Malayalam—*Kappal-melaka*; Kannada—*Mena-sina-kayi*; Sanskrit—*Marichi- phalam*; Persian—*Filfile-surkh, pilpile-surkh*; Family—Solanaceae.

It is a herb, 2 or 3 feet in height, with entire ovate leaves, white flowers with a rotate corolla, and many-seeded fruits, which are technically berries.

Uses. The fruit when green is used for pickling and when ripe is mixed with tomatoes to make sauces. It is also dried and ground for use. The consumption of chillies is very great, and both rich and poor daily use them. The chillies form the principal ingredient in all chutneys and curries. They are ground into a paste, between two stones (Silbatta), with a little mustard oil, ginger and salt, they form the only seasoning which the millions of poor can obtain to eat with rice.

Caraway

Carum carvi Linn.; English— Caraway; Hindi—*Shiajira, zira*; Bengali—*Jira*; Punjabi—*Zira siyah*; Kashmiri—*Gunyun*; Ladakh—*Unbu*; Tamil—*Shimai-shombu*; Telugu— *Shimai-sapu*; Sanskrit—*Sushavi*; Persian— *Karoya*; Family— Umbelliferae (Apiaceae).

A herb; native of Europe and West Asia, now cultivated in Bihar, Orissa, the Punjab, Bengal and Andhra Pradesh, as a cold season crop. It is frequently cultivated on the hills, as a summer crop in Kashmir and Garhwal at an altitude of between 9,000 and 12,000 feet. It is a perennial with thick roots, compound leaves with linear segments and small white flowers. The fruits are brown in colour, slightly curved and tapering. The spice seems to have come into use in Europe about the thirteenth century, and it was known in England at the close of the fourteenth century.

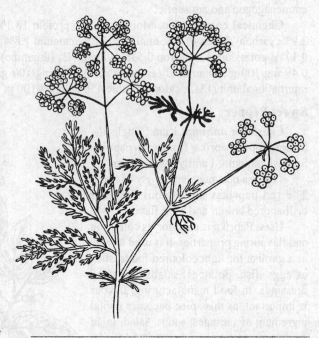

Fig. 14.7. Spices and condiments. *Carum carvi* Linn.; Eng. Caraway (Umbelliferae, Apiaceae). A flowering twig.

Uses. The fruit (seed) is used parched and powdered, or raw and entire. In the former case it is employed to flavour curries; in the latter it is put in cakes. It is used in confectionery and in flavouring drinks. It also produces a spirit cordial. It is carminative and largely used in curry powder.

A valuable essential oil is obtained from the "seeds" called caraway oil. The oil is a mixture of a hydrocarbon $C_{10}H_{16}$ (*carvene*) and an oxygenated oil, $C_{10}H_{14}O$ (*carvol*). The oil possesses a strong odour and flavour of the fruit. It is used medicinally and to flavour curries.

Chemical composition of fruit of *Carum carvi* Linn. Moisture 4.5%; protein 7.6%; fat 8.8%; fibre 25.2%; carbohydrates 50.2%; total ash 3.7%; calcium 1.0%; phosphorus 0.11%; sodium 0.02%; potassium 1.9%; iron 0.09%; vitamin B_1 (thiamine) 0.38 mg/100 g.; vitamin B_2 (riboflavin) 0.38 mg/100 g.; vitamin C (ascorbic acid) 12.0 mg/100 g.; niacin 8.1 mg/100 g.; vitamin A 580 International Units (I.U.); calorific value 465 calories/100 g. of spice.

Coriander

Coriandrum sativum Linn.; English—Coriander; Hindi—*Dhaniya*; Bengali—*Dhane*; Sanskrit— *Dhanyaka*; Tamil—*Kotamalli*; Telugu—*Danyalu, kotimiri*; Kannada—*Kotambari*; Nepali—*Danya*; Persian—*Kushniz*; Family—Umbelliferae (Apiaceae).

It is a native of the Mediterranean region. It is grown extensively in India, Russia, Central Europe, Asia Minor and Morocco. In India, it is cultivated in all the States. The more important States for its cultivation are - Andhra Pradesh, Assam, Maharashtra, Tamil Nadu, Uttar Pradesh, Karnataka, Himachal Pradesh and Madhya Pradesh.

The plant is generally 2-3 feet in height, with white or pinkish flowers. The lower leaves have broad segments, while the upper are very narrow. The fruits are small, oval and aromatic. Technically the fruit is known as "cremocarp". Each fruit consists of two one-seeded carpels, or mericarps with numerous oil ducts (vittae).

Uses. The fruits and leaves are aromatic and used as flavouring materials. The fruits are used extensively in the preparation of curry powder, pickles, sauces, soups, sausages and seasonings. They are also employed for flavouring pastries, cookies, buns and cakes and tobacco products. It is also used for flavouring liqueurs, particularly gin. The fruits are used both as spice and condiment. It is an important condiment used widely in all parts of India. A major part of the produce is used within the country. The fruits are also used as stimulant, carminative, stomachic, diuretic, antibilous, refrigerant, aphrodisiac and tonic. Oil of Coriander is used in medicine and for flavouring beverages. The Coriander leaves make one of the richest sources of vitamin C (*i.e.*, 250 mg/100 g.) and vitamin A (*i.e.*, 5200 I.U./100 g.).

Cumin

Cuminum cyminum Linn.; English—*Cumin*; Hindi—*Zira*; Bengali—*Jira*; Gujarati—*Jiru, jira-utmi*; Marathi—*Jire*; Tamil—*Shirangam*; Telugu—*Jiraka, Jilakarra*; Kannada—*Jiringe, jirage*; Malayalam—*Jirakam*; Sanskrit—*Jiraka, jirana*; Persian—*Zira*; Arabic—*Kamun*; Family—Umbelliferae (Apiaceae).

It is native of Mediterranean region. In India, it is cultivated mainly in the Punjab, Rajasthan, Haryana and Uttar Pradesh. The plant is a little annual herb with small pinkish flowers. The elongated oval fruits are aromatic and light brown in colour.

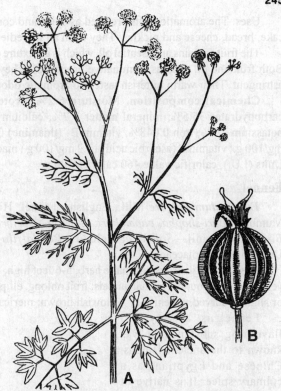

Fig. 14.8. Spices and condiments. *Coriandrum sativum* Linn.; Eng. Coriander (Umbelliferae, Apiaceae). A, a flowering twig; B, a fruit. India produces, on an average, 80,000 tons per year from about 2.5 lakh hectares.

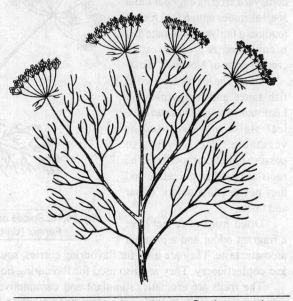

Fig. 14.9. Spices and condiments. *Cuminum cyminum* Linn.; Eng. Cumin (Umbelliferae, Apiaceae). A flowering

Uses. The aromatic fruits are used as spice and condiment. The fruits are used in soup, curries, cake, bread, cheese and pickles. They form an ingredient of some curry powders and pickles.

The fruit contains an essential oil, which is a mixture of cymol and cuminol and other hydrocarbons. Both fruit and oil possess carminative properties. They are also aromatic, stimulant, stomachic and astringent. Their warm bitterish taste and aromatic odour reside in the volatile oil.

Chemical composition. Moisture 6.2%; protein 17.7%; fat 23.8%; crude fibre 9.1%; carbohydrates 35.5%; mineral matter 7.7%; calcium 0.9%; phosphorus 0.45%; sodium 0.16%; potassium 2.1%; iron 0.048%; vitamin B_1 (thiamine) 0.73 mg/100 g.; vitamin B_2 (riboflavin) 0.38 mg/100 g.; vitamin C (ascorbic acid) 17.2 mg/100 g.; niacin 2.5 mg/100 g.; vitamin A 175 International Units (I.U.); calorific value 460 calories/100 g.

Fennel

Foeniculum vulgare Mill.; English—Fennel; Hindi—*Saunf*; Bengali—*Mauri, pan-muhori*; Mumbai—*Bari-shopha, panmohuri*; Gujarati—*variari, Variyali*; Marathi—*Badishep*; Kannada—*Badisopu*; Tamil—*Sohikira*; Telugu—*Pedda-jila-kurra*; Sanskrit—*Madhurika*; Family—Umbelliferae (Apiaceae).

It is a stout, glabrous, aromatic herb, 5-6 feet high; leaves pinnately decompound; flowers small, yellow, in compound terminal umbels; fruit oblong, ellipsoid or cylindrical, 6-7 mm. in length, straight or slightly curved, greenish or yellowish brown; mericarp 5-ridged with prominent vittae.

Fennel is a very old flavouring substance. It was known to the ancient Hindus, Chinese and Egyptians as a culinary spice. It is native of Mediterranean region. In India, it is cultivated mainly in the Punjab, Uttar Pradesh, Assam, Maharashtra and Baroda. It is cultivated mostly as a garden or homeyard crop throughout India at all altitudes upto 6,000 feet. It requires a fairly mild climate and is cultivated as a cold weather crop in parts of Northern India.

Uses. The leaves are used in fish sauce and for garnishing. Leaf stalks are used in salad. The leaf stalks are also used as vegetable. The leaves also possess diuretic properties. The roots are used as purgative and they possess an aromatic odour and taste.

Dried fruits of fennel have a fragrant odour and a pleasant

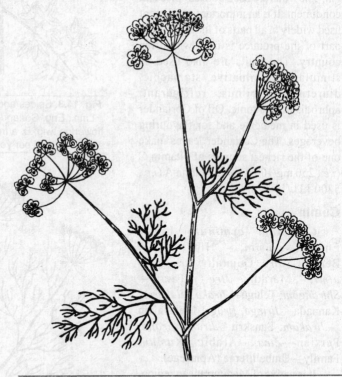

Fig. 14.10. Spices and condiments. *Foeniculum vulgare* Mill.; Eng. Fennel (Umbelliferae, Apiaceae). A flowering twig.

aromatic taste. They are used for flavouring curries, soups, meat dishes, sauces, bread rolls, pastries and confectionery. They are also used for flavouring liqueurs and in the manufacturing of pickles.

The fruits are aromatic, stimulant and carminative. They are useful in the diseases of chest, spleen and kidney. It is used as one of the condiments in liquorice powder. A hot infusion of the fruits is used to increase lacteal secretion and to stimulate sweating. Fennel fruits from Lucknow are considered to be the best and are priced higher than those from other areas.

Fennel oil. The fruit of fennel also contains a volatile oil. The oil is obtained by steam distillation of crushed fruits. It is a colourless or pale yellow liquid with a characteristic taste and odour. The main constituent of the fennel oil is anethole. Oil of good quality contains 50-60% anethole. Fennel oil is largely used as a flavouring agent in culinary preparations, confectionery, cordials and liqueurs. It is a good aromatic and widely carminative. It is used in colic and flatulence of infants. It makes a good vermicide against hookworm. It is used in the preparation of fennel water. It is used in perfumery and in scenting soaps.

Chemical composition. Moisture 6.3%; protein 9.5%; fat 1.0%; crude fibre 18.5%; carbohydrates 42.3%; mineral matter 13.4%; calcium 1.3%; phosphorus 0.48%; sodium 0.09%; potassium 1.7%; iron 0.01%; vitamin B_1 (thiamine) 0.41 mg/100 g.; vitamin B_2 (riboflavin) 0.36 mg/100 g.; vitamin C (ascorbic acid) 12.0 mg/100 g.; niacin 6.0 mg/100 g.; vitamin A 1040 International Units (I.U.); calorific value 370 calories/100 g.

Allspice

Pimenta dioica (Linn) Merrill syn. *P. officinalis* Lindl.; English—Allspice tree, Jamaica Pepper tree; Family—Myrtaceae.

It is a bushy evergreen tree, 6-9 m. high. It is native of West Indies and tropical America. It is grown in gardens in India. Leaves oblong-lanceolate, coriaceous; flowers white, in terminal and axillary trichotomous paniculate cymes; fruit a globose berry, about the size of a pea seed, black or purple, two seeded; seeds deep brown, reniform.

Fig. 14.11. Spices and condiments *Pimenta dioica* (Linn.) Merrill, syn. *P. officinalis* Lindl.; Eng. All spice tree, Pimento tree, Jamaica pepper tree (Myrtaceae). A flowering twig.

Uses. The berries are used as a condiment, as a flavouring agent in sauces, soups, pickles, canned meats, sausages, etc., It is an important ingredient of whole mixed pickling spice, and spice mixtures, *viz.*, curry powders, mincemeat spice, poultry dressing, pastry spice, etc., They are used for flavouring liqueurs. Pimenta berry oil is used for flavouring condiments and food products. The oil is used also as a carminative and stimulant.

Chemical composition of ground berries. Moisture 8.8%; protein 6.0%; fat 6.6%; fibre 21.6%; carbohydrates 52.8%; total ash 4.2%; calcium 0.8%; potassium 1.1%; iron 7.5%; vitamin B_1 (thiamine) 0.1 mg/100 g.; vitamin B_2 (riboflavin) 0.06 mg/100 g.; vitamin C (ascorbic acid) 39.2 mg/100 g.; niacin 2.9 mg/100 g.; vitamin A 1445 International Units (I.U.); calorific value 380 calories/100 g.

Anise

Pimpinella anisum Linn.; English—Aniseed, Hindi—*Saunf, badian*; Bengali—*Muhuri, mitha-jira*; Marathi—*Somp*; Gujarati—*Anisa*; Telugu—*Kuppi*; Tamil—*Shombu*; Kannada—*Shombu*; Oriya—*Sop*; Family—Umbelliferae (Apiaceae).

It is native of the Eastern Mediterranean region. It is widely cultivated in Europe, Russia, North Africa, Mexico and South America. In India, it is grown to a small extent. It is grown in Uttar Pradesh, the Punjab and Orissa. It is stated that a commodity commonly available in Indian market under the name *Lucknow saunf* is called Indian Aniseed.

The plant is an annual about 2 feet in height with simple based leaves and pinnately dissected steam leaves. The small fruits are greyish brown and covered with short hairs.

Aniseed on steam distillation yields an essential oil, known as oil of anise, anise oil is a colourless or pale yellow liquid having the characteristic odour and taste of the fruit.

Uses. The fruits are used as condiment. Now, oil of anise replaces the fruits for medicinal and flavouring purposes. Aniseed possesses a sweet aromatic taste and emits when crushed, a characteristic agreeable odour and is used for flavouring food, confectionery, bakery products, beverages and other liqueurs. The fruits are expectorant, stimulating, carminative, diuretic and diaphoretic.

Fig. 14.12. Spices and condiments. *Pimpinella anisum* Linn.; Eng. Anise, Aniseed (Umbelliferae, Apiaceae). A flowering twig.

Fresh leaves of the plant are used as a garnish and for flavouring salads.

Chemical composition of fruits. Moisture 9-13%; protein 18%; fatty oil 8-23%; essential oil 2-7%; sugars 3-5%; starch 5%; nitrogen free extract 22-28%; fibre 12-25%; ash 6-10%; choline is also present.

Black Pepper

Piper nigrum Linn.; English—Black pepper; Hindi—*Kalimirch, golmirch, choca mirch*; Bengali—*Kalamorich, golmorich*; Marathi—*Kalimirch, mire*; Gujarati—*Kalamari, kalomirich*; Tamil—*Milagu*; Telugu—*Miriyala tige*; Kannada—*Kare menasu*; Malayalam—*Kurumulaku, nallamulaku*; Punjabi—*Golmirich*; Kashmiri—*Martz*; Sanskrit—*Maricha, ushana, hapusha*; Family—Piperaceae.

A branching, climbing perennial shrub, mostly found cultivated in the hot and moist parts of India, Ceylon and other tropical countries. Branches stout, trailing and rooting at the nodes; leaves entire, 12.5-17.5 by 5.0-12.5 cm., very variable in breadth, sometimes glaucous beneath, base acute rounded or cordate, equal or unequal; flowers minute in spikes, usually dioecious; fruiting spikes very variable in length and robustness, rachis glabrous; fruits ovoid or globose, bright red when ripe; seeds usually globose, testa thin, albumin hard.

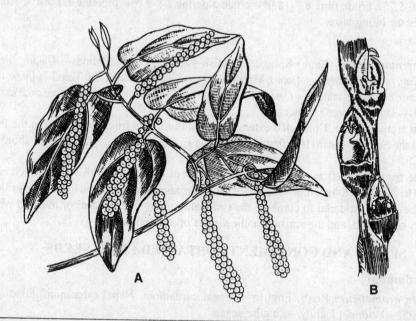

Fig. 14.13. *Piper nigrum* (Black pepper—**Kali mirch** or **golmirch**). The dried berries are used as black pepper. A, a branch with fruits; B, Part of a spike.

In India, the average yield of commercial black pepper has been found to vary from 110 to 335 kg. per hectare.

Black Pepper. Black pepper consists of the dried, fully developed unripe fruits. It is nearly globular in shape, about 4-5 mm in diameter with the characteristic coat with deep set wrinkles. The freshly harvested spikes are spread on cement floors or mats and dried in the sun for about a week. During drying the green or red fruits gradually change in colour to dark brown or almost black and their skin becomes tough and wrinkled. The fruits are detached from the stalks by beating the heaped up material with sticks or treading upon it barefooted. The outturn of dried black pepper obtained from green fruits varies from 26-29% depending upon the type.

White Pepper. It consists of dried ripe fruits, freed of their pericarp. In preparing white pepper the separation is done through the zone of fibro-vascular bundles, *i.e.*, only a part of the mesocarp is removed. In India, the production is limited to very small quantities, by some households in Kerala, for medicinal and domestic usage. For this purpose, the fully ripe fruits are rubbed with hand to remove the soft rind, and dried. The white fruits obtained are then washed and finally dried.

Uses. Pepper fruits are used as spice or condiment. In Kerala, fresh green pepper is sometimes used for preparing pickles. Black and white pepper make the major condiments employed for seasoning freshly cooked and prepared foods. In U.S.A. and other European countries they are used mainly for preserving meat. The whole fruits are added to pickles, certain types of sausages, etc., but the bulk of the product is generally ground before use. Black pepper is mostly used for its characteristic aroma and pungent taste. White pepper is less pungent. The aromatic odour of pepper is due to a volatile oil, while the pungent taste is caused by an *oleoresin*. An alkaloid is also present. Pepper stimulates the flow of saliva and the gastric juices and has a cooling effect. In modern Indian medicine, it is much employed as an aromatic stimulant in cholera, weakness following fevers, coma, etc., as a stomachic in dyspepsia, as an antiperiodic in malarial fever.

Chemical composition of different type of black pepper (*Piper nigrum* Linn.) varies. Moisture 8.7-14.1%; total nitrogen 1.55-2.60%; nitrogen in non-volatile ether extract 2.70-4.22%; volatile ether extract 0.3-4.2%; non-volatile ether extract 3.9-11.5%; alcohol extract 4.4-12.0%; starch 28.0-49.0%; ash 3.6-5.7%; crude fibre 8.7-18.0%; crude piperine 2.8-9.0%; piperine 1.7-7.4%; Alkaloid piperine makes the biting taste.

Ammi

Trachyspermum ammi (Linn.) Sprague; English—Ammi, Lovage; Hindi—*Ajwain, ajowan*; Bengali—*Jowan, juvani*; Gujarati—*Ajamo*; Marathi—*Owa*; Kashmiri—*Jawind*; Tamil—*Aman, oman*; Telugu—*Omami, omamu*; Kannada—*Omu, oma*; Mumbai—*Ajwan owa*; Sanskrit—*Yamani*; Persian—*Zinian*; Family—Umbelliferae (Apiaceae).

This is an aromatic herb. Cultivated extensively in India for its fruits (seeds); from the Punjab and Bengal to the South Deccan. It is first mentioned in Europe as brought from Egypt about 1549 A.D.

Uses. The fruits are used as spice. They yield an oil of distillation with water, which is used medicinally. The fruits (seeds) are much valued for their antispasmodic, stimulant, tonic and carminative properties. They are considered to combine the stimulant quality of capsicum or mustard with the bitter property of chiretta, and the antispasmodic virtues of asafoetida.

SPICES AND CONDIMENTS OBTAINED FROM SEEDS

Bengal Cardamom

Amomum aromaticum Roxb; English—Bengal cardamom, Nepal cardamom; Hindi—*Bari elaichi*; Marathi—*Veldode*; Family—Zingiberaceae.

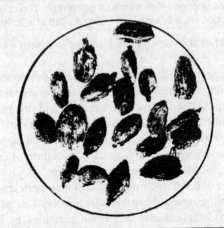

Fig. 14.14. *Amomum aromaticum* (**Bari elaichi**). The fruits and the seeds are used as spice.

It is a perennial herb, grown in North Bengal and Khasia hills. The fruit ripens in September; the capsules are then carefully gathered by the natives and sold to the druggists.

Uses. The fruits and seeds are used as a condiment. It is one of the chief ingredients of 'garam masala'.

White Mustard

Brassica hirta Moench; Syn. *B. alba* (Linn.) Boiss.; English—White mustard; Hindi—*Safed rai, safed rayan*; Bengali—*Dhop-rai*; Marathi—*Pandhora-mohare*; Gujarati—*Ujlo-rai*; Tamil—*Vellai-Kadugu*; Telugu—*Tella-avalu*; Malayalam—*Vella-Katuka*; Kannada—*Bili-sasave*; Sanskrit—*Siddhartha*; Persian—*Sipandane-supid*; Family— Cruciferae (Brassicaceae).

This is considered native of Europe and Western Asia. It is a herb, 2-6 feet high, with yellow flowers, hairy lobed leaves and a long-beaked pod with bristles. The small round seeds are yellow on the outside and white within. The seeds contain a glucoside, *sinalbin*. When ground seeds, are treated with water, the glucoside breaks down through enzyme action, and yields a sulphur compound with a characteristic sharp and pungent taste.

Uses. It is used as a condiment in food stuffs and pickles. The powdered seeds made into a paste with cold water act as a stimulant. It is used also in medicine. The seeds yield fatty oil.

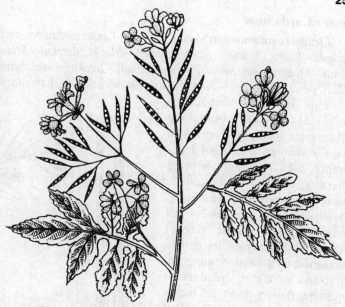

Fig. 14.15. Spices and condiments. *Brassica* spp.; Eng. Mustard (Cruciferae, Brassicaceae). *Brassica hirta* Moench. (White mustard); *B. juncea* (Linn.) Czern. & Coss., (Indian mustard); *B. nigra* Koch (black mustard).

Indian Mustard

Brassica juncea (Linn.) Czern. & Coss; English—Indian Mustard; Hindi—*Rai, sarson, sarson-lahi, gohna-sarson, barirai, barlai, badshahi-rai, shahzada-rai, khas-rai*; Bengali—*Rai sarisha*; Kashmiri—*Asur*; Gujarati—*Rai*; Mumbai—*Rai, sarson, rajika*; Marathi—*Mohari, rayan*; Sanskrit—*Rajika*; Family—Cruciferae (Brassicaceae).

A tall, erect annual herb, 3-5 feet high, with bright green foliage; racemes terminal, with a rough reticulate testa. It is cultivated chiefly in the Punjab, West Bengal and Uttar Pradesh. It is sown in October-November and cut in March-April.

Uses. The seeds are used as a condiment in pickles. The seed oil is used for pickles and cooking purposes.

Black Mustard

Brassica nigra Koch; English—Black mustard; Hindi—*Kali rai, rai, tira, tara mira, lahi, jag rai, makra rai*; Bengali—*Rai sarisha*; Gujarati—*Rai, kalirai*; Mumbai—*Rai, sarson*; Tamil—*Kadagho*; Telugu—*Avalo*; Kannada—*Bile sasive*; Sanskrit—*Rajika*; Persian—*Jarshaf*; Family—Cruciferae (Brassicaceae).

It is a native of Eurasia. In India, it is cultivated mainly in the Punjab, Uttar Pradesh and Tamil Nadu. The plant is smaller than the white mustard. It has smooth pods with dark brown seeds, which are yellow inside. The seeds contain a glucoside, sinigrin. This glucoside yields on decomposition a volatile oil containing sulphur, which is responsible for the aromatic odour and pungency.

Uses. Ground black mustard seeds are used as a condiment in pickles. The seed oil is used for cooking purposes.

Chemical composition of Brassica seeds. Moisture 7.6%; nitrogen substances 29.1%; nitrogen free extract 19.2%; ether extract 28.2%; crude fibre 11%; ash 5%; seed oil 27-33%.

Lesser Cardamom

Elettaria cardamomum Maton; English—Lesser cardamom, cardamom; Hindi—*Chhoti elaichi*; Bengali—*Ilachi*; Gujarati—*elachi*; Punjabi—*Illachi*; Mumbai—*Malabari elachi*; Marathi—*Velloda*; Tamil—*Ellakay, aila-cheddi, elakaya*; Telugu—*Ellakay, elaki chettu, ela-kaya*; Kannada—*Yalakki, yelaki, yerakki*; Sanskrit—*Prith weeka, chundruvala, ela, bahoola*; Family—Zingiberaceae.

This is a tall herbaceous perennial, with branching subterranean rootstock, from which arise a number of upright leafy shoots, 5-18 feet high, bearing alternate, elliptical or lanceolate sheathing leaves, 1-3 feet long. Flowers borne in panicles 2-4 feet long, arising from the base of vegetative shoots; panicles upright throughout their length or upright at first and ultimately pendent or prostrate; flowers about 1.5 inches long, white or pale green in colour with a central lip streaked with violet, borne in a close series on the rachis; bisexual. Fruits trilocular capsules, fusiform to ovoid, pale green to yellow in colour, containing 15-20 hard, brownish black, angled and rugose seeds, covered by a thin mucilaginous membrane.

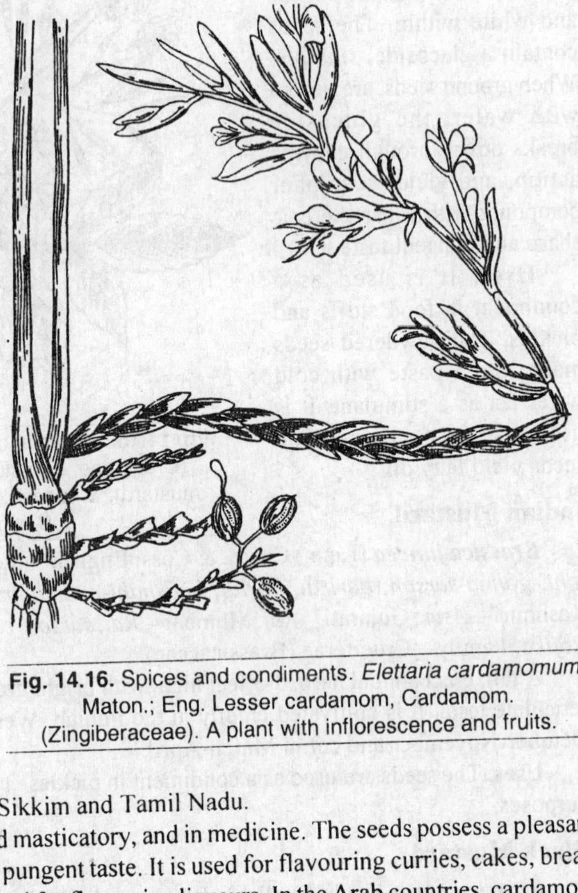

Fig. 14.16. Spices and condiments. *Elettaria cardamomum.* Maton.; Eng. Lesser cardamom, Cardamom. (Zingiberaceae). A plant with inflorescence and fruits.

Distribution. It is usually cultivated in those regions which form the natural habitat of the species. They are chiefly cultivated in Kerala, Mysore, Maharashtra, Assam, Sikkim and Tamil Nadu.

Uses. Cardamom is used as a spice and masticatory, and in medicine. The seeds possess a pleasant aroma and a characteristic, warm, slightly pungent taste. It is used for flavouring curries, cakes, bread and for other culinary purposes. It is also used for flavouring liqueurs. In the Arab countries, cardamom is used for flavouring coffee and tea. In medicine, it is used as an aromatic, stimulant, carminative and flavouring agent.

The cardamom capsules contain—Moisture 20%; protein 10.2%; ether extract 2.2% mineral matter 5.4% crude fibre 20.1% carbohydrate 42.1% calcium 0.13% phosphorous 0.16% iron 5.0 mg/ 100 g. The seeds of cardamom contain 2-8% volatile oil. Seeds of green cardamom yield appreciably more oil than those of bleached cardamom.

Chemical composition of seeds. Moisture 8.3%; volatile oil 8.3%; total ash 3.7%; non-volatile ether extract 2.9%; crude fibre 9.2%; crude protein 10.3%; calcium 0.3%; phosphorus 0.21%; sodium 0.01%; potassium 1.2%; iron 0.012%; vitamin B_1 (thiamine) 0.18 mg/100 g.; vitamin B_2 (riboflavin) 0.23 mg/100 g.; vitamin C (ascorbic acid) 12.0 mg/100 g.; niacin 2.3 mg/100 g.; vitamin A 175 International Units (I.U.) per 100 g. of seeds.

Cardamom oil of commerce is obtained by the distillation of the whole fruits of *E. cardamomum*. The cardamom oil is a colourless or pale yellow liquid with a penetrating, camphoraceous odour and a strong pungent taste. The main constituents of the oil are - cineol, terpineol, terpinene, limonene, sabinene and terpineol in the form of formic and acetic esters. Cardamom oil is used in flavouring beverages.

The chief importing countries of Indian cardamom are - Arabia, Sweden, U.K., U.S.A., Germany and Middle East countries.

Nutmeg and Mace

Myristica fragrans Houtt.; English—Nutmeg tree; Hindi—Jaiphal (fruit kernel), Japatri (aril); Bengali—Jaiphal (nut), jotri (aril); Punjabi—Japhal (nut), jauntari (aril); Marathi—Jaiphala (fruit), jayapatri (aril); Gujarati—Jayephal (nut), javantari, japatri (aril); Tamil—Jadikkay (nut), jadi-pattiri (aril); Telugu—Zevangam, jajikaya (nut), japatri (aril); Malayalam—Jatikka (nut), jati-pattiri (aril); Sanskrit—Jajiphalam (nut), jajipatri (aril); Family—Myristicaceae.

It is native of the Moluccas Islands. In India, it is grown in the Nilgiris, Kerala, Mysore, Andhra Pradesh, Assam and West Bengal.

This is a dioecious or rarely monoecious evergreen aromatic tree, usually 30-40 feet high. The bark is greyish black and longitudinally fissured in old trees. The leaves are elliptic or oblong-lanceolate, coriaceous. The flowers are arranged in umbellate cymes. The flowers are creamy-yellow and fragrant. The fruits are yellow, broadly pyriform or globose, 6-9 cm. long, glabrous often drooping. The pericarp is fleshy, 1.25 cm. thick, splitting into two halves at maturity. The seeds are broadly ovoid, arillate, albuminous, with a shell like purplish brown testa. The aril is red and fleshy.

Preparation of nutmeg and mace. The harvested ripe fruit with the valves split, discloses the seed with a shell-like testa covered by a scarlet fibrous aril. After collection, the pericarp is removed and the seed separated from the aril and dried. Drying is complete when the kernel rattles in the shell. The shells are cracked off with wooden hammers and the kernels removed and sorted. Dried kernels make the nutmeg of commerce.

Mace is the dried fibrous aril covering the testa. It is obtained by separating the arils and drying in the sun. Mace of superior quality is produced by drying in specially constructed ovens. During drying the arils at first become dark red and brittle, and in about six weeks they become bright amber coloured.

Fig. 14.17. Spices and condiments. *Myristica fragrans* Houtt; Eng. Nutmeg (kernel) and mace (aril) (Myristicaceae). A twig with an opened fruit.

Nutmeg. The commercial nutmeg is ovoid, 2.0-3.5 cm. long × 1.5-2.8 cm. diameter, greyish brown in colour with minute reddish brown spots and lines and reticulately furrowed. East Indian nutmeg is of three grades - 1. Banda nutmeg is supposed to be the best which contains upto 8% essential oil; 2. Siauw nutmeg is of second grade containing 6.5% essential oil and 3. Penag nutmeg, which is suitable only for distillation purposes.

Composition. The nutmeg contains - Moisture 14.3%; protein 7.5%; ether extract 36.4%; fibre 11.6%; carbohydrates 28.5%; mineral matter 1.7%; calcium 0.12%; phosphorus 0.24%; iron 4.6 mg/100 g.; Nutmeg contains a volatile oil (6-16%), starch (14.6-24.2%); pentosans (2.25%); furfural (1.5%), and pectin (0.5-0.6%). The flavour and therapeutic action are due to the volatile oil.

Nutmeg oil. The percentage of volatile oil varies from 6-16% according to the origin and quality of the spice. Commercial oil is derived from broken and wormy nutmegs. The material is comminuted, pressed to remove fixed oil, and immediately subjected to steam distillation.

The nutmeg oil is a mobile, colourless or pale yellow liquid with a characteristic odour. The major constituents of the oil are *d*-pinene and *d*-camphene.

Nutmeg butter. Commercial nutmeg butter, a highly aromatic fat, is obtained from undersized, damaged or worm-eaten kernels which are unfit for sale as spice. The material is ground and cooked or steamed before pressing.

The nutmeg butter is a soft solid, yellow or yellowish red in colour, with the odour and taste of nutmeg.

Mace. Commercial mace consists of flattened lobed pieces, 2.5 cm. or more in length, somewhat less in breadth and 1 mm. thick. When soaked in water the lobes swell up and regain their original form. It is dull yellowish red in colour, translucent and brittle. It is nutmeg-like in odour and taste. There are three grades of mace.

1. *Banda mace* is supposed to be finest — it is bright orange in colour and possesses fine aroma; 2. *Java Estate mace* is golden yellow in colour with brilliant crimson streaks; 3. *Siauw mace* is of light colour and contains less volatile oil.

Mumbai mace is derived from *Myristica malabarica*, it is dark red in colour and consists of narrow pieces, divided into numerous lobes twisted together at the apex. It is almost devoid of aroma, and is useless as a spice.

Composition. Mace contains — Moisture 15.9%; protein 6.5%; ether extract 24.4%; fibre 3.8%; carbohydrates 47.8%; mineral matter 1.6%; calcium 0.18%; phosphorus 0.10%; iron 12.6 mg/100 g. It contains a volatile oil (4-15%; average 10%), amylodextrin (25%), reducing sugars, pectin and resinous colouring matter. The chief constituents are volatile oils and amylodextrin.

Uses. Both nutmeg and mace are used as condiment and in medicine. They are commonly used more as a drug than as condiment. Nutmeg is stimulant, carminative, astringent and aphrodisiac. It is used in tonics and forms a constituent of preparations prescribed for dysentery, flatulence, nausea, vomiting, malaria, rheumatism, sciatica and leprosy.

Nutmeg oil and mace are used for flavouring food products and liqueurs. Nutmeg butter is used as mild external stimulant in ointments, hair lotions and plasters, and forms a useful application in case of rheumatism.

Black Cumin

Nigella sativa Linn; English—Black cumin, small fennel; Hindi—*Kalonji, kalajira*; Bengali—*Mugrela, kala-jira*; Kashmiri—*Tukm-i-gandna*; Mumbai—*Kalonji, kalenjire*; Tamil—*Karunshirogam*; Telugu—*Nalla-jilakra*; Kannada—*Karijirigi, kare-jirage*; Malayalam— *Karun-chirakam*; Sanskrit—*Krishna-jirata*; Persian—*Siyah-danah*; Myanmar—*Samonne*; Family—Ranunculaceae.

A herb. It is a native of Southern Europe. In India, it is cultivated in the Punjab, Bengal, Assam and Bihar for its seeds. Its Sanskrit names indicate, its introduction at a very early period.

Uses. The seeds, possess a strong, pungent, aromatic taste, and therefore, are much used in curries, pickles and other dishes. They are also frequently sprinkled over the surface of bread along with sesamum seed. French cooks employ the seeds of this plant under the name of *Quatre epices* or *toute epices*, and they were formerly used as a substitute for pepper.

Poppy Seeds

Papaver somniferum Linn. var. album; English—Poppy seeds; Hindi—*Post*; Bengali—*Pasto*; Marathi—*Posta*; Gujarati—*Posta*; Family—Papaveraceae.

It is native of West Asia. In India, it is cultivated in the East Punjab, Uttar Pradesh, Rajasthan and Madhya Pradesh. The plant is an erect, rarely branched, usually glaucous annual herb, 60-120 cm. in height. Leaves ovate-oblong or linear-oblong, amplexicaul, lobed, dentate or serrate; flowers large, usually bluish white with a purplish base or white, purple or variegated; capsules large, 2.5 cm. diameter, globose, stalked; seeds white or black, very minute, reniform.

As we know poppy is cultivated also for its seeds. In India, var. *album*, with white seeds has been cultivated for many years for the production of seeds (*post*) under licence in Dehradun and Tehri Garhwal districts of Uttar Pradesh, and in Jalandhar, Kapurthala, Hoshiarpur and Patiala districts of the Punjab. In India, best seeds are obtained when the capsules have not been incised for extraction of opium. The crop yields 220-275 kg. of seeds per hectare.

Uses. Poppy seeds are considered nutritive and are used in breads, curries, sweets and confectionery. Poppy seeds contain upto 50% of an edible oil. The oil is odourless and possesses a pleasant almond - like taste. In India the oil is extracted by cold-pressing the seed in small presses. The oil is widely used for culinary purposes. It is free from narcotic properties and used as a salad oil. The cake or the meal left after extraction of the oil from the seeds is sweet and nutritious and is eaten by poor people.

Fig. 14.18. Spices and condiments. *Papaver somniferum* Linn. var. *album*; Eng. Poppy seeds (Papaveraceae). A flowering twig. The poppy seeds are white and very small.

Chemical composition of seeds. Moisture 4.3-5.2%; protein 22.3-24.4%; ether extract 46.5-49.1%; nitrogen free extract 11.7-14.3%; crude fibre 4.8-5.8%; ash 5.6-6.0%; calcium 1.03-1.45%; phosphorus 0.79-0.89%; iron 8.5-11.1 mg/100 g.; thiamine 740-1181 ug/100 g.; riboflavin 756-1203 ug/100 g.; nicotinic acid 800-1280 ug/100 g; iodine 6 ug/kg.; manganese 29 mg/kg.; copper 22.9 mg/kg.; magnesium 15.6 g/kg.; zinc 130 mg/kg.; lecithin 2.80%; Oxalic acid 1.62%; pentosans 3.0-3.6%; traces of narcotin, an amorphous alkaloid and enzymes—diastase, emulsin.

Pomegranate

Punica granatum Linn.; English—Pomegranate; Hindi—*Anardana*; Assamese—*Dalim*; Bengali—*Dalimb*; Gujarati—*Dalamb*; Kannada—*Dalimbari*; Kashmiri—*Daan*; Malayalam—*Mathalam pazham*; Marathi—*Dalimb*; Tamil—*Mathalam pazham*; Telugu—*Dannima pandu*; Punjabi—*Anardana*; Sanskrit—*Dadima*; Family—Punicaceae.

A shrub or small tree, 5-10 m. high, native of Iran, Afghanistan and Baluchistan, found growing wild in the warm valleys and outer hills of the Himalayas between 900 and 1,800 m. and cultivated throughout India. Leaves 2.0-8.0 cm. long, oblong or obvate, shining above; flowers usually scarlet red; fruits globose, crowned by persistent calyx, with a coriaceous woody rind and an interior septate with membranous walls, containing numerous seeds; seeds angular with a fleshy testa which is red, pink or whitish.

Though mostly found cultivated in many parts of India, the tree is also very common and gregarious in the gravel and boulder deposits of dry ravines in the outer Himalayas, upto about 1,800 m. In Jammu, it is found gregariously on dry limestone soils in the upper extremities of sub-tropical forests;

it is also found in Chamba, Kangra and Mandi districts of Himachal Pradesh and valleys below 1,800 m. in Jaunsar and Tehri - Garhwal districts of Uttar Pradesh. As a cultivated crop, maximum area is said to be devoted to it in Maharashtra, particularly in Pune, Sholapur and Satara districts. In Gujarat, its cultivation is concentrated in Dholka taluka. It is cultivated in the districts of Almora, Aligarh, Tehri - Garhwal, Meerut and Farrukhabad in Uttar Pradesh; Uthukuli, Michaelpatti, Vellodu and Dindigul in Tamil Nadu state; Penukonda and Madakasira in Andhra Pradesh; Tumkur, Kolar, Bangalore and Mysore districts in Karnataka state.

Among the numerous types grown in India, the *Bedana* and *Kandhari* are considered the best.

The pomegranate is a sub-tropical fruit tree, growing best in semiarid climate where cool winters and hot summers prevail.

The fruit is a good source of sugars and vitamin C, and a fair source of iron but is poor in calcium. The sugar content increases with the age of the fruit and of the tree. The fruit contains 0.27% of pectin. During ripening, the insoluble pectin changes into soluble pectin. The concentration of vitamin C is said to increase with maturity and ripening of the fruit, and in most cases the maximum amount is deserved in the nearly ripe fruit.

Anardana of commerce. The seeds along with the fleshy portions are dried and commercially marketed as *anardana* and are widely used as condiment. The source of *anardana* of commerce is said to be the wild trees, covering vast tracts of hill slopes in Jammu, and parts of Chamba, Kangra and Mandi districts of Himachal Pradesh. The main areas from where *anardana* is collected are the Riasu, Udhampur, Ramban, Kishtwar and Bhadarwah Forest Divisions. In these areas, fruits are hand-picked towards the middle of October, when they are ripe and brown red in colour. Seeds with the pulp are separated by hand from the rind and are dried in the sun for about 10-15 days when the colour of the seeds turns reddish brown. The main assembling centre for *anardana* is Udhampur (J & K State) from where distribution is done all over the country.

Fenugreek

Trigonella foenum-graecum Linn.; English—Fenugreek; Hindi—*Methi, muthi*; Bengali—*Methi, methika*; Punjabi—*Methi, methri*; Gujarati—*Methi, methini*; Tamil—*Vendayam*; Telugu—*Menti kura*; Kannada—*Menthya*; Malayalam—*Ventayam*; Sanskrit—*Methi, methika*; Persian—*Shanbalid*; Family—Papilionaceae.

It is a native of Southern Europe and Asia. It is grown mainly in Northern India. It is an annual legume with white flowers and long slender pods with a pronounced beak. The crop is sown in October-November. It is ready to harvest in April.

Uses. The seeds are chiefly used as a condiment to flavour curries made of rice, pulse, flour and meat, or as a relish with unleavened bread. The aromatic leaves are used as vegetable. The seeds are carminative, tonic and aphrodisiac.

SPICES AND CONDIMENTS OBTAINED FROM LICHENS

Parmelia

Parmelia abessinica Kremp.; Telugu—*Rathipoovvu*; Family—Parmeliaceae.

This is a crustaceous lichen found in rocky areas of Bellary, Anantpur and Guddapah districts of Andhra Pradesh. The lichen is available in large quantities in the market and used as food material and condiment. It contains atranorin (1.1%), lecanoric acid (3.3%), salazinic acid (0.1-0.5%) and isolichenin (3.4%).

Parmelia tinctorum Despr. is a foliose lichen commonly found in the plains of India and in the Himalayas on tree bark and rocks. It is commonly used in certain parts of South India as a component of various food preparations. It contains—crude protein, 13.8; ether extract, 6.0; isolichenin, 25.0; crude fibre, 13.4; and ash, 12.6%; calcium 1,728 mg.; ascorbic acid, 5.0 mg.; and riboflavin 100 mg./100 g.

Uses. The above mentioned lichens are used as spice and condiment.

CHAPTER 15

The Medicinal Plants— Pharmacognosy

The branch of medical science which deals with the drug plants is known as *pharmacognosy*. This science is concerned with the history, commerce, collection, selection, identification and preservation of crude drugs and raw materials. The study of the action of the drugs is known as *pharmacology*. There are several thousand drug yielding plants all over the world. Most of the plants are known and utilized by herb doctors and *ayurevdic vaids*. Only a few drug plants are cultivated. Most of the supply of drugs is obtained from wild plants growing in all parts of the world and especially in tropical regions. These drug-yielding wild plants are popularly known as *jari-butis* in India. The drug plants are collected and prepared in crude indigenous way. The medicinal value of drug plants is due to the presence of some chemical substances in the plant tissues which produce a definite physiological action on the human body. The most important chemical substances are alkaloids, carbon compounds, hydrogen, oxygen, nitrogen, glucosides, essential oils, fatty oils, resins, mucilages, tannins, gum, etc. Some of these substances are powerful poisons, and, therefore, the preparation and administering of drugs should be done by competent physicians.

CLASSIFICATION OF DRUGS

The classification of drugs in the present text is based on the morphology of the plant organ from which the drug is obtained. Here the drug plants have been considered and arranged on a morphological basis. The general categories of the drug plants are as follows:

1. **Drugs obtained from roots.**
2. **Drugs obtained from underground stems.**
3. **Drugs obtained from bark.**
4. **Drugs obtained from stem and wood.**
5. **Drugs obtained from leaves.**
6. **Drugs obtained from flowers.**
7. **Drugs obtained from fruits.**
8. **Drugs obtained from seeds.**
9. **Drugs obtained from all parts of plant.**

DRUGS OBTAINED FROM ROOTS

Aconite

Aconitum heterophyllum Wall., of family Ranuncualceae; Eng. Aconite; Hindi—*Atis*; Sanskrit—*Ativisha*.

This herb is commonly found in the subalpine and alpine zones of the Himalayas from the Indus to Kumaon, from 6,000 to 15,000 feet.

Uses. The drug commonly known as aconite is obtained from the roots. The roots are used as astringent, tonic, antiperiodic in diarrhoea, dyspepsia and cough. It contains the alkaloids, atisine, dihydroatisine, heteratisine and hetisine. It is used externally for rheumatism and internally to relieve pain and fever.

Total alkaloidal content is 0.79 per cent. Plant is considered a valuable febrifuge and bitter tonic. Roots are used for hysteria, throat infections, dyspepsia and vomiting, abdominal pain and diabetes.

Indian Belladona

Atropa acuminata Royle ex Lindley, of family Solanaceae; Eng. Indian belladonna; Hindi—*Sagangur*.

This is tall erect herb, 3-5 feet high. It is found in Kashmir and Himachal Pradesh.

Uses. The roots are used in the manufacture of tinctures and plasters. It is used as an anodyne of rheumatism, neuralgia and local inflammations.

Belladona

Atropa belladonna Linn., of family Solanaceae; Eng. Belladona; Hindi—*Sag angur*.

This is also a tall erect herb. It is native of Europe, now cultivated in Kashmir.

Uses. The roots are used as sedative, stimulant and antispasmodic. It is used externally to relieve pain and internally to check excessive sweat, cough, etc.

Dried roots and leaves are used as sedative, antispasmodic, and anodyne; also used in ophthalmology to dilate pupils. Leaves are stimulant and narcotic, contains atropine and hyoscyamine, extremely toxic alkaloids.

Liquorice

Glycyrrhiza glabra Linn., of family Papilionaceae, Eng. Liquorice, sweetwood; Hindi—*Mulhatti*; Sanskrit—*Madhuka*; Bengali—*Jashtimadhu*; Marathi—*Jestha madha*; Gujarati—*Jethi madha*; Telugu—*Atimadhuramu*; Tamil—*Atimadhuram*; Kannda—*Atimadhura*; Malayalam—*Iratimadhuram*.

This is a perennial herb; native of the Mediterranean region but grown in Himachal Pradesh, Jammu and Kashmir.

Uses. The root contains glycyrrhizic acid. It is sweet demulcent, emollient, pectoral, alterative; laxative and expectorant; it is given in cough, bronchitis and other chest complaints, catarrhal condition of bowels, urinary passages, asthma, hoarseness of voice, etc. Its infusion is given in sore throat. It is also used in preparation of nauseous drugs.

Liquorice is also chewed with betel leaves. Principal constituents of liquorice to which it owes its characteristic sweet taste is *glycyrrhizin*, 2 to 14 per cent.

Serpentine

Rauvolfia serpentina Benth., of family Apocynaceae; Eng. Serpentine; Hindi—*Sarpagandha*; Sanskrit—*Sarpagandha*; Bengali—*Chandra*; Marathi—*Harkaya*; Telugu—*Paataalagani*; Tamil—*Chivan amelpodi*; Kannda—*Sarpagandhi*; Malayalam—*Chuvannavilpori*; Oriya—*Patalgarur*; Mundari—*Simjenga*; Assam—*Arachontita*; Khasi Hills—*Todong-pait-parao*; Trade—*Rauvolfia*.

Habitat. A large climbing or twining shrub, found in the tropical Himalayas and plains near the foot of the hills from Sirhind and Moradabad to Sikkim. It occurs also in Assam (up to 4000') and in South India Peninsula along the Ghats to Travancore and Kerala. The genus is distributed in the tropics, *i.e.*, Central and South America, Africa, India, Sri Lanka, Burma, China and Japan. The largest number of species are found in Africa and South America. It is also distributed to Malaysia and Java.

Medicine. In India and Malaysia the root of this plant has been, from ancient times, much valued as an antidote for the bites of poisonous reptiles and the stings of insects, also as febrifuge, and as a remedy for dysentery and other painful affections of the intestinal canal. In Sanskrit works it is mentioned under the name of *Sarpagandha.*

Besides the alkaloids, the roots contain oleoresins, a sterol, unsaturated alcohols, oleic acid, fumaric acid, glucose, sucrose, a derivative or oxymethylantheraquinone, a strongly fluorescent substance and mineral salts. Of these, the oleoresin is said to be physiologically active and shows typical hypnotic and sedative action of the drug.

Uses as a drug. Vast developments have been made in the chemistry of its different alkaloids and their role in hypertension, neuropsychiatric and other pharmacodynamics. The two main

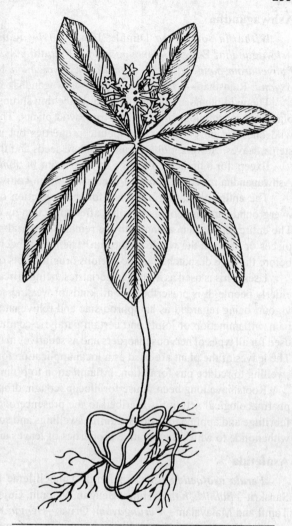

Fig. 15.1. *Rauvolfia serpentina* (*Sarpa-gandha*). The roots are used as medicine.

pharmacological actions of reserpine, *viz.*, lowering the blood pressure and sedative influence, have led to successful trials of the drug in hypertension, neuropsychiatric, gynaecological and geriatrics. With a moderate hypotensive action it controls mainly subjective symptom of high blood pressure when given alone. The drug is also reported to be useful in certain gynaecological conditions, such as menstrual, moliminia, frigidity and women complaining of menopausal syndrome. In the clinical use of reserpine in geriatrics it is reported to be of value in hypertension, nervousness, insomnia, etc.

Some important preparations are as follows:

Rauvolfia serpentina (tablets)—Gluconate Limited Calcutta.

Ralfen (alcoholic preparation) (tablets)—Bengal Chemical and Pharmaceutical Works, Calcutta.

Serpina or S 117—Himalaya Drug Company, Dehradun.

Raudixin (tablets)—Sarabhai Chemicals, Ahmedabad.

Adelphene-CIBA India Limited, Mumbai.

Serpasil—CIBA Pharma Limited, Basle, Switzerland.

Ashwagandha

Withania somnifera Dunal.; Hindi— *Ashwagandha* of family Solanaceae; Sanskrit— *Ashwagandha*; Bengali— *Ashwagandha*; Marathi— *Askandha*; Gujarati— *Ghodakun*; Telugu— *Pulivendram, panneru*; Tamil— *Amukkura*; *aswagandhi*; Kannada— *Panneru, aswagandhi*; Punjab— *Asgand*; Rajasthan— *Chirpotan*; Trade— Aswagandha.

The wild plants are generally erect branching shrubs up to one metre in height. The cultivated plants are morphologically distinct from wild plants. The cultivated plants are "different from the wild ones not only in their therapeutic properties but in all morphological characters like roots, stems, leaves, flowers, pollen grains, mature seeds and the enlarged calyx." (Kaul, K.N., 1957).

Except for a limited collection of roots from *W. somnifera* plants growing wild, the supplies of Ashwagandha roots are obtained exclusively from cultivated sources.

The entire plants are uprooted for the collection of roots. The roots are separated from the overground parts as soon as possible after collection by cutting the stems 1-2 cm. above the crown. The entire root system along with the remains of aerial stems is either cut transversely into smaller pieces or dried in the whole in the sun. The roots undergo further cleaning, trimming and grading before they are despatched to the various drug markets of India.

Uses. This is used as a tonic in geriatrics, being efficacious in relieving hand and limb tremors of elderly people. It is prescribed for all kinds of weaknesses and is supposed to promote strength and vigour, being regarded as an aphrodisiac and rejuvenator. It is used for the treatment of rheumatic pain, inflammation of joints and certain paralytic conditions. Several preparations of this drug are used for all types of nervous disorders and as sedatives in the treatment of insanity and in hypertension. The leaves of the plant are used as a local application for all types of skin lesions, ulcers, boils, and swelling to reduce pus formation, inflammation to promote healing processes.

Roots have long been in use for hiccup, cough, dropsy, rheumatism, and female disorders. The pharmacological activity is ascribed to the presence of several alkaloids. The leaves are used as a febrifuge and applied to lesions, painful swellings and sore eyes. Withaferin A is the most important withanolide to which the curative properties of leaves are attributed.

Asafetida

Ferula asafoetida Linn., of family Umbelliferae (Apiaceae); Eng. Asafetida; Hindi— *Hing*; Sanskrit— *Balhika, hingu*; Hindi, Bengali, Marathi, Gujarati and Kannada— *Hing*; Telugu— *Inguva*; Tamil and Malayalam— *Perungayam*; Oriya— *Hengu*; Kashmir— *Yang*; Mumbai— *Hing*.

This is an unpleasant smelling perennial herb, commonly grown in the Punjab and Kashmir.

Uses. The oleo-resin gum that exudes from the root-stock is carminative, antispasmodic, nervine, stimulant, digestive, sedative, expectorant, diuretic, anthelmintic and emmenagogue. It is prescribed in flatulent colic, dyspepsia, asthma, hysteria, convulsions, cholera, chronic constipation, chronic bronchitis, whooping cough, cough, spasmodic disorders of the bowels and angina pectoris. The fried gum is given either as a solution or emulsion or pills, preferably as pills.

DRUGS OBTAINED FROM UNDERGROUND STEM

Turmeric

Curcuma longa Linn., of family Zingiberaceae; Eng. Turmeric; Hindi— *Haldi*; Sanskrit— *Haridra*; Hindi, Bengali, Marathi and Gujarati— *Haldi, Halada*; Tamil— *Manjal*; Telugu— *Pasupa*; Kannada— *Arishina*.

A herb, cultivated commonly in Maharashtra, Bengal, Tamil Nadu, Andhra Pradesh and Orissa for its rhizomes.

Uses. The rhizome is aromatic, stimulant, antiperiodic, tonic, alterative and carminative. It is given in diarrhoea, intermittent fevers, dropsy, jaundice, liver disorders and urinary troubles. The fresh juice of rhizome is used as an anthelmintic. It is commonly used for cleaning foul ulcers. Along with lime or alum it makes a good dressing for sprains, bruises, wounds, etc. Its decotion is an effective eye wash in ophthalmia. The fresh juice is also used as antiparasitic for many skin affections.

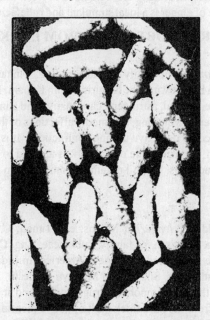

Fig. 15.2. The rhizomes/corms of turmeric – a medicinal plant.

Curcuma paper is used as an indicator of chemicals. Rhizomes yield an oil used as a carminative, stomachic and tonic.

Garlic

Allium sativum Linn., of family Liliaceae; Eng. Garlic; Verna. *Lahsuna*; Sanskrit—*Arishta*, *lashuna*; Hindi, Gujarati, Bengali and Marathi—*Lasun, lasan*; Telugu and Malayalam—*Velluli*, *tellagadda*; Tamil—*Vellaipundu*; Kannada—*Bellulli*; Punjab—*Thom*.

This is a strong smelling, glabrous, bulbous-rooted, perennial about a foot in height. The bulbs are short, compressed, breaking up into 10-12 bulbils or cloves, surrounded by a few, dry membranous scales. It is cultivated throughout the country.

Uses. Garlic is of great medicinal value. It is given in fevers, coughs, flatulence, disorders of the nervous system, pulmonary phthisis, whooping cough and dilated bronchitis. It has diuretic properties. A decoction of garlic made with milk and water is given in small doses in hysteria, flatulence, sciatica, etc. In the form of syrup, it is a valuable remedy for asthma, and disorders of the chest and lungs. It is used as an anthelmintic. Externally it is used as rubefacient, vesicant and disinfectant. Its juice is introduced in the ear for relief of earache. The oil in which garlic has been fried is a useful liniment for rheumatic pains, nervous diseases like scabies and maggot infested wounds.

Ginger

Zingiber officinale Rosc., of family Zingiberaceae; Eng. Ginger; Hindi—*Adrak*; Sanskrit—*Ardraka*; Bengali—*Ada*; Marathi—*Ale*; Telugu—*Allamu, sonthi* (dry); Tamil—*Allam*; Kannada—*Hasisunti*; Malayalam—*Andrakam, inchi.*

This is a perennial herb; the root stock is horizontal, tuberous and aromatic; native of South-East Asia but now cultivated mainly in Kerala, Uttar Pradesh, West Bengal, Maharashtra, Himachal Pradesh and Andhra Pradesh for the rhizomes.

Uses. The rhizome is used as a stimulant, carminative and flavouring agent. It is given in dyspepsia and flatulent colic. It is administered as an adjunct to many tonic and stimulating remedies. It makes a valuable drug for disorders of the digestive system, rheumatism, piles, pulmonary and catarrhal diseases, dropsy, febrile diseases, neuralgia, etc. The juice of fresh rhizome, with honey is a remedy for coughs and asthma. A paste of ginger is a local stimulant and rubefacient in headache and toothache.

DRUGS OBTAINED FROM BARKS

Cinnamon

Cinnamomum zeylanicum Bl., of family Lauraceae; Eng. Cinnamon; Hindi—*Dalchini.*

This is native of Sri Lanka but grown in the Nilgiris, South Kanara, Malabar, Assam and Kumaon.

Uses. The bark is aromatic, cordial, astringent, carminative and stimulant; it is given in diarrhoea, nausea, gastric irritation, flatulence, vomiting, spasmodic affections of the bowels, toothache, paralysis of the tongue and labour caused by defective uterine contractions. It is administered in the form of a powder, infusion or decoction. A paste made of the bark is applied to the temples to get relief from neuralgic pains and severe headaches. The oil obtained from the stem bark is used as a carminative, antiseptic and astringent.

Quinine

Cinchona calisaya Wedd., *C. ledgerina* Moens. ex Trimen; *C. officinalis* Linn; *C. robusta* How., *C. succirubra* Pavon ex Klotzsch. of family Rubiaceae; Eng. Quinine; Hindi—*Kunain.*

The quinine tree is native to the Andes of South America. In India it is found in West Bengal, the Khasia hills, Nilgiris, South India, Sikkim and Madhya Pradesh.

Uses. Quinine is one of the most important drugs known and it is the only adequate cure for malaria. Quinine is obtained from the hard thick bark of above mentioned species of *Cinchona.* The most important constituent of Cinchona bark is quinine, a very bitter, white, granular substance. In addition to its use in the treatment of Malaria, it is a valuable tonic and antiseptic. It is also used in the treatment of other fevers. Some 29 other alkaloids have been isolated from the bark, including cinchonidine, cinchonine, and quinidine, all of which are useful in medicine.

Asoka Tree

Saraca indica Linn., of family Caesalpiniaceae; Eng. Asoka tree; Hindi—*Ashok*; Sanskrit, Hindi and Bengali—*Asok, ashoka*; Marathi—*Ashoka*; Gujarati—*Ashopalava*; Telugu—*Asoka*; Tamil—*Asogam*; Kannada—*Asokadamara*; Malayalam—*Asokam*; Oriya—*Oshoko*; Khasi Hills—*Dieng-sohkyrkha.*

This is a spreading evergreen tree; native of India; commonly found in Central and East Himalayas, Bengal and West Peninsula.

Uses. The bark is astringent. Its decoction is given in uterine disorders, especially in menorrhagia and leucorrhoea. The decoction is also an efficacious remedy for piles and dysentery. The dried flowers are given in diabetes. The dried flowers of it are fried and used even by common people in Kerala.

Arjun Tree

Terminalia arjuna (Roxb. ex DC.) Wight and Arn., of family Combretaceae; Eng. Arjun tree; Hindi—*Arjuna.*

A tree, commonly found in Madhya Pradesh, Bihar and the Western Peninsula.

Uses. The bark is astringent, febrifuge, cooling, cardiac stimulant, cholagogal, lithontriptic and vulnerary. It is an excellent remedy for heart diseases. The decoction with milk is given every morning on an empty stomach. The decoction is also used for cleaning sores and ulcers.

DRUGS OBTAINED FROM STEMS AND WOODS

Ephedrine

Ephedra gerardiana Wall., of family Gnetaceae or Ephedraceae; Eng. Ephedrine; Hindi—*Khanda.*

A small shrub, found in the drier regions of the temperate and Alpine Himalayas from Kashmir to Sikkim at 7,000 to 16,000 feet elevation.

Uses. The stems are the source of famous drug ephedrine. The liquid extract of stem is used for controlling asthma. The tincture of the plant is cardiac and circulatory stimulant. The decoction of stems and roots is used as a remedy for rheumatism and syphilis in Russia. Juice of berries is used in affections of the respiratory passages. The stems contain the alkaloids—ephedrine and pseudo-ephedrine.

White Sandal Wood

Santalum album Linn., of family Santalaceae; Eng. White sandalwood; Hindi—*Safed chandan*.

A tree, found in the Western Peninsula, Karnataka, Tamil Nadu, and forests of Kerala.

Uses. The wood is cooling, astringent, bitter, sedative, cardiac, tonic and diuretic. It is given in fevers and thirst. The powder of wood is given in gonorrhoea, fevers and bilious disorders. A paste of wood is a cooling dressing in inflammatory eruptive skin diseases. The paste is also applied to the temple in headache and fever. The essential oil of wood is stimulant, antiseptic demulcent and diuretic. It is used in gonorrhoea, chronic catarrh of the bladder,

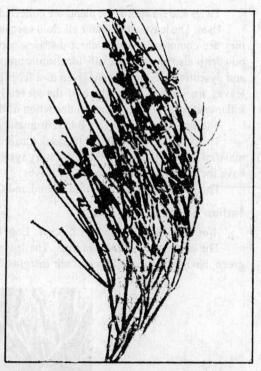

Fig. 15.3. *Ephedra.* The stems are the source of famous drug '*ephedrine*'.

urethral haemorrhage, chronic bronchitis and intermittent fevers. The oil is applied over scabies and other skin diseases.

Catechu

Acacia catechu Wild., of family Mimosaceae; Eng.. Catechu tree; Verna. *Kattha, Khair*.

Uses. It is a valuable astringent. It is generally used for disorders in which a mild, non-irritating and powerful astringent is required, such as chronic diarrhoea, dysentery, bleeding piles, uterine haemorrhage, leucorrhoea, etc. It is very efficacious for mercurial salivation bleeding or ulcerated or spongy gums, hypertrophy of the tonsils, enlarged uvula, aphthous ulceration of the mouth, etc. It may be used as lozenge made with the addition of gum arabic and sugar. A powder of catechu is used for plugging the cavity of an aching tooth to relieve pain. A tincture of catechu is useful for bed sores and painful mammary glands. A mixture of catechu and myrh, known as *Kathbol*, is used as a tonic, as a galactagogue for nursing mothers. Khersal or catechuic acid, found in small fragments in cavities of the wood, is a useful drug for chest diseases. The juice of the fresh bark is given with asafoetida in haemoptysis.

DRUGS OBTAINED FROM LEAVES

Vasaka

Adhatoda vasica Nees., of family Acanthaceae; Eng. Malabo nut; Verna—*Arusi, rusa*.

This is a perennial shrub. An evergreen shrub about 4-8 feet in height. Leaves elliptic, lanceolate, acuminate, dark green above, pale beneath. Flowers in short dense—axillary peduncled spikes, white with pink or purple stripes. Flowers after rainy season.

It is found throughout the plains of India and in the sub—Himalayan tract up to 4,000 feet.

Twigs and flowers of the plants are collected in March-April. The dried drug is sold in the market.

Uses. The leaves contain the alkaloid vascine; they are a powerful expectorant and antispasmodic; they are commonly used in chest diseases, especially phthisis. A decoction of the leaves or their powder is also given, especially for chronic bronchitis and asthma. The leaf juice is given in diarrhoea and dysentery. The leaves are given as a febrifuge in malarial fevers. For relief of asthma the dried leaves are smoked. A poultice of the leaves is applied over fresh wounds, rheumatic joints and inflammatory swellings. A warm decoction of the leaves is used for scabies and other skin diseases.

The flowers and fruits are bitter, aromatic and antispasmodic.

The root is expectorant, antispasmodic, antiseptic, antiperiodic and anthelmintic. It is given in malarial fevers, diseases of the respiratory system, diphtheria and gonorrhoea. The root and the bark have the same medicinal uses as the leaves.

The preparations are—Vansa Khand and Chyavanprash.

Indian Aloe

Aloe vera Mill., of family Liliaceae; Eng. Indian Aloe; Verna. *Gheekunvar*, *ghrita kumari*.

The plant is about 2-3 feet high. The leaves are fleshly tapering to a blunt point, smooth, pale green, having horny prickles on their margins. The plant is found throughout our country.

Fig. 15.4. *Aloe vera*. A common medicinal plant with succulent leaves. The pulp of leaves is given in fever and liver enlargement.

Uses. After removing the skin of leaves they are given in fevers, enlargement of the liver, spleen and other glands, skin diseases, gonorrhoea, constipation, menstrual suppression, piles, jaundice and rheumatic affections. In the diseases of liver and spleen the pulp of one leaf is administered with black salt and ginger. The juice of roasted leaf is being given with honey for cough and cold. The pulp of one leaf is being given daily in abdominal tumors, dropsy, carbuncles, piles, sciatica, rheumatism and retention of urine in fevers. A salad of leaves is eaten in indigestion, constipation and flatulence. The leaf juice is given as a remedy for intestinal worms in children. A poultice of the leaves is applied to tumours, cysts, inflamed parts and scalds.

Life Plant

Bryophyllum pinnatum Kurz., of family Crassulaceae; Eng. Life plant; Hindi—*Ghamari*.

This is a succulent perennial plant. Distributed throughout India.

Uses. The leaf juice is given in diarrhoea, dysentery, calculous affections and cholera. The leaves are styptic, astringent and antiseptic; they are slightly toasted before they are applied to wounds, bruises, boils, cuts, ulcers, bites of venomous insects; by its application swelling is prevented, incised wounds heal rapidly and irritation is allayed.

Indian Pennywort

Centella asiatica (L.) Urban., of family Umbelliferae (Apiaceae); Eng. Indian pennywort; Hindi—*Brahmi*.

This is a common trailing herb, rooting at the nodes. Commonly found throughout India.

Uses. The weed is alterative, tonic, diuretic, antiphlogistic, blood purifier and local stimulant. It is a remedy for skin diseases, like chronic eczema, chronic ulcers etc., enlargement of glands, chronic rheumatism, chronic nervous diseases, madness, cholera, amenorrhoea and piles. The leaves are a household remedy in early stages of dysentery of children. The powder of leaves is given with milk in small doses in mental weakness and to improve memory. The fresh juice of leaves mixed with milk is given as an alterative in gonorrhoea, jaundice and fevers; this is also useful for children in skin diseases and for improving the blood and nervous system. An ointment made of leaf juice and lanoline is of great value in elephantiasis.

Holy Basil

Ocimum sanctum Linn., of family Labiatae; Eng. Holy basil; Hindi—*Tulsi*.

This is an erect softy hairy aromatic herb or undershrub. Found throughout India.

Uses. The leaves are expectorant, stomachic, anticatarrhal, diaphoretic and aromatic; their decoction or infusion is given in malaria, gastric diseases of children and liver disorders; as a prophylactic against malaria fresh leaves are taken with black pepper in the morning. The leaf juice is given in chronic fever, haemorrhage dysentery and dyspepsia; it is also used to check vomiting and as an anthelmintic.

Betel Pepper

Piper betle Linn., of family Piperaceae; Eng. Betel pepper; Hindi—*Pan*.

This is a climbing shrub cultivated for its leaves.

Uses. The leaves are astringent, aromatic, antiseptic, carminative, aphrodisiac, stimulant, expectorant and sialogogue. The leaf juice with honey is given to children in colic, indigestion, diarrhoea and laryngitis. The leaves are chewed to remove foul odour from the mouth. The leaf juice is used as eye drops in ophthalmia, and other painful eye diseases and night blindness. Oil coated leaves are a useful dressing for blistered surfaces and ulcers. The essential oil extracted from the leaves, is given in catarrhal and pulmonary diseases.

Tylophora

Tylophora asthmatica; Syn. *Tylo-phora indica*; Hindi—*Jangli Pikavan* or *Antamul*; Family—Asclepiadaceae.

It is a trailing creeper, growing abundantly in Northern India, Bengal, Assam; the Western Ghats, Burma and Sri Lanka. The leaves are thick and deep green, 5 to 12 cm long and 2 to 6 cm wide. In dry state, they are rather, thick and of a pale-yellow colour.

Uses. The chewing and swallowing of leaves by the patient of asthma have shown wonderful results. The leaf was also tried at Vallabhbhai Patel Chest Institute, Delhi on the patients suffering from bronchial asthma, the results were quite satisfactory.

DRUGS OBTAINED FROM FLOWERS

Saffron

Crocus sativus Linn., of family Iridaceae; Eng. Saffron; Hindi—*Kesar*.

This is a herb, cultivated in Kashmir (Pampur), Bhersar and Chaubattia in Uttar Pradesh.

Uses. The dried stigmas and tops of the styles make the saffron of commerce. It is of medicinal value. It contains the bitter principle picrocrocin. Saffron is mild stimulant, stomachic, carminative, antispasmodic, nerve sedative, mild narcotic, diuretic and emmenagogue. It is a remedy for promoting menstruation. It is also used in fevers, hysteria, flatulent colic, asthma, leucorrhoea, piles and catarrhal diseases of children.

Iron Wood

Mesua ferrea Linn., of family Guttiferae; Eng. Ironwood; Hindi—*Nagkesar*.

A tree, found in the Eastern Himalayas, Assam, West Bengal, the Western Ghats, Travancore and the Andaman Islands.

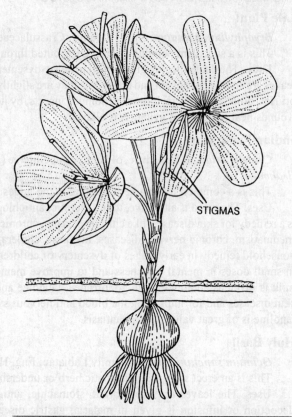

Fig. 15.5. *Crocus sativus* (Saffron). The stigmas and tops of the styles make the saffron of commerce.

Uses. The flowers are astringent and stomachic. The dried flowers are given in vomiting, dysentery, coughs, thirst, irritability of the stomach, excessive perspiration and bleeding pile.

Violet

Viola odorata Linn., of family Violaceae; Eng. Violet; Hindi—*Banafsha*.

A herb; native of Europe but now cultivated in Kashmir.

Uses. The flowers are demulcent astringent, diuretic, emollient, diaphoretic and laxative. They are given in biliousness and lung troubles. The flowers are used for the treatment of coughs, sore throat, kidney diseases, liver disorders and infantile affections.

DRUGS OBTAINED FROM FRUITS

Bael

Aegle marmelos Corr., of family Rutaceae; Eng. Bael tree; Verna. Bael, *Siriphal*.
This is a tree.

Uses. The fruit is of great medicinal value. The ripe fruit is aromatic, astringent, cooling and laxative. The unripe or half-ripe fruit is astringent, stomachic, antiscorbutic and digestive. It is best given in sub-acute or chronic cases of diarrhoea and dysentery and in irritation of the elementary canal; it is a useful adjunct in after treatment of bacillary dysentery. The ripe fruit is prescribed in intestinal disorders and certain forms of dyspepsia characterized by alternate constipation and diarrhoea. A sherbet of the ripe fruit is given for chronic constipation and dyspepsia.

Coriander

Coriandrum sativum Linn., of family Umbelliferae (Apiaceae); Eng. Coriander: Hindi—*Dhaniya.*

This is an aromatic herb; native of the Mediterranean region now cultivated in Madhya Pradesh, Maharashtra, Karnataka, Bihar and throughout India.

Uses. The fruit is aromatic, stimulant, carminative antispasmodis, correctivem diuretic, aphrodisiac, and refrigerant. A decoction of the dried fruits is given in flatulent colic, rehumatism and neuralgia. The volatile oil distilled from the fruits is given in flatulent colic, rheumatism and neuralgia. The watery paste of seeds is used for the cure of ulcers of the mouth and throat.

Cumin

Cuminum cyminum Linn., of family Umbelliferae (Apiaceae); Eng. Cumin; Hindi—*Zira.*

This is an annula aromatic 1-3 feet high herb. It is native of Mediterranean region but now commonly grown in the Punjab and Uttar Pradesh fro aromatic fruits.

North Gujarat especially Unja is well known for its cultivation and market.

Uses. The fruit is a good source of thymol; it is a stomachic, diuretic, carminative, stimulant, astringent and emmenagouge. It is prescribed in dyspepsia, diarrhoea, and hoarseness of voice. The fruit is given with lime juice to pregnant women for checking nausea; for promoting secretion of milk, cumin seeds are given after childbirth.

Emblic

Emblica officinalis Gaertn., of family Euphorbiaceae; Eng. Emblic; Hindi—*Amla.*

A tree found throughout India.

Uses. The fruit is of great medicinal value. It is one of the richest sources of vitamin C. The fresh fruit is refrigerant, tonic, antiscorbutic, diuretic and laxative. It is used in fevers, vomiting, indigestion, habitual constipation and other digestion troubles. The dried fruit is a good astringent, refrigerant, stomachic, antiscorbutic and blood purifier. It is given in diarrhoea, dysentery and haemorrhage. The infusion of seeds is a useful eye-wash in ophthalmic diseases.

Fennel

Foeniculum vulgare Mill., of family Umbelliferae (Apiaceae, Fennel; Hindi—*Saunf.*

This is an aromatic herb. It is native of Mediterranean region, now cultivated mainly in the Punjab, Assam, Maharashtra and Baroda.

Uses. The fruit is sweet, laxative, aphrodisiac, stomachic, stimulant, aromatic, corrective of flatulence, appetizer, anthelmintic, carminative, lactagogue, diuretic, stimulant and antidotal. It is administered in eye diseases, burning sensation, fever, thirst, wounds, dysentery, diseases of the chest, spleen and kidney, headache, amenorrhoea and bellyache of children; it also promotes female monthly regularity. In dysentery a decoction of fruit is given; in fever a decoction of fruit is given with sugar. The oil extracted from the seed is an anthelmintic against hookworms. The leaves are diuretic, digestive, stimulant and aromatic; they are useful in cough, flatulence, colic and thirst. They are also eaten to improve the eyesight.

Opium

Papaver somniferum Linn., of family Papaveraceae; Eng. Opium; Hindi—*Afim.*

A herb; native of W. Asia, now grown in Uttar Pradesh, in the East Punjab, Rajasthan and Madhya Pradesh.

An inspissated juice obtained by scratching the unripe capsules of *Papaver somniferum* Linn.; and allowing the milky sap, which exudes thereby, to dry spontaneously. The bulk of the medicinal article is obtained from Asia Minor, at the present day, as it has been for nearly the past 2,000 years. Indian Opium is, however, the most important form commercially, being that which is smoked, eaten or drunk, in various preparations by the inhabitants of Asiatic countries, chiefly the Chinese.

In India the opium-poppy is grown here and there throughout the country, but its cultivation is mainly confined to three centres, which afford the following opiums—'Patna Opium' in Bihar, 'Benares Opium' in Uttar Pradesh, and 'Malwa Opium' in Madhya Pradesh and certain parts of Rajasthan.

Medicinal properties of opium. Opium is well known to the medical profession. The medicinal drug of Europe is mainly derived from Asia Minor and is the produce of *P. somniferum* var. *glabrum*.

In the words of Pharmacopaeia of India it may be said that opium in its primary effects medicinally is stimulant, and its secondary action narcotic, anodyne, and antispasmodic. "It operates chiefly on the cerebrospinal system, and, through the nerves arising therefrom, it affects more or less every organ of the body. It tends to diminish every secretion excepting that of the skin, which increases under its use. In overdoses it is a powerful poison." In inflammation, especially of serious membranes, it has been employed extensively either alone, or in combination with calomel, antimony, and other remedies. As a general rule it

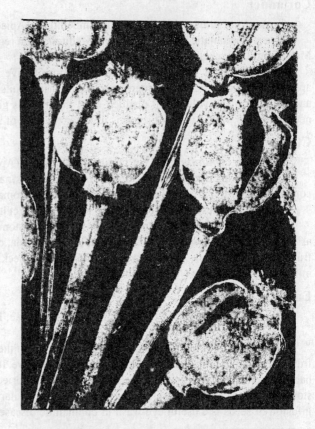

Fig. 15.6. *Papaver somniferum (Afim)*—The latex is obtained by scrapping the capsules. The latex, obtained from the immature fruits; is the source of opium, which is used to induce sleep, relieve pain, and relax spasms.

is less applicable to inflammatory and other diseases, in which the tendency to death is by coma or by apnoea, then to those which produce death by asthenia. In the latter, as in peritonitis, it holds the first place as a remedial agent. In fevers, especially in the advanced stages, it is of the highest value, either alone or in combination with antimony, camphor, allaying vascular and nervous excitement, and procuring sleep; but as a general rule, it is inadmissible when contraction of the pupil is strongly marked. In painful spasmodic affections, opium in large and repeated doses often affords immediate relief. In various morbid states of the abdominal viscera, *e.g.*, simple or cancerous ulceration of the stomach, chronic gastritis, gastrodynia, nervous and sympathetic vomiting, diarrhoea, dysentery, colica pictonum, strangulated hernia, visceral destructions, it is often given with the best results. In diseases of the genito-urinary system, *e.g.*, cystitis, cistirrhoea, spasmodic stricture of the urethra, also in menorrhagia, dysmenorrhoea, irritable states of the uterus, metritis, it is a remedy of the highest value. Tetanus, acute rheumatism, and delirium tremens are amongst the other diseases in which opium has been employed as a sheet anchor. In cholera it has been used but with doubtful results. In cancerous and gangrenous ulceration, opium, by allaying constitutional disturbances, often exercises a favourable influence on the local symptoms. As an external application, opium proves valuable in various rheumatic, neuralgic, and other painful affections; also in ophthalmia and other diseases of the eye".

"*Dose.* From a quarter of a grain to two grains or more according to circumstances, in many painful affections the sole criterion for the regulation of the dose is the amount of relief afforded"

Long Pepper

Piper longum Linn., of family Piperaceae, Eng. Long pepper; Hindi—*Pipar, Piplamul.*

This is a slender creeping undershrub. It is native of India and cultivated in the Western Ghats, Karnataka and Tamil Nadu for the fruits.

Uses. The sun-dried unripe fruit (berries) or the spike of the small flowers is known as long pepper. It is a cardiac, stimulant carminative, alterative tonic, laxative, digestive, emollient, stomachic and antiseptic. It is given with honey for indigestion, dyspepsia, cough, bronchitis, asthma, hysteria, cholera, fever, leprosy, piles, gout, etc. To prevent fever after childbirth it is an efficacious remedy. The dried root (*Piplamul*) possesses the same medicinal qualities as the berries but in an inferior degree.

Ammi

Trachyspermum ammi (L.) Sprague of family Umbelliferae. Eng. Ammi; Hindi *Ajwain.*

A herb, cultivated throughout India.

Uses. The fruits are carminative, stimulant, antispasmodic and tonic. They are given in colic, flatulence, dyspepsia, indigestion, diarrhoea, cholera, tympanites, hysteria, etc. The fruit yields an essential oil containing thymol.

Chebulic Myrobalan

Terminalia chebula Retz., of family Combretaceae; Eng. Chebulic myrobalan; Hindi—*Harara, Haritaki.*

A tree. Commonly found in Northern India. Also found in South India in the Deccan tablelands at 1,000–3,000 feet and up to 6,000 feet in Travancore; higher forests of the Mumbai Ghats, Satpuras, Belgaum and Kanara.

Uses. The fruit is the chebulic myrobalan of commerce. It is an efficacious laxative, astringent, stomachic, tonic and alterative. The fruit pulp is given in chronic diarrhoea, dysentery, flatulence, asthma, urinary disorders, vomiting, enlarged spleen and liver, etc. It is used externally as a local application to chronic ulcers and wounds and as a gargle in stomatitis. Fine powder of fruit is used as a dentrifice and considered useful in various teeth, bleeding and ulcerations of the gums.

Solanum

Solanum viarum Dunal; Syn. *Solanum khasianum* var. *Chatterjeeanum*, Sengupta; family Solanaceae.

Solanum viarum, is a wild perennial herb. It grows well in the hilly areas particularly of Khasia and Jaintia hills (Assam) in North East and Nilgiri hills of South India.

Morphology. It is a stout herb, with a woody stem, of about 2 feet in height. Nearly whole body of the plant is covered with yellow hairs (hirsute). The stem bears two types of prickles, hooked and straight. Stem is cymosely branched.

Leaf is 7" to 5" long and is deeply lobed, hirsute and bears only straight prickles.

Flowers are white in colour, and are produced in large number. The berry is about 2.5 cms. in diameter which contains about 350 seeds.

Alkaloid and medicinal uses. The berries of *S. viarum* contain the alkaloid *Solasodine*. It is a glycon which is used by pharmaceutical companies for the preparation of many important drugs. It is a nitrogen analogue of diosyenin and is a good source of *sapogenin*. Sapogenin is used as a base for the preparation of *Cortisone* and allied products. The synthetic substitutes are not known for these drugs, hence the importance of this source.

The gluco-alkaloid percentage of the berries is about 6 per cent which in turn produces one-third or 2 per cent of *Solasodine*. It can be extracted from dry as well as fresh berries.

Cortisone, a steroidal hormone prepared from solasodine, is found to be effective in the treatment of acute stages of rheumatoid arthritis, chronic cases of asthma, leukemia, obesity and many skin diseases.

Induced mutations have yielded favourable results regarding the increases in alkaloid content of the berries. (Dhyansagar and Pingle). *Material received from P.N. Purekar.*

DRUGS OBTAINED FROM SEEDS

Carrot

Daucus carota Linn. var *sativa* D.C. of family Umbelliferae (Apiaceae); Eng. Carrot; Hindi— *Gajar.*

An annual or biennial herb, grown chiefly in the Punjab, Uttar Pradesh and Madhya Pradesh.

Uses. The seeds are aromatic, stimulant, carminative, useful in the diseases of the kidney and in dropsy, nervine tonic, aphrodisiac, given in uterine pain.

Lesser Cardamom

Elettaria cardamomum Maton., of family Zingiberaceae; Eng. Lesser cardamom; Hindi—*Chotti ilaichi.*

This is a herb; native of India, cultivated in Kerala, Karnataka, Maharashtra, Assam and Tamil Nadu.

Uses. The seeds are aromatic, stimulant, stomachic, carminative, diuretic, cooling, abortifacient, emmenagogue and antidotal; they are useful in asthma, bronchitis, piles, diseases of the bladder, kidney, liver, uterus, rectum and throat. They are also remedy of scabies, headache, earache and toothache.

Blonde Psyllium

Plantago ovata Forsk., of family Plantaginaceae. Blonde psyllium; Hindi—*Isafgol.*

This is an annual herb. It is cultivated in parts of Rajasthan and Maharashtra.

Uses. The seeds are mildly laxative, demulcent, mucilaginous cooling, emollient, astringent and diuretic. They are used in the treatment of dysentery, constipation and disorders of the digestive system. The mucilaginous matter is found in the seed coat, and therefore, the seed coat or husk is used.

Castor Oil Plant

Ricinus communis Linn. of family Euphorbiaceae; Eng. Castor oil plant; Hindi—*Arand.*

This is a small tree, cultivated chiefly in Andhra Pradesh, Maharashtra, Karnataka and Orissa.

Uses. The seeds contain the alkaloid ricinine; the cold drawn oil from the seed is medicinally the most useful part of the plant; it is an effective purgative generally given in acute diarrhoea. As an enema the oil is given in constipation. The oil is locally applied in conjunctivitis. The leaves are applied to the head to relieve headache and as poultice for boils.

Nux-Vomica

Strychnos nux-vomica Linn., of family Loganiaceae; Eng. Nuxvomica; Hindi—*Kuchla.*

A tree, found in Orissa, Bihar, Andhra Pradesh and Tamil Nadu.

Uses. The dried ripe seeds are the source of a drug nux vomica which is used as a tonic stimulant and in the treatment of paralysis and nervous disorders. The powdered seeds are also given in general debility, chronic rheumatism, dyspepsia, intermittent fevers, diarrhoea, hysteria, general constipation, hydrophobia, impotence, cholera and epilepsy.

Fenugreek

Tirgonella foenumgraecum Linn., of family Papilionaceae; Eng. Fenugreek; Hindi—*Methi*.
A herb; native of South Europe, grown mainly in Northern India.

Uses. The seeds are aromatic, diuretic, nutritive, tonic, lactagogue, astringent, emollient, carminative and aphrodisiac. The seeds are given, boiled or roasted in dyspepsia, diarrhoea, dysentery, colic, flatulence, dropsy, rheumatism, chronic cough, liver and spleen enlargement. The seeds contain the alkaloid trigonelline.

DRUGS OBTAINED FROM ALL PARTS OF PLANTS

Absinthe

Artemisia absinthum Linn. of family Compositae (Asteraceae); Eng. Absinthe; Verna; *Vilayati Afsanthin.*

This is an aromatic, bitter, herbaceous hairy perennial herb. It is found in Kashmir from 5,000 to 7,000 feet elevation.

Uses. The whole herb is used medicinally but the leaves are preferred. The fresh plant is more efficacious than the dry plant. It is a tonic, stomachic and anthelmintic. Small doses of its infusion are given for dispersing the yellow bile of jaundice from the skin. It is also given in the disease of the digestive system, nocturnal pollution, anaemia, wasting diseases, etc. The poultice of its leaves is applied for fomentation to gouty or rheumatic joints. It is a useful antiseptic and detergent in skin diseases. An infusion of the leaves is given as an enema for killing worms in the rectum.

Neem Tree

Azadirachta indica A. Juss., (Syn. *Melia azadirachta* Linn)., of family Meliaceae; Eng. Margosa tree, Neem tree; Hindi—*Nim*.

It is native of Myanmar but grown all over India.

Uses. The leaves are carminative, expectorant, anthelmintic, antidotal, diuretic and insecticidal. The fresh juice of the leaves is given for intestinal worms; with honey the juice is prescribed for jaundice and skin diseases. An infusion of the fresh leaves is a bitter vegetable tonic and alterative, especially in chronic malarial fevers, because of its action on the liver. Externally the leaves are applied over skin diseases as a discutient, stimulant and antiseptic; they are specially used for boils, chronic ulcers, eruptions of small pox, syphilitic sores, glandular swellings, wounds, etc. The bark is also a bitter tonic, astringent, alterative, anthelmintic, antispasmodic and stimulant. It is used in the same way as the leaves. The root bark has the same properties as the bark of the stem. The nim gum is a stimulant and demulcent tonic. The fermented sap that exudes from the trunk is a refrigerant, nutrient, stomachic and alterative tonic.

The fruit is recommended for urinary diseases, piles, leprosy, intestinal worms, etc. The seeds are emetic, laxative and anthelmintic. Seed oil is applied as an antiseptic dressing in leprosy and chronic skin diseases.

Spiny Bamboo

Bambusa bambos Voss., of family Gramineae (Poaceae); Eng. Spiny bamboo; Hindi—*Bans*.

This is a tall woody grass, found throughout India, particularly along river valleys and in moist situations.

Uses. The leaf buds are administered for thread-worms. The leaf juice is given with aromatics in vomiting of blood. A decoction of the leaves is used to induce lochia after childbirth.

The young shoots contain hydrocyanic and benzoic acids; they are stomachic and stimulant; they are used in lung diseases. A decoction of the joints of bamboo stem is a useful emmenagogue; it is also used as an abortifacient.

Banslochan, a silicious crystalline secretion found in the culms of the female plants, is a febrifuge, expectorant, tonic, aphrodisiac, demulcent and pectoral. It is given in hectic fever, phthisis, asthma, paralytic complaints, etc.

Apple of Peru

Datura metel Linn., of family Solanaceae, Eng. Apple of Peru; Hindi— *Dhatura*.

This is a herbaceous plant covered with fine, minute hairs. Commonly found throughout India.

Uses. All parts of the plant are strongly intoxicant, narcotic, aphrodisiac, toxic, antispasmodic and anodynous. The young leaves and seeds contain the drugs hyoscine, hyoscyamine and atropine. The dried leaves and twigs of the plants are smoked as an antispasmodic in asthma, whooping cough, bronchitis, etc. The juice of the fruits is a useful dressing for the scalp to check dandruff and falling of the hair. The seeds are astringent, antispasmodic, narcotic, anodynous, intoxicating, aphrodisiac, bitter, carminative and stomachic. The paste of seeds is used for decaying teeth, piles, fistula, tumors and parasitic skin diseases.

Fig. 15.7. *Datura*. A twig with leaves, flower and fruits. All parts are intoxicant, narcotic, aphrodisiac, toxic, antispasmodic and anodyne.

Achyranthes

Achyranthes aspera Linn., Hindi—*Chirchita, Latzira, Apamarg*; family Amarantaceae.

This is a common roadside weed with spike inflorescence. Flowering throughout year. It is of common occurrence throughout India.

Uses. The plants are used medicinally for several diseases such as piles, colic, boils, etc. It is pungent, purgative, diuretic and astringent. Roots are used for pyrrhoea. Also used in cough and fevers.

Pedalium

Pedalium murex Linn., of family Pedaliaceae; Hindi—*Bada gokru*.

This is a low, thick stemmed succulent annual herb; found in Gujarat, Konkan and Andhra Pradesh.

Uses. Fresh plants infused in water or milk become mucilaginous. This infusion is diuretic and demulcent; it is given in disorders of urinary system, such as ardour urine, dysuria, gonorrhoea, spermatorrhoea, impotence, nocturnal seminal emission, calculous affections and dropsy. If the fresh plant is not available the dried fruits are used for the diseases for which the mucilaginous infusion of the leaves is recommended.

Black Nightshade

Solanum nigrum Linn., of family Solanaceae; Eng. Black Nightshade; Hindi—*Makoy*.

This herb is found throughout India.

Uses. The herb is a cardiac tonic, alterative, diuretic, sedative, diaphoretic, cathartic, anodyne, expectorant and hydragogue. It is used as a decoction in dropsy; enlargement of the liver and jaundice. The syrup of herb is given as an expectorant. In fevers it is given as a cooling drink. The leaf juice is given in inflammation of the kidneys and bladder and in gonorrhoea, dropsy, heart diseases, piles and enlargement of spleen. Hot leaves are applied over the swollen and painful testicles. The berries are alterative, and tonic. They are given in fevers, diarrhoea and heart diseases.

Indian Solanum

Solanum xanthocarpum Schrad & Wendl., of family Solanaceae; Eng. Indian Solanum; Hindi—*Kateli.*

A common prickly herb found throughout India.

Uses. The herb is expectorant, bitter, stomachic, astringent, diuretic, alterative and anthelmintic. Its decoction is given in fevers, coughs, asthma, dropsy, flatulence, gonorrhoea, pain in the chest and heart disease.

Chiretta

Swertia chirata Buch-Ham., of family Gentianaceae; Eng. Chiretta; Hindi—*Charayatah.*

This is a shrub commonly found in temperate Himalayas from Kashmir to Bhutan and the Khasia hills.

Uses. The shrub contains two bitter principles ophelic acid and chiratin. It is a bitter tonic, stomachic, febrifuge, appetizer, anthelmintic, alterative, laxative, antidiarrhoeic, and antiperiodic. It makes a good drug for skin diseases, intermittent fevers, intestinal worms, bronchial asthma and regulating the bowels. It is given as an infusion or tincture.

Heart-leaved Moonseed

Tinospora cordifolia (Willd.) Miers of family Menispermaceae; Eng. Heart-leaved moonseed; Hindi—*Gulancha.*

A common climbing shrub (liane). Found throughout tropical India and the Andamans.

Uses. The fresh plant is antiperiodic, alterative, tonic, hepatic, stimulant and diuretic; its watery extract is very effective in fevers. The plant is commonly used in rheumatism, urinary diseases, dyspepsia, general debility, syphilis, skin diseases, piles, bronchitis, impotence, gonorrhoea and jaundice. The fecula prepared from the roots and stem, known as *sat giloe* is a valued drug for intermittent fevers, chronic diarrhoea, chronic dysentery, jaundice and rheumatism.

Lochnera

Lochnera rosea (Linn.) Reichb.,—*Catharanthus roseus* G. Don. Syn. *Vinca rosea* Hindi—*Sadabahar*; family Apocynaceae.

An erect annual or perennial herb; native of Madagascar but now commonly grown in India as an ornamental plant. Leaves opposite, oval, obovate or oblong, glossy; flowers usually 2-3, in cymose axillary clusters; fruit a cylindrical follicle, manyseeded. Flowers whife or pink.

Alkaloids. All parts of the plant, particularly the root bark contain alkaloids; these include three alkaloids of the Rauvolfia group; *viz.,* ajmalicine, serpentine and reserpine. The alkaloids of this plant possess hypotensive, sedative and tranquillizing properties. They also cause relaxation of plain muscles and depression of the central nervous system.

Uses. The plant has been used as a folk remedy for diabetes in various parts of South Africa and also in India and Sri Lanka. It is reported to be toxic to cattle. The juice of the leaves is used as an application for wasp stings. An infusion of the leaves is given in the treatment of menorrhagia. The root is considered tonic and stomachic. The alkaloids possess hypotensive, sedative and tranquillizing properties. The alkaloids inhibit the growth of Vibrio cholerae and Micrococcus pyogenes var. aureus. Vindoline and the other alkaloids from leaves are active against M. pyogenes var. aureus and var. albus, Streptococcus haemolyticus, Corynebacterium diphtheriae and a few other bacteria; leaf extracts form a useful anti-bacterial agent for the treatment of staphylococcal and streptococcal infections.

Non-Alcoholic Beverages and Beverage Plants

The beverages containing caffeine are used all over the world for their stimulating and refreshing qualities. Caffeine is an alkaloid, which has definite medicinal values and acts as a diuretic and nerve stimulant. The most important non-alcoholic beverages are—*tea*, *coffee* and *cocoa*. Caffeine is harmful in large quantities, it is present in these beverages in very small amounts, not exceeding two per cent. The other beverages which do not contain alcohol are commonly known as *soft drinks*. They contain high sugar content and make a good source of energy. The fruit juices are the simplest soft drinks.

INDIAN TEA

Tea

Camellia sinensis (Linn.) O. Kuntze; Eng.—Tea; Hindi—*Cha*; Family—Theaceae.

The Story of Indian Tea

The fascinating story of tea from the seed to your cup is one filled with colourful legend and romance of modern organisation and commerce in India. It is end product of the patient toil of tens of thousands of tea-growers, the ingenuity of scientists, the expert skill of the blenders, business acumen of traders, care and promptness of shippers and the service and courtesy of retailers. It has passed through many phases, thousands of hands, and across the oceans of the world to reach you and to give you satisfaction.

The tea plant is an evergreen of the *Camellia* genus and is known as *Camellia sinensis* and flourishes in warm tropical and subtropical rainy regions. The highest yield will be obtained from tea which is grown in tropical climate. Paradoxically, the finest quality teas are produced from leaves grown in the cooler altitudes of 1,000 to 2,000 metres. The great 'Darjeeling teas' are grown against the background of *Mount Kanchenjungha* of the Himalayas; nowhere else in the world has the 'Darjeeling flavour' been duplicated. From here come the most delicate, the most fragrant teas ever produced.

Our story starts with the tea seeds, round and hard like brown marbles. The seed itself is taken from the tea trees. Many estates have a plot of selected trees which are allowed to grow to their full size of 5 metres to 10 metres. During July to October the trees blossom and tea flowers appear. But only after a year will the seed be ripe. When the shells crack the seeds are removed and planted in the nursery beds. Within a month they germinate into seedlings and green shoots start to grow. In 9 to 12 months the young plants are ready for removal to the tea garden—their permanent home. For another four years the plants must be expertly pruned before they are ready for the first plucking. By this time they have become wide and flat-topped like a waist-high table to make the plucking easier. If tea plants were left unpruned, they would grow as high as 30 feet.

Fig. 16.1. *Camellia sinensis.* Indian tea. The cured leaves are used as a beverage.

Plucking. Plucking takes place over 7 to 14 days and the deft fingers of the expert plucker (mostly women) can gather as much as 60 lb. of leaf in one day, or enough to make 15 lb. of black tea. Only two small leaves and a bud are gathered from each shoot.

In North India, during March or April the spring or 'First Flush' materialises; the 'Second Flush' comes a month later in May. After the 'Second Flush', the other flushes are not so well marked and the bush gives more or less a continuous supply of green leaf until November.

In India, plucking is carried on throughout the year. Even then, there are two big flushing periods, from April to May when about 25 per cent of the annual crop is gathered, and a second flush in September to December when about 35 to 40 per cent of the annual crop is harvested.

Commercially, tea may be divided into three basic classes:

(1) Black or fermented (2) Green or unfermented and (3) Oblong or semi-fermented.

Black tea is most important commercially and the production of major world supplies—viz., India, Ceylon, Indonesia and recently East Africa—is mostly of this type.

There are four principal operations in the preparation of black tea: (1) withering, (2) rolling; (3) fermenting, and (4) firing.

Withering. About 75% of the weight of a fresh leaf consists of water even on a dry day and nearly half of this has to be removed before the fibre of the leaf and stalk will stand the strain of rolling, without breaking up. The leaf is spread thinly over withering racks arranged one above the other horizontally, and allowed to remain there for 12 to 18 hours to lose its excessive moisture. Sometimes, heated air is forced over these racks if the atmosphere around is humid. The leaf slowly and evenly becomes soft and flaccid like soft leather and is ready for rolling.

Rolling. It imparts the characteristic twist to the leaf, breaks the leaf cells, exposes the juices to the air for fermentation to set in. After half-an-hour's rolling the leaf is removed in aluminium trolleys to a sifter and ball breaker. This machine consists of a long and flat metal sheet with perforations fixed on a frame which makes reciprocating motion. The movement causes the broken leaf and fine particles to fall below and the rest is taken out after sieving. The latter is again rolled for the second time with increased pressure. After the second roll, all the leaf still more or less green and quite flaccid removed to the fermenting room.

Fermentation. During fermentation, the tannin in tea is partly oxidised and the leaf changes colour and turns bright coppery-red. The rolled leaf is spread on tiles or aluminium or even glass sheets and the oxidation which has commenced during rolling continues, the leaf coming into contact with air. The period of fermentation generally extends from 3 to 3 1/2 hours, but this includes rolling time as well. As a general rule, the *shorter* the fermentation the more pungent the liquor: and the *longer* the fermentation the softer the liquor and deeper the colour.

Orange Pekoe (O.P.): This consists of long, thin, wiry leaves containing tip or bud leaf. These teas generally come from the finer portions of the shoot that is the bud, first leaf and softer parts of the stalk. The liquors are generally light or pale in colour and, it produced from high grown teas, usually flavoury.

Pekoe (P): The leaves are slightly shorter and so not wiry as those of O.P., the buds also are present. The liquors, however, have more colour and this grade is generally quicker brewing than the O.P.

Pekoe Souchong (P.S.): A bold and round leaf with pale liquors.

Broken Grades

These are of smaller and broken leaves and are roughly 80% of the crop including the dust varieties, which are also strictly to be classified under broken grades. There are 4 main grades in this category.

Broken Orange Pekoe (B.O.P.): They are much smaller than any of the leaf grades and usually contain tips, hence the word orange is added. The liquors have good colour and strength and this is one of the chief attractions.

Broken Pekoe (B.P): They are slightly larger than B.O.P. but tips or buds will be absent. The liquors are paler and are less coloury in the cup. These are mainly used as 'fillers'.

Broken Pekoe Souchong (B.P.S.): They are a little large or bolder than B.P. and in consequence lighter in the cup, but useful as 'fillers'.

Fannings or Pekoe Fannings: These are much smaller than B.P.S. and are quick brewing and give good coloured liquors.

Dusts

Finally, the smallest particles excluding 'fluff' and 'stalk' are graded as Dusts. These teas are useful in quick brewing, the liquors produced have both strength and colour. They are in a good demand for catering purposes.

Tea Board of India

The Tea Board's major functions at present are: promotion of the tea habit; helping the development of the Industry, more especially of its marginal units; mediation to secure essential goods and services; provision of educational facilities for the dependants of garden workers. For the buyers from abroad it is enabled by the Act to render effective assistance in ensuring the standard of tea shipments from India. But, the Tea Board is more important than its functions would signify. For it embodies the organised knowledge and experience of all tea interests, reflects the attitudes of the industry as a whole and is the only statutorily recognised link between the Industry and the Government.

Five Golden Steps to a Good Cup of Tea

1. Take fresh water from the cold tap and boil.
2. Warm teapot by rinsing out with hot water.
3. Put into teapot one teaspoonful of tea leaf for each cup.

4. Pour boiling water into the teapot. Cover and wait for three minutes. Give more time for bigger leaf teas.

5. Pour liquid tea from teapot into cup. Add milk or a slice of lemon and sugar to taste. Enjoy the taste and flavour of Indian tea.

INDIAN COFFEE

Location and area. Coffee is grown in India on the sunny slopes of the Western Ghats and it spurs extending eastwards where the ecological conditions are ideal for the growth of firstclass coffee. The F.A.O. has listed India as one of the eight countries in the world possessing optimum conditions for the growing of coffee.

The total area under coffee in India is 3,20,570 acres (or 1,29,730 hectares). About 58% of this coffee area is in the Karnataka State, 20% is in the Tamil Nadu State and 21% in the Kerala State. The remaining 1% is scattered, in small pockets in Andhra Pradesh, Maharashtra, Orissa, Assam and West Bengal States, besides the Andamans.

India produces about 100,000 metric tonnes of coffee every year. About 60,000 metric tonnes are exported to different destinations like U.S.A., Russia, West Germany, France, Italy, Netherlands, Sweden, U.K., Belgium and Canada. Indian Coffee in all grades—is among the best in the world and is used to blend with coffees of other origin to improve the quality.

Fig. 16.2. *Coffee berries.* There was a record production of coffee in India, one lakh and twenty thousand tonnes valued at Rs. 89 crores were exported in 1977-78.

Two varieties. Two main varieties of coffee are grown in India. They are *Coffea arabica* Linn.; and *Coffea robusta* Linden.

Indian Coffee is processed in two ways, i.e., by wet process (washed coffee) and by dry process (unwashed coffee). The washed coffee is known as Plantation or Parchment coffee. The unwashed coffee is called cherry coffee. Thus according to the process, coffee under arabica and robusta is described as under:

	ARABICA	ROBUSTA
Wet Process (*i.e.*, washed coffee)	Plantation	Parchment
Dry Process (*i.e.*, unwashed coffee)	Cherry	Cherry

Plantation coffee. Arabica coffee processed by the wet or washed method is called Plantation coffee. This is an elaborate and time-consuming process in which the outer skin of the fruit and the mucilaginous matter beneath it are removed, by pulping and subsequent washing with fresh water, channelled from the springs in coffee-growing areas. The pulping and washing release the coffee beans from the coffee berries. But each bean is still encased in a soft parchment covering. The parchment-covered coffee is then dried in the sun on barbecues in the estates. Coffee in this form is known as Parchment coffee.

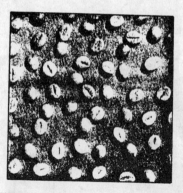

Fig. 16.3. Indian coffee. Coffee beans of *Coffea arabica*.

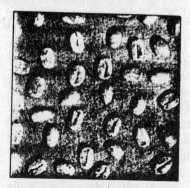

Fig. 16.4. Indian coffee. Coffee beans of *Coffea robusta*.

Curing. Parchment coffee is sent to curing works where it is further dried in the sun, if necessary, to a moisture content of not more than 10 per cent. The well-dried parchment coffee is fed through the peeling machine to remove the thin brittle parchment cover.

The beans obtained are then graded according to shape and size, and carefully garbled by hand, or using electronic sorters and pneumatic separators to remove blemished and defective beans. The final product of these processes gives the Plantation coffee of commerce.

Cherry coffee. The other method of preparing Arabica coffee for the market is simpler. The berries are harvested, dried in the sun till their outer skin, the parchment cover and pulpy matter in between, dry up to form a thick husk leaving the beans loose inside. The dried cherry is then decorticated by passing through a huller, graded and garbled according to prescribed standards. The final produce of this process is known as Arabica cherry coffee or simply cherry coffee.

Robusta coffee. Robusta coffee is also processed by both wet and dry methods, and the resultant beans are known in trade parlance as Robusta Parchment or washed Robusta and Robusta cherry respectively.

Characteristics. The two types of coffee have certain characteristics:

Variety	Type	Characteristics
Arabica	Plantation	Long and wide beans, greyish or bluish in colour.
	Cherry	Same as above, but colour golden brown to brown.
Robusta	Plantation	Broad oval beans, smaller in size than (Parchment) Arabica, greyish in colour.
	Cherry	Same as above, but colour golden brown to brown.

Grading. Both Arabica and Robusta can have round beans, called PEABERRY (PB) or flat seeds called FLATS. Classification into A or B or AB is done according to the size of seeds.

The main grades of coffee released for export are Plantation A, B and Triage; Arabica Cherry AB and Triage; Robusta Cherry AB and Triage; Robusta Parchment AB. The main grades are tabulated below:

Arabica Plantation		Arabica Cherry		Robusta Parchment		Robusta Cherry	
Grade	Sieve Size (mm)	Grade	Sieve Size (mm)	Grade	Sieve Size (mm)	Grade	Sieve Size (mm)
PB	—	PB	—	PB	—	PB	
A	6.65 and above	AB	6.00	AB	6.00	AB	6.00
B	6.00						
T	5.50	T	5.50	T	5.50	T	5.50

Coffee board. The production, internal marketing, export marketing, quality control, research, etc., are controlled by the Coffee Board which is a Statutory Body under the Ministry of Commerce of the Government of India. All coffee produced in India is delivered to the Coffee Board, Bangalore, a statutory organization, comprising representatives of coffee growers, curers, traders, workers, consumers and others connected with the industry.

Many of the different growths of Indian coffee, like Biligiris, Bababudans, other Mysores, Coorgs, Nilgiris, Naidubattams, Shevaroys, Anamallais, Pulneys, Nelliampathis, and Nilagiris Wynaad are familiar to importers of coffee in different countries of the world, as being synonymous, with supreme quality coffee. This is because the Indian Coffee Industry has to its credit three hundred years of continuous service in growing and making available high grown, good quality, mild coffee.

Indian coffee has a high reputation in the world market. This is because of the high quality of Indian coffee and the infinite care taken by the Coffee Board to maintain high standard at each stage of processing Indian coffee from the seed to the cup and special attention given to the screening and selection of only the best coffee for export, so that coffee connoisseurs around the world can always enjoy the superior and fine aroma of India's high-grown mild coffees.

CHAPTER 17

Rubber and its Products

Rubber is obtained from the *latex*, of various plants of tropical or sub-tropical regions. Most of the rubber plants belong to the Moraceae, Euphorbiaceae and Apocynaceae families. Though several species are available as sources of rubber, yet *Hevea brasiliensis* supersedes all. The cultivated *Hevea* trees, the so-called plantation rubber furnish about 98% of the supply. Rubber is the most recent of the major crops of the world. The industry is little more than a century old, and cultivation has been carried on about 80 years or so.

The latex occurs in latex tubes or latex vessels found in the various parts of the plants. Generally the commercial rubber is obtained from the lower part of the stem of tree. Latex is a gummy white liquid full of minute globules. It is mixture of water, hydrocarbons, resins, oils, proteins, acids, salts, sugars and caoutchouc. The physical and chemical properties of rubber have been considered separately in the following paragraph :

PROPERTIES OF RUBBER

Physical properties. The physical properties of rubber vary with temperature. Natural rubber is soft and translucent at 20°C ; when chilled to 0–10°C, it becomes hard and opaque ; at the temperature of liquid air, it is brittle and transparent like glass. At temperatures exceeding 25°, rubber loses elasticity and becomes sticky. Rubber melts to a viscous fluid at about 200°C. Rubber is insoluble in water and is unaffected by alkalies or moderately strong acids. It is soluble in benzene, naphtha, carbon disulphide, ether, chloroform and chlorinated hydrocarbons. When rubber is dissolved in a solvent, it first swells to gel-like consistency and then forms a solution. The elastic property of rubber is closely related to its molecular structure. Rubber is amorphous in the unstretched state, but shows crystalline behaviour when kept at 0° for a long time or when stretched. Rubber is one of the best insulating and dielectric materials available.

Chemical properties. First grade latex plantation rubber contains : rubber hydrocarbon 92–94%, resin 3%, protein 2% and ash 0.2% in Hevea rubber. Rubber hydrocarbon, also known as caoutchouc, is colourless, odourless, transparent and elastic. It consists of long chains of isoprene units connected end to end through 1 : 4 linkages. Rubber forms compounds with halogens, halogen acids and metallic halides, ozone and oxides of nitrogen. Hydrogenation at elevated temperatures and pressures in the presence of a catalyst gives fully saturated hydrorubber. Rubber is oxidised by nitric acid, potassium permanganate and hydrogen peroxide.

Hevea Aubl. (Euphorbiaceae).

A small genus of trees distributed chiefly in the Amazon region of South America. One species *Hevea brasiliensis* ; the source of Para Rubber, has been introduced in India and cultivated as a plantation crop.

Hevea brasiliensis (H.B.K.) Muell. Arg. (Eng. Para rubber ; Verna. *Rabar*). It is a large tree attaining a height of 60–100 ft. or more and a girth of 8–12 ft. The stem is smooth, straight, generally unbranched up to a considerable height, with a much branched leafy canopy. It is considered indigenous to the Amazon valley of Brazil, Venezuela, Peru, Ecuador and Colombia.

The rubber plantation industry in South-East Asia dates back to 1876 ; when 1,900 seedlings raised at Kew, were despatched to Ceylon. Plantations were raised and by 1930 a number of strains had been developed by breeding and selection, some of them superior to the stock originally obtained from Kew.

In India, rubber plantations were first started in Kerala state in 1905. Since then many other areas have been brought under rubber cultivation. At present, Kerala is the most important rubber producing state in India with plantations concentrated particularly in Kottayam and Quilon districts. Kanyakumari district in Tamil Nadu state is also an important rubber-growing area; there are small areas in Coimbatore and Nilgiris in Tamil Nadu state, Coorg in Karnataka state and in Andaman Islands. Rubber is produced in India, in plantations ranging from less than one acre to about 3,000 acres in area. Areas above 50 acres are classified as large estates and those of 50 acres and below, as Holdings.

Fig. 17.1. The rubber plantations in India registered phenomenal growth since independence. Production increased ten-fold in a span of 30 years and area enhanced four-fold while average yield shot up 2½ times. As a result from an importer of 35,000 tonnes of natural rubber in 1963, India gradually attained self-sufficiency and emerged a net exporter since 1973. Natural rubber, has spread now to over 230,000 hectares producing annually over 150,000 tonnes valued at Rs. 1200 million. Over a million people depend on this industry for their livelihood.

Hevea brasiliensis thrives in the tropical belt of the equator, in which the climate is warm, humid and equable and the temperature ranges from 74°F to 95°F. It requires a well distributed rainfall of 70 to 100 inches per annum. In South India, the plantations are located mostly in areas with a prolonged dry season and severe South West monsoon. The temperature ranges from 60°F to 95°F and there is a large variation between winter and summer temperatures.

Hevea brasiliensis thrives best in deep, well drained loamy soils. The soils in the rubber plantations of South India are red lateritic or clayey loams. The soils are generally deep and well drained. They are fairly rich in nitrogen, but poor in mineral constituents.

Rubber is a long duration tree crop which stays on the ground for several years. The economic life of rubber tree is 30–35 years. Newly opened jungle is considered to be the most suitable for rubber cultivation. The area to be planted is cleared of the jungle by cutting down the undergrowth and felling the trees. The cleared area is then lined and marked and terraces prepared. Provision is made for roads and drainage.

Tapping. Para rubber (*Hevea brasiliensis*) is valued for the latex obtained by tapping, *i.e.*, opening up the latex vessels situated in the bark with a sharp incision on the main trunk. When the vessels are cut, the latex flows out, quickly at first, then slowly, and finally coagulating on the cut surface. The tree is rested after each cut for varying periods according to age, climate and condition of the tree. When the tree is tapped again, the coagulated latex of 'plug' from the old cut surface is removed and a thin strip of bark is cut off. During the first tapping, only a small amount of viscous latex exudes. The flow increases with each successive tapping, the cuts being opened always at an angle to the horizontal. Usually, the cut extends half way around the trunk, but quite often, may completely encircle it.

Yield. The average yield of latex per acre in India from unselected ordinary seedling trees is 300 lb. The yield from budgrafted trees of approved clones and from clonal seedlings of approved parentage is twice, or more. An average yield of 700–800 lb. per acre has been obtained with improved planting materials in India.

Latex. Fresh latex is usually milky white in colour. The latex drawn from a tree which has been rested for sometime is yellow. The latex obtained by tapping is essentially a colloidal suspension of rubber particles in an aqueous serum.

Fresh latex is readily susceptible to enzymic and bacterial action leading to acid formation, and preservatives and bactericides are usually added to latex at the time of collection to inhibit acid development and consequent coagulation.

Raw rubber. Rubber of commerce is obtained from latex of *Hevea brasiliensis* by coagulation; rolling and drying. Two forms of raw rubber are known in trade, namely, *Smoked Sheet Rubber* and *Crepe Rubber.*

Grading. The system adopted in our country for grading raw rubber is based on the type description of the Rubber Manufacturers' Association and endorsed by the Rubber Trade Association of New York. These types are recognised as universal standards by producing and consuming countries alike.

Packing. The raw rubber is packed in bales in accordance with R.M.A. packing specifications.

Marketing. The raw rubber is marketed in the form of dry rubber. About two-thirds of total production is marketed by managing agents after grading. Petty merchants and dealers sell the collection to the nearest depot of a purchasing firm or take them to dealers in Kottayam, Trivandrum, Trichur or other market centres.

Uses. The raw rubber as such has few important applications. Its chief uses are in making insulation tapes, shoe soles, adhesives and erasers.

Rubber is used for the production of a wide variety of products utilized in industries and services, and for domestic purposes. It has been estimated that about 50,000 different products are fabricated from rubber directly or indirectly. Tyres and tubes for automobiles and cycles account for about 75% of the total rubber consumption. About 6% is used for footwear ; about 4% for wire and cable insulations. Among miscellaneous manufactured articles mention may be made of rubberised fabrics, motor mountings for absorbing vibrations and shocks, washers and gaskets, transmission and conveyor belting, garden hose, fire hose and hose for gasoline, pneumatic tools, paints, sports goods, household and hospital supplies, such as sheets, hot water bags, ice bags, surgeon's gloves, bathing caps and prophylactics, toys, such as balls, dolls and balloons, erasers and rubber bands and adhesives. Metals are coated with rubber to protect them from wear and corrosion. Sponge rubber from foamed latex finds uses in cushioning, seating and bedding. Elastic fabrics are made from latex threads. It is also employed in the fabrication of battery boxes, fountain pen barrels, tobacco pipe stems, telephones and combs.

Natural rubber latex, in preserved and concentrated forms, finds many commercial applications. Compounded latex is largely replacing rubber solutions for the manufacture of such articles as balloons, gloves, contraceptive appliances, finger stalls and teats. Over 65% of the latex is used in the manufacture of foam rubber and the rest for dipped goods, fabric coatings, impregnation and moulded goods. Uncured latex is used as an adhesive in footwear manufacture. The bulk of latex goods is made from vulcanised latex.

Reclaimed rubber prepared from discarded rubber products and rubber scrap, is used alone or in admixture with raw rubber in the manufacture of heels, soles, mechanical rubber goods, tyres and adhesives for use in fabric dipping, carpet backing, flooring, etc., and hard rubber used for battery containers, tubes and rods.

18

CHAPTER

Food Adulteration

There are three basic necessities of man, *i.e.*, (1) food, (2) shelter and (3) clothing. Considering the importance of food as one of the three basic needs, the food which we take in should be healthy and nutritious one. Further it should contain all the required components. But it was true only in ancient times when there was plenty of healthy nutrition. In those times even poor people could afford healthy and nutritious food. But now the situation has been changed, and there is a problem to get healthy and nutritious food. This seems to be due to exploding population. Due to increase in population, the supply of common foodstuff has fallen short. To keep pace with the increasing needs of food, the production has to be increased, but it is not always possible. So some traders resort to food adulteration without considering its hazardous effects. Although it is a crime but lack of public awareness has allowed it to continue. Due to scarcity of food the price index has also gone up. This has further made, well balanced food, out of reach of common people.

Survey of Food Adulteration in Uttar Pradesh. Survey for this problem has been made in U.P. during recent years. For the purpose, the samples of different foodstuff were taken from different parts of U.P. The samples were analysed at the Government Public Laboratory, Lucknow. The results found were rather disappointing and disgusting.

About 4,09,200 samples were taken for testing but amazingly 1,03,044 samples were found adulterated in some way or other. So, approximately 25% adulteration was there.

Now the Central Food and Technological Research Institute, Mysore (CFTRI, Mysore) is engaged in giving information about the food adulterations.

Danger Signal to Health. Thus we see that the food articles on an average have 25% adulteration which we consume daily in one form or other. These adulterations are responsible for many diseases. When these adulterated foodstuffs reach in our body, they affect the metabolism. The chemicals used for checking the skimming-curding of milk in summer, are responsible for many diseases of colon and deudenum.

Pigeonpea adulterated with *Lathyrus sativus* when taken causes **Lathyrism**, which is paralytic disease. Both human beings and livestock are susceptible to lathyrism and severe epidemics have been reported in the past from Bihar, M.P. and some eastern districts of U.P. Lathyrism is characterized by partial or complete paralysis of the lower limbs and degenerative changes in spinal cord. The onset of the disease is sudden. In the early stages the patient finds difficulty in walking, the gait becomes jerky and the legs may have to be crossed while walking. High and calf muscles become rigid and lower limbs are paralysed. The toxic principle has been identified as anicnopopionitrite ($C_8H_{13}O_3N_3$) which is present in concentration varying from 58 to 160 mg/100 gm and selenium which interferes with methionine metabolism.

1. *Cotton Seed Oil*—Cotton seed oil is detected when present in oil mixture with other oils by the *Halphen cotton test*. The test is carried out as follows:

  (*i*) 1—3 c.c. of the oil is dissolved in an equal volume of aryl alcohol.

  (*ii*) 1—3 c.c. of 1% solution of flowers of sulphur in carbon disulphide is added and the mixture is heated for 2 hours.

  (*iii*) Red colour indicates the presence of cotton seed oil.

2. *Milk*—Milk is usually adulterated with water or separated milk. In summer it is usually adulterated with calcium hydroxide, sodium carbonate and sodium bicarbonate chemicals to prevent it from skimming (without cream).

The specific gravity of the milk should be detected with the help of Lactometer for detecting any adulteration. Pure milk shows the specific gravity 1.030—1.034.

3. *Ghee*—Ghee obtained from animal sources (*i.e.,* Buffalo, Cow. etc.) is usually an adulterant with vegetable ghee or other cheap oils. The adulterated ghee is detected by the following test:

  (*i*) 1 spoon sugar is mixed with 10 c.c. HCl.

  (*ii*) (Sugar + HCl) mixture is added to 10 c.c. of melted sample ghee.

  (*iii*) Keep for 10 minutes — Red colouration develops over the surface.

4. *Brassica or Mustard Oil*—The oil is usually adulterated with the oil of seeds of *Argemone mexicana* or the chemical alayl isothiocynate which is cheaper than mustard oil. The adulteration can be detected by the following tests—

  (1) HCl + Ferric chloride + oil.

  (2) Brownish red precipitate develops. This shows the adulteration of oil of seeds of *Argemone mexicana.*

5. *Boora (Powdered Sugar Khandsari)*—This sugary white article is adulterated with sodium bicarbonate which is cheaper than *Boora.* To detect the adulteration the following test is performed:

  (1) 5 gm. Boora + 10 c.c. of water → Red litmus paper is applied.

6. *Coffee*—Coffee is adulterated with powder of roasted wheat, gram, sunflower seeds, etc. The purity of coffee is tested as follows:

Coffee sample is mixed with water and allowed to settle; pure coffee powder floats over the surface of water, while adulterants become submerged and settle at the bottom.

7. *Tea leaves*—Tea leaves are adulterated with leaves of other plant sources, finely powdered and treated with yellow, pink or red non-permitted colours which are cheap enough to be mixed in fresh tea leaves or in used dried tea leaves. The purity of tea leaves is tested as follows:

These adulterants can be detected by keeping the adulterated tea leaves on wet white paper sheet. The wet paper receives the colouration (pink, yellow or red) which shows that the tea sample is adulterated.

8. *Turmeric*—This spice is used in every household of India either poor or rich and thus is the source of bigger adulteration by many adulterants.

  (1) If adulterated with wheat or sorghum flour—dissolve 1 gm. of turmeric powder in 3 c.c. water and add 1 c.c. iodine solution — Blue colour is produced (starch).

  (2) If adulterated with colours

1 gm. turmeric powder + 3 c.c. water + 3 c.c. HCl → colouration develops. (If no colouration is produced then the turmeric is not adulterated with colours).

  (3) If adulterated with *geru:*

Burn spoonful of turmeric powder → Brown ash more than half in quantity than of the sample.

9. *Cut Areca Nuts and Powdered Chillies*—These two articles are usually adulterated with fine sieved saw dust. To observe adulteration the sample of powdered chillies or cut areca nuts are added to the water. The saw dust will float at the surface of the water while areca nut or chillies will settle down in the bottom. If they are mixed with colours also the water becomes coloured.

10. *Asafoetida (Hing)*—Asafoetida is mixed and adulterated with cheap resins and gums. This type of adulteration can be judged by the following process. A spoonful of *Hing* is dissolved in 1/2 glass of water, pure *Hing* changes the water into milky water.

11. *Cumin (Zeera)*—Cumin is adulterated by charcoal powder or some other seed powders which are easily available. *Zeera* powder is pressed keeping it on palm with the help of thumb—Tip of thumb turns black, due to the colour of adulterants.

12. *Black Pepper (Piper nigrum;* **Kali Mirch**)—This is adulterated with papaya (*Carica papaya*) seeds as such or powdered. Test—This sample is mixed with water; the pepper powder settles at the bottom while the papaya seeds float at the surface of the water.

13. *Crocus sativus (Kesar)*—*Kesar*, the stigmas of *Crocus sativus*, adulterated with the stamens and stigmas of other plants coloured with non-permitted colouring agents and coloured starch threads. The purity is tested as follows:

(*i*) Dissolve the *Kesar* into water, the pure *Kesar* dissolves rapidly in water while other substances are not dissolved easily.

(*ii*) A glass rod dipped in sulphuric acid placed over *Kesar* vapour — the glass rod first changes to blue, then to violet and then to brown — the *Kesar* is pure.

14. *Cardamom (Chotti Ilaichi)*—Cardamom fruits are often adulterated with orange seeds or unroasted coffee grains. The adulterants of seeds are small pebbles and seeds of *Amomum* spp., powdered seeds are adulterated with the powder of hulls.

15. *Pigeon Pea (Cajanus cajan—Arhar)*—*Arhar* is usually adulterated with *Khesari dal* (*Lathyrus sativus*) which is cheap and easy to cultivate. Consuming *Khesari* as the principal diet are known to be affected by a paralytic disease known as *lathyrism*. Prohibited colour methanil yellow is used to colour these pulses. If these coloured pulses are kept in water for some time, the water becomes coloured. Sometimes, lead chromate is used instead of methanil yellow.

16. *Fennel (Faeniculum vulgare;* **Saunf**)—*Saunf* is adulterated with exhausted or partially exhausted fruits, or with undeveloped or mold attacked fruits, or with the seeds of anise (*Pimpinella anisum*). Pure fennel passes easily through 54 mesh screen and has distinct features and flavours. Pure seeds contain 1.4% volatile oil and 1.5% acid insoluble ash.

17. *Licorice (Glycyrhiza glabra;* **Mulhati**)—Licorice which is used as expectorant, demulcent, laxative and for allaying coughs and in irritable conditions of mucous membrane has been found adulterated with rods of *Rati* (*Abrus precatorius*) and with *G. uralensis* by CFTRI, Mysore. Licorice is imported into India from Asia Minor, Iraq, Persia and other Central Asian countries. Pure licorice is soft, flexible and fibrous, internally of a light yellow colour with a characteristic sweet pleasant taste, while adulterants contain only a small percentage of sugar and gives a rather pungent taste.

18. *Surti and Pan Masala*—Adulterated with other leaves without *Nicotiana* leaves and prohibited colours, *i.e.,* lead chromate and methanil yellow.

19. *Khoya Sweets*—Adulterated with starch and prohibited colours. Test: Khoya + 1 c.c. Iodine solution → Blue colour (starch is adulterant).

20. *Honey*—Adulterated with sugar, saccharine and prohibited colours. The honey should be examined under the microscope for pollen and other natural crystals.

Oils adulterated with *Argemone mexicana* causes the disease epidemic dropsy which causes swelling of feet fingers and heart. Vegetable ghee industry uses nickel as a catalyst in hydrogenation process. When vegetable ghee is yellow in colour the nickel is in excess. The nickel in excess quantity causes respiratory diseases.

21. *Perfumes*—Perfume oils such as *Cananga odorata*, *Citronella* and *Palmarasa* have been found adulterated with coconut oil. It may be detected by the fact that oils, so adulterated will solidify wholly in freezing mixture. Coconut oil melts at 68–82°F; its sp. gr. at 212°F is 0.868 to 0.874 and its saponification value from 209 to 229.

22. *Tomato Ketchup*—In the manufacture of tomato ketchup the tomato solid is adulterated by carrot, gourd, pumpkin, sweet potato, papaya and apple pulp. The adulteration can be detected by

determining the lycopene content of the ketchup. Tomato ketchup contains 475 hg/gm or 7.8 mg/100 gm. of lycopene. Lycopene is the colouring matter of tomato when adulterated with other solids artificial colouring matter is added.

23. *Almond Oil*—The almond oil is adulterated with the fatty oils from peach, apricot and plum seeds which resemble it to a great extent. The adulteration is determined by examining the specific gravity of almond oil which is 1.049– 1.058 at 25°C; saponification value is 208.

24. *Orange Juice*—Pressed juice from carrot is adulterated in orange juice (carrot has sp. gr. 1.3; total acids as citric acid 1.3 and sucrose 17.8%) and the adulteration can be detected by analysis.

25. *Til Oil (Sesamum Oil)*—*Carthamus tinctorius* seed oil which is straw coloured. Nitrogen 3.19 sp. gr.; 0.9224 at 15°C is generally added to *Til oil* as adulterant.

26. *Animal Ghee (Clarified Butter)*—The chief articles used in the adulteration of ghee are vegetable oils such as — coconut, groundnut, cotton seed, sunflower, poppy and *sesamum oils*. These are harmless, several cheaper but injurious oils are also used as adulterants, especially *Salvadora* oil, castor oil, *Madhuca latifolia* oil and animal fats (especially mutton and meat are largely utilized). Starches such as that of rice, bajra, potato and corn are frequently resorted to in order to thicken oily compositions. Adulterated ghee is also often remade with milk or curd to render detection difficult. The simplest method of ascertaining adulteration is to boil a given quantity of ghee; and when it is in a state of complete ebullition add cold water on it. The oil will rise to the surface.

To face the challenge of food adulteration following measures should be taken:

(1) Consumers' councils should be organised at 1000 population level, taking the co-operation of active citizens and consumers.

(2) Organization of anti-adulteration board at district level with legal powers to deal with the adulterators.

(3) Consumers' council members should have the powers of drawing the sample for analysis.

(4) Effective enforcements of prevention of food adulteration. (Rules—Ministry of Health, Government of India 1959 by the administration).

(5) More heavy punishment should be awarded to the offenders (Even capital punishment should not be spared for serious offenders).

(6) Number of analysing laboratories should be increased to facilitate effective and early analysis of samples (at present in U.P. only one lab. exists).

(7) Number of persons concerning food and drug administration should be increased in proportion to the number of shops and population.

(8) At present administration charges Rs. 35/- per sample from citizen for analysing any sample. The charges should be moderate, so that poor section of the society may also be benefitted.

(9) Consumers should be taught about the common adulterants and the simple test to detect them. If these measures are taken effectively, we can meet the challenge of food adulteration.

19

CHAPTER

Forests and Action Plans

Forests are Nature's most bountiful and versatile renewable resources, providing simultaneously a wide range of economic, social, environmental and culture benefits and services. The world wide demands for their numerous functions and outputs increasing with the expanding population, while the global forest resource is shrinking either as a result of over harvesting, deforestation and permanent conversion of other forms of land use, in many tropical regions, or as a consequence of forest decline associated with air borne pollutants in temperate regions.

The forests of India occupy an area of about 75 million hectares, *i.e.*, 22 per cent of the land area with a great variety of species. During the British Period, these forests were treated as a source of revenue and to supply the demands of people for timber, fuelwood, and minor forest products such as cane, resins and lac. Nearly a 100 million poor people including tribals live in and around forests. The forests supply, almost free of cost their food requirements water, fodder for livestock, firewood, timber of agricultural implement and house construction as well as medicinal plants. In addition these people make their living by collecting and selling minor forest products. They have a symbiotic relationship with the forest since ages. Like indigenous people all over the world, the tribal communities that live in forests respect the trees, and the birds and animals that give them sustenance. Strategies are being developed for a greater degree of people's participation in forest management. The role of forest communities in restoring and conserving forests is now being increasingly recognized. The challenge is to integrate modern knowledge and skills in the area of forestry with the traditional knowledge and experience of the local communities, and to evolve more effective strategies for the joint management of forests.

Nature has endowed India with a large variety of plants, about 45,000 species in number, of which 15,000 are flowering plants, 1,676 algae, 1,940 lichens, 12,480 fungi, 64 gymnosperms, 2,843 bryophytes and 1,012 pteridophytes. About 5,000 species are endemic occurring only in India. Also 28 species are now extinct, 399 are endangered and 1500 species are threatened.

India can be divided into eight floristic regions, namely, (1) Western Himalayas, (2) Eastern Himalayas, (3) Assam, (4) Indus Plain, (5) Ganaga Plain, (6) Deccan, (7) Malabar and (8) Andamans.

The temperate zone of Western Himalayan region is rich in forests of chir pine (*Pinus roxburghii*), other conifers and broad leaved temperate trees. Higher up, forests of deodar (*Cedrus deodara*), blue pine (*Pinus wallichiana*), spruce (*Picea smithiana*) and silver fir occur. The alpine zone extends from the upper limit of the temperate zone to about 4,750 metres or even higher. The characteristic trees of this zone are the higher level silver fir, silver birch and junipers which are characteristic of this high altitude area.

The temperate zone of the Eastern Himalayan region has forests of Oak (*Quercus spp.*) laurel (*Calophyllum spp.*), maple (*Acer spp.*) rhododendron, alder (*Alnus spp.*) and birch (*Betula spp.*), many conifers, junipers and dwarf willows.

The Assam region comprises evergreen forests, occasional thick clumps of bamboo and tall grasses.

Some small areas of the Ganga Plain support forests of widely different types.

The Deccan region comprises the entire tableland of the Indian Peninsula and supports vegetations of various kinds from scrub jungles to mixed deciduous forests.

The Malabar region besides being rich in forest vegetation produces important commercial crops, such as coconut (*Cocos nucifera*), betelnut (*Areca catechu*), pepper (*Piper nigrum*), coffee (*Coffe arabica*) and tea (*Camellia sinensis*). Rubber (*Hevea brasiliensis*), cashewnut (*Anacardium occidentale*) and eucalyptus trees have also been successfully grown in some parts of this region.

The Andaman region abounds in evergreen, semi-evergreen, mangrove, beach and diluvial forests.

In India, forest resources are an important factor of socio–economic development, more specially of rural development, and it is the responsibility of our generation to safeguard these for future generations. The importance of the renewable goods and services provided by trees and forests, including the positive role they play in water and carbon cycles, soil protection, and the conservation of biodiversity, is well understood, yet forests face an onslaught due to the growing demand for construction materials, fuel, food, fodder, recreation areas and the like. Techniques are available for the sustainable management of trees and forests which can ensure the permanence, and even lead to increasing their ability to provide goods, and services, though these are too often ignored. Long term planning for the management of forest resources, however, can help avoid irreversible damage to the biosphere.

The real challenge is to reconcile the economic use of natural resources with the protection of the environment, through integrated and sustainable development. Any solution of forest problem requires common efforts to reduce poverty, to increase agricultural productivity, to guarantee food security and energy supplies, and to promote development.

Thus, sustainable development is an integrated approach to all round development, keeping mind its effect on the environment. What needs to be done is to increase the productivity of the "**producer systems**" and the efficiency of the "**user systems**".

GENETIC DIVERSITY OF ECONOMIC PLANTS

India is endowed with a rich genetic variety of cereals and pulses. The cereal basket includes rich (*Oryza sativa*), wheat (*Triticum aestivum*), barley (*Hordeum vulgare*), oat (*Avena sativa*), rye (*Secale cereale*) and maize (*Zea mays*); the millets include jower (*Sorghum vulgare*), bajra (*Pennisetum typhoides*), ragi (*Elucine coracana*), fox-tail millet (*Setaria italica*), etc., and also pseudocereals like amaranth (*Amaranthus spp.*), Buck wheat or Kutu (*Fagophyrum esculentuam*), *etc.* The pulses include various types of gram such as green gram (moong), black gram (urad) and gram (chana), and different types of pea (matar). It has also a wealth of oilseeds both edible and non-edible.

India's fruit basket is fabulously rich and diverse. It consists of a variety of mangoes (*Mangifera indica*), bananas (*Musa paradiciaca*) and various types of citrus fruits like mandarin (*Citrus reticulata*), sweet orange (*Citrus sinensis*) and lime (*Citrus aurantiefolia*). Other fruits are papaya (*Carica papaya*), guava (*Psidium guajava*), apple (*Malus sylvestris*), grapes (*Vitis vinijera*), pinapple (*Ananas comosus*), *etc.*

The oriental spices are well known. India produces a wealth of spices such as ginger (*Zingiber officinale*), cardamom (*Elettaria cardamomum*), black pepper (*Piper nigrum*), red pepper (*Capsicum frutescens*), clove (*Syzygium aromaticum*) and nutmeg (*Myristica fragrans*).

The plant wealth of India also includes a variety of aromatic and medicinal plants. Some of these are the sandal (*Santalum album*), lemon-grass (*Cymbopogon flexuosus*), palm-rose (*Cymbopogon martini*), eucalyptus (*Eucalyptus globulus*) and keora (*Pandanus tectorius*).

ACTION PLANS

The concern for environmental conservation has long been an integral part of Indian thought and social process and is also reflected in the Constitution of India. The Government has enunciated policy statements on forestry and on abatement of pollution and formulated a National Conservation Strategy. In addition, there are laws for the protection of environment, the Wild life Protection Act, 1972, the Forest Conservation Act, 1980, and the Environment Protection, Act 1986. Significant amendments have been made in the various acts from time to time to make them more effective.

The priorities before us are conservation and sustainable utilization of natural resources, afforestation, wastelands development, control and management of industrial and related pollution.

National Forestry Action Plan

This programme envisages a review of the forestry sector covering critical issues affecting forestry development in the country, a perspective action programme for the long, mid and short term development of forestry at national and state levels. The focus of the National Forestry Action Plan would be the increase in the sustainable management of forest and tree resources contributing to biodiversity and conservational and climatic needs.

National Afforestation and Eco-development Board (NAEB)

The programme of wasteland development through afforestation and tree planting in 1985 laid emphasis on people's participation, harnessing inputs of science and technology and achieving interdisciplinary coordination in programme planning and implementation.

The National Afforestation and Eco-development Board (NAEB), set up in the ministry of Environment and Forests, Government of India in August, 1992, is responsible for promoting afforestation, tree-planting, ecological restoration and eco-development activities in the country.

The National Wastelands Development Programme on a large scale was launched in the country in May, 1985, to deal with the ecological crisis caused by land degradation. The National Wastelands Development Board (NWDB) established in 1985 in the Ministry of Environment and Forests was the forerunner of NAEB.

The Integrated Afforestation and Eco-development Project Scheme (IAEPS) promotes an integrated approach for the development of mini-watershed by creating fuel wood and fodder plantation and treating the lands against soil and moisture losses.

The Area-Oriented Fuelwood and Fodder Projects Scheme (AOFFPS) aims at creation of plantation of fuelwood and fodder. The Minor Forest Produce including Medicinal Plant Scheme provides assistance to State Governments for increasing the production of non-timber forest produce including medicinal plants with a special focus on tribal population for whom non-timber forest produce is an important source of livelihood. There are also schemes for seed development, aerial seedling and wasteland mapping.

Wild Life Conservation

The threat to biological diversity due to over exploitation and habitat destruction is a major challenge. Realising the fact that many species of plants and animals have become endangered, several initiatives have been taken in India for their conservation. Hunting of animals is banned throughout the country.

National Parks and Sanctuaries

Today India has a wide network of 75 National Parks, 421 Wild Life Sanctuaries, 21 Project Tiger areas and eight Biosphere Reserves covering an area of 140,675.46 sq. kms., which is approximately 4.3% of the total land area. Years of protection and scientific management have pulled out many species from the brink of extinction. Not only have individual species been saved, but also their habitats and entire ecosystems have been restored to health.

Biosphere Reserves

Biosphere Reserves would afford conservation of large ecosystems representing a number of rare and endangered species of animals that exist in these habitats.

The setting up of Biosphere Reserves for conserving the biological diversity that exists in representative ecosystems is a concept evolved under the Man and Biosphere Programme by the UNESCO. The major objectives of the Biosphere Reserve are (*i*) To conserve diversity and genetic integrity of plants, animals and micro-organisms in their totality as part of the natural ecosystems, so as to ensure their self-perpetuation and unhindered revolution of the living resources.

(*ii*) To promote research on ecological conservation, both within and in areas adjacent to these reserves.

(*iii*) To provide facilities for international cooperation and people-environment interaction in various bioclimatic and biogeographical situations of the biosphere.

(*iv*) To provide opportunities for people's participation in achieving these objectives.

In India 14 representative ecosystems have been identified for setting up of Biosphere Reserves of which eight have already been set up at Nilgiris, Nanda Devi, Nokrek, Great Nikobar, Gulf of Mannar, Manas, the Sunderbans and Simlipal. Others that the proposed to be set up are the Kanha, Uttarakhand, Thar Desert, Kaziranga, the little Rann of Kutch, and North Andaman.

Botanical Survey of India

The Botanical Survey of India (BSI) was established in 1890 with the objective of surveying and identifying the plant resources of the country. The survey has its headquarters at Calcutta and nine circles located in different phytogeographical regions of the country.

The Botanical Survey of India has been serving the nation through inventorisation of the plant resources and advising on all matters related to plants. About 65% of the total area of the country has been surveyed and the herbaria of the BSI hold about three million plant specimens including about 15,000 type specimens. The research wing has flora, ecology, cryptogams, plant chemistry and pharmacognosy units.

The schemes of setting up of many Botanic Gardens and Field Centres have also been taken up during 1991-92 to augment the activities for conservation and propagation of plant genetic resources in different regions of the country through a network of these centres. Under this scheme, a one time non-recurring financial assistance is provided to botanic gardens in different phytogeographic regions of the country for strengthening their existing facilities for conservation and propagation of threatened and endangered endemic plant species of that region, and education and public awareness of endemic plant species.

The Indian Botanic Garden in Howrah is the largest Botanic Garden in the country and is used for study, introduction and conservation of flora, educational and secretarial purposes. It is a living repository of about 15,000 trees and shrubs distributed over 2,000 species. The greatest attraction of this Garden are the Great Banyan Tree, Giant Water Lilies and the large Palm House in addition to a number of interesting botanical specimens from different parts of the India and other countries.

Forest Survey of India

The Forest Survey of India with its headquarters at Dehradun and four zonal offices has been set up with the following objectives:-

(*i*) To assess the extent of forest cover and monitor on two–year cycle the broad changes in forest vegetation cover of the country by using multisatellite data.

(*ii*) To prepare thematic maps through the use of remote sensing data with maximum essential ground with verification on a 10–year cycle.

(*iii*) To collect, store and retrieve necessary forestry related data for national and state level planning and to create a computer based National Basic Forestry Inventory System.

(*iv*) To design methodologies relating to forest surveys and subsequent updating.

(*v*) To support and oversee techniques/inventory work undertaken by State/Union Territory Forest departments.

Indian Council for Forestry Research and Education (ICFRE)

The ICFRE in Dehradun, an autonomous body of the Ministry of Environment and Forests holds the mandate to organise, direct and manage research and education in the field of forestry. It is also responsible for framing the overall Forestry Research Policy of the country and ensuring the best method of application of all sources of scientific knowledge to the solution of problems facing the forestry sector.

Convention of Biological Diversity

India along with 170 other countries signed the Convention on Biological Diversity during the Earth Summit held at Rio de Janeiro, Brazil in June, 1992. The Convention has come into force with effect from December 29, 1993. India has ratified the Convention in February, 1994.

The Convention through its 42 articles establishes commitments on conservation, access to genetic resources, transfer of technology, biotechnology and biosafety, benefit sharing and finance, besides establishing sovereign rights of the state on their biological resources.

CHAPTER

Indian Raw Materials and Industrial Products

The economic botany deals with the direct relationship of plants with man. The use of processed, improved, or otherwise modified plant products and their commerce by man primarily is **economic botany**. The primary necessities of man are threefold—**food, clothing** and **shelter**. This food primarily comes from plants in the form of cereals, millets, pulses, vegetables and fruits. For clothing again plants are indispensable. The plants that yield fibres are second only to food plants. From the time immemorial, shelter from the wheather inclemencies and as a protection against natural enemy, has been felt too much. In this respect, the forest products have been of service to mankind from the very beginning of his history. The most familiar and most important of these products is wood, which is used in all types of construction work. With the advancement of civilization, the need of man also ever on the increase. To meet his requirements he has tried to tap plants as sources for his comforts and varied uses by exploiting his scientific knowledge and has been successful in this direction to a great extent. Other useful plant products include drugs, tannins, dyes, paper, sugar, starch gum, resin, rubber, vegetable fats, fatty oils, essential oils, tea, coffee, cocoa, tobacco, spices, condiments, cork, *etc*. It becomes quiet evident that a knowledge of botany and its proper application led to well-being of humanity in different ways.

A list of the genera of Indian raw-materials is undermentioned alphabetically.

Beverages

Anacardium (Cashewnut tree), *Ananas* (Pine apple), *Arenga* (Malacca sugar palm), *Borassus* (Sweet toddy and toddy), *Camellia* (Tea), *Caryota* (Sago palm), *Cichorium* (Chicory, endive), *Coffea* (Coffee), *Cola* (Kola), *Elaeis* (African oil palm), *Gaultheria* (Indian winter green), *Hemidesmus* (Indian sarsaparilla), *Hordeum* (barley), *Ilex* (Paraguay tea), *Musa* (Banana, plantain), *Oryza* (Rice), *Phoenix* (Date palm), *Theobroma* (Cocoa), *Vitis* (Grape), *Zingiber* (Ginger).

Dyes and Tans

Acacia (Babul, Cutch, Wattle), *Bixa* (Annatta), *Bruguiera*, *Butea* (Flame of the forest), *Caesalpinia* (Divi-divi), *Cassia* (Avaram), *Ceriops* (Cochineal), *Cotinus* (Indian sumach), *Crocos* (Saffron), *Curcuma* (Turmeric), *Datisca* (Akalbir), *Diospyros* (Persimmon), *Emblica* (Emblic Myrobalan), *Flemingia* (Warrus), *Galium* (Cheese Rennet), *Garcinia* (Gomboge), *Haematoxylon* (Logwood), *Hedyotis* (Chayroot), *Heritiera* (Sundri), *Indigofera* (Common Indigo), *Juglans* (walnut),

Kandelia, Lawsonia (Henna), *Lichens, Mallotus* (Kamala), *Myrica* (Box Myrtle), *Onosma, Oroxylum, Paeonia* (Peony), *Peltophorum* (Copper pod), *Pistacia* (Galls of pistachio),

Pterocarpus (Red sanders, Malay Padauk, Andaman Padauk, Indian or Malabar kino tree), *Quercus* (Oak), *Punica* (Pomegranate), *Rhizophora* (Mangrove), *Rhus, Rubia* (Madder), *Semecarpus* (Marking-nut tree), *Sonneratia, Tagetes* (Marigold), *Tamarix, Terminalia, Uncaria* (Gambir), *Wagatea, Xylia, Xylocarpa.*

Essential Oils

Alpinia (Galangal), *Amomum* (Greater Cardamom), *Anethum* (Dill), *Apium* (Celery), *Artemisia* (Oil of Taragon), *Bursera* (Linaloe), *Cananga* (Ylang-ylang), *Carum* (Caraway), *Cedrus* (Cedar wood), *Cinnamomum* (Cinnamon bark oil, camphor), *Citrus* (Lime, Lemon and Oranges), *Coriandrum* (Coriander), *Cuminum* (Cumin), *Cymbopogon* (Lemon grass), *Dianthus* (Carnation), *Elettaria* (Cardamom), *Eucalyptus, Foeniculum* (Fennel), *Gaultheria* (Indian Wintergreen), *Hibiscus* (Ambrette seed), *Illicium* (Star Anise), *Iris* (Orris), *Jasminum* (Jasmine), *Juniperus* (Juniper), *Lavandula* (Lavender), *Melaleuca* (Cajuput), *Mentha* (Mint), *Murraya* (Curry leaf), *Narcissus* (Jonquil), *Nyctanthes* (Night Jasmine), *Ocimum* (Basil), *Pandanus* (Screw pine), *Pavonia* (Hina), *Pelargonium* (Geranium), *Pogostemon* (Patchouli), *Polianthes* (Tuberose), *Rosa* (Rose), *Rosmarinus* (Rosemary), *Salvia* (Sage), *Santalum* (Sandal wood oil), *Saussurea* (Costus), *Tagetes* (Marigold), *Tanacetum* (Tansy), *Thalictrum, Thuja, Thymus* (Thyme), *Vanilla, Vetiveria, Viola Zanthoxylum.*

Fats and Oils

Aleurites (Tung, wood oil tree), *Arachis* (Groundnut), *Brassica* (Mustard, Rape), *Carthamus* (Saffflower), *Cocos* (Coconut), *Croton* (Oleum Crotonis, Oleum Tigli), *Cucumis* (Wild Muskmelon), *Cucurbita* (Pumpkin), *Diploknema* (Phulwara, Indian Butter Tree), *Elaeis* (African oil Palm), *Eruca* (Taramira), *Glycine* (Soyabean), *Gossypium* (Cotton seed), *Helianthus* (Sunflower), *Hydnocarpus* (Chaulmoogra), *Juglans* (Walnut), *Linum* (Linseed), *Madhuca* (Mahua), *Mesua* (Nagkesar), *Olea* (Olive), *Pongamia* (Pongam oil), *Prunus* (Almonds oil), *Ricinus* (Castor), *Salvadora, Sapindus* (Soapnut tree), *Schleichera* (Lac Tree), *Sesamum* (Sesame), *Shorea* (Sal Butter), *Telfairia* (Oysternut), *Theobroma* (Cocoa), *Xanthium, Ximenia.*

Fibres and Pulps

Agave (Sisal), *Aloe* (Indian Aloe), *Boehmeria* (Ramie), *Borassus* (Palmyra, Bassine), *Calotropis, Cannabis* (True Hemp), *Caryota* (Kittul), *Ceiba* (Kapok, white silkcotton), *Cocos* (Coir), *Corchorus* (Jute), *Corypha* (Fan palm), *Crotaloria* (Sunnhemp), *Eriophorum* (False Bhabar), *Erythrina* (Indian Coral Tree), *Furcraea* (Mauritius Hemp), *Girardinia* (Nettle), *Gossypium* (Cotton), *Helicteres* (Isora Fibre), *Hibiscus* (Kenaf, Mesta), *Linum* (Flax), *Lonicera* (Honeysuckle), *Luffa* (Ridged Gourd), *Musa* (Banana), *Pandanus, Pergularia, Phoenix* (Date-palm), *Phormium* (New Zealand Flax or Hemp), *Sabal* (Cabbage-Palm), *Salmalia* (Silk-cotton Tree), *Sansevieria, Tillandsia, Triumfetta, Typha, Urena, Urtica, Yucca.*

Food and Fodder

Avena (Oat), *Bothriochloa* (Sour Grass), *Brachiaria* (Crab Grass), *Cajanus* (Redgram), *Caryota* (Sago Palm), *Cicer* (Bengal-gram), *Cyamopsis* (Cluster Bean), *Cynodon* (Dub), *Dioscroea* (Yams), *Dolichos* (Horse bean, Indian butter bean, Field bean), *Echinochloa* (Barnyard Millet), *Eleusine* (Finger Millet), *Eragrostis* (Teff Grass), *Fagopyrum* (Buck wheat), *Fungi* (Edible Mushrooms), *Glycine* (Soyabean), *Hordeum* (Barley), *Hymenachne* (Dal Grass), *Ipomoea* (Sweet Potato), *Lens* (Lentil), *Manihot* (Tapioca), *Maranta* (West Indian Arrowroot), *Melilotus* (Sweet clover), *Mucuna* (Common Cowitch), *Musa* (Plantain), *Oryza* (Rice), *Pachyrrhizus* (Yan-bean), *Panicum* (Guinea grass, Proso or Hog Millet), *Pennisetum* (Pearl Millet, Napier , or Elephant grass), *Phoenix* (Date-palm), *Pueraria* (Kudzu), *Saccharum* (Sugarcane), *Secale* (Rye), *Sesbania* (Agathi, Sesban), *Setaria* (Italian or Fox-tail Millet), *Sorghum* (Jowar), *Theobroma* (Cocoa), *Trapa* (Water-chestnut), *Trifolium*

(Clover), *Triticum* (Wheat), *Vaccinium* (Blueberry), *Vicia, Vigna* (Cowpea, Black and Greengram), Yeast.

Fruits and Nuts

Achras (Sapota), *Aegle* (Bael Tree), *Anacardium* (Cashewnut), *Ananas* (Pineapple), *Annona* (Custard Apple), *Areca* (Betelnut), *Artocarpus* (Jack Fruit), *Averrhoa* (Carambola), *Borassus* (Palmyra), *Carica* (Papaya), *Carissa* (Karaunda), *Cicca Citrullus* (Watermelon), *Citrus* (Lime, Lemon and Orange), *Cocos* (Coconut), *Corylus* (Hazel nut), *Cucumis* (Melon), *Cydonia* (Quince), *Diospyros* (Persimmon), *Durio* (Durian Civet Fruit), *Emblica* (Indian Gooseberry), *Eriobotrya* (Loquat), *Ficus* (Fig), *Fragaria* (Strawbarry), *Garcinia* (Mangosteen), *Grewia* (Phalsa), *Hyphaene* (Egyptian Doum Palm), *Juglans* (Walnut), *Litchi* (Litchi), *Malus* (Apple), *Mangifera* (Mango), *Morus* (Mullberry), *Musa* (Banana), *Passiflora* (Passion Fruit), *Persea* (Avocado), *Phoenix* (Dates), *Physalis* (Cape Goseberry), *Pinus* (Chilgoza pine), *Pistacia* (Pistachio nut), *Prunus* (Almond, Apricot, Cherry, Plum), *Psidium* (Guava), *Punica* (Pomegranate), *Pyrus* (Pears), *Ribes* (Black Currant, Red Currant), *Rubus* (Raspberry, Blackberry), *Sorbus* (Rowan Tree), *Spondias* (Hogplum), *Telfairia* (Oysternut), *Vitis* (Grape), *Ziziphus* (Ber).

Gums, Latex and Resins

Acacia (Gum Arabic), *Algae* (Agar-agar), *Aquilaria* (Agar), *Astragalus* (Tragacanth), *Boswellia* (Indian olibanum), *Butea* (Bengal kino), *Conarium* (Black Dammar), *Cannabis* (Hemp Resin), *Ceratonia* (Carob), *Cochlospermum* (Kaitira Gum), *Commiphora* (Indian Bedellium), *Cyamposis* (Guar Gum), *Daemonorops* (Dragon's blood), *Dipterocarpus* (Gurjan Balsam), *Excoecaria* (Agallocha), *Ferula* (Asafoetida), *Garcinia* (Gamboge), *Guaiacum* (Guaiacum Resin), *Hevea* (Para Rubber), *Hopea* (Rock Dammar), *Kingiodendron* (Piney), *Liquidamber* (Storax), *Macarange* (Gum kino), *Melanorrhoea* (Burmese Lacquer), *Myroxylon* (Tolu), *Palaquium* (Gutta Percha), *Pterocarpus* (Indian or Malabar kino Tree), *Salmalia* (Semal Gum), *Schinus* (Mastic-Tree), *Semecarpus* (Markingnut Tree), *Shorea* (Dammar Gum), *Sterculia, Stereospermum, Styrax, Tamarindus* (Tamarind), *Taraxacum, Tieghemopanax, Trachylobium, Vateria* (Dammar).

Medicinal Plants

Aconitum (Aconites), *Acorus* (Sweet Flag), *Adhatoda, Aloe* (Indian Aloe), *Alstonia* (Ditabark), *Artemisia* (Absinthe, Wormseed, Santonica), *Atropa* (Belladonna), *Azadirachta* (Neem, Margosa), *Cannabis* (Hemp Drug), *Carica* (Papaya), *Cassia* (Senna), *Centella* (Indian Pennywort), *Cephalia* (Ipecacuanha), *Cinchona* (Quinine), *Cinnamomum* (Cinnamon, Camphor), *Citrullus* (Colocynith), *Claviceps* (Ergot), *Croton* (Purging-Nut, Croton Oil), *Datura* (Stramonium), *Derris* (Tuba), *Digitalis, Dryopteris* (Filix-Mas), *Emblica* (Indian Goose-berry, Emblic, Myrobalan), *Ephedra, Erythroxylum* (Cocaine), *Eucalyptus, Euphorbia, Fumaria* (Fumitory), *Fungi (Penicillium, etc.)*, *Gentiana* (Gentian), *Glycyrrhiza* (Liquorice), *Gymnema, Hemidesmus* (Indian Sarsaparilla), *Holarrhena* (Kurchi), *Hydnocarpus* (Chaulmoogra), *Hyoscyamus* (Henbane), *Ipomoea* (Kaladana), *Jateorhiza* (Calumba), *Matricaria* (Chamomile), *Mentha* (Mint), *Myristica* (Nutmeg), *Nardostachys* (Indian Nard), *Nerium* (Indian Oleander), *Nigella* (Black Cumin), *Onosma, Pimpinella* (Anise), *Plantago* (Isafgol), *Polygala* (Senega), *Psoralea* (Bebchi), *Quassia, Randia* (Emetic Nut), *Rauvolfia* (Sarpagandha), *Rheum* (Rhubarb), *Ruta* (Garden Rue, Common Rue), *Sambucus* (European or Black Elder), *Saraca* (Asoka), *Sassafras* (Ague Tree), *Saussurea* (Costus), *Scilla* (South Indian Squill), *Sida* (Country Mallow), *Smilax* (China Root), *Strophanthus, Strychnos* (Kuchla), *Svertica, Tanacetum* (Tansy), *Tephrosia, Thalictrum, Thevetia* (Yellow Oleander), *Thymus* (Thyme), *Trachyspermum* (Carum), *Tylophora* (Antamul), *Ulex, Urtica, Valeriana, Vinca* (Periwinkle, Sadabahar), *Withania* (Asgandh), *Xanthium*.

Spices and Flavourings

Allium (Garlic), *Anethum* (Dill), *Artemisia* (Davanamu), *Brassica* (Mustard), *Capsicum* (Chillies), *Carcum* (Caraway), *Cinnamomum* (Cinnamon), *Coriandrum* (Coriander), *Crocus* (Saffron), *Cuminum* (Cumin), *Curcuma* (Turmeric), *Elettaria* (Cardamom), *Ferula* (Asafoetida), *Foeniculum* (Fennel), *Glycyrrhiza* (Liquorice), *Hyssopus* (Hyssop), *Illicium* (Star Anise), *Iris* (Orris), *Laurus* (True Laurel), *Mentha* (Mint), *Murraya* (Curry leaf), *Myristica* (Nutmeg and Mace), *Pastinaca* (Parsnip), *Origanum* (Wild or Common Marjoram), *Ocimum* (Basil), *Piper* (Pepper), *Pimenta* (Allspice Tree), *Rosemarinus* (Rosemary), *Salvia* (Sage), *Syzygium* (Laung), *Tamarindus* (Tamarind), *Tetragonia* (New Zealand spinach), *Tanacetum* (Tansy), *Thymus* (Thyme), *Trachyspermum* (Carum), *Trigonella* (Fenugreek), *Vanilla*, *Zingiber* (Ginger).

Timber and Forest Products

Abies (Fir), *Albizzia* (Siris Tree, East Indian Walnut), *Anogeissus* (Axle Wood), *Bambusa* (Bamboos), *Betula* (Birch), *Boswellia* (Salai), *Buxus* (Boxwood), *Calamus* (Cane), *Calophyllum* (Poonspar, Alexandrian Laurel), *Canarium* (Black Dammar, Dhup), *Cedrela* (Toon), *Cedrus* (Deodar), *Chloroxylon* (Indian Satinwood), *Chukrasia* (Chickrassy), *Cupressus* (Cypress), *Dalbergia* (Sissoo, Indian Rosewood), *Dendrocalamus* (Male or Solid Bamboo), *Diospyros* (Ebony), *Dipterocarpus* (Gurjun), *Duabanga* (Lampati), *Dysoxylum* (White Cedar), *Eucalyptus* (Safeda), *Eulaliopsis* (Sabai Grass), *Gardenia, Gmelina* (Gumhar), *Grewia* (Dhaman), *Hardwickia* (Anjan), *Heritiera* (Sundri), *Holoptella* (Indian Elm), *Juglans* (Walnut), *Juniperus* (Juniper, Pencil Cedar), *Melia* (Bakain), *Mesua* (Mesua), *Millingtonia* (Indian Cork Tree), *Mimusops* (Bulletwood), *Morus* (Mulberry), *Oroxylum, Ougeinia* (Sandan), *Pinus* (Chir), *Populus* (Poplar), *Pseudotsuga* (Green Douglas Fir), *Quercus* (Oak), *Robinia* (False-Acacia, Black-Locust), *Salix* (Willow), *Salmalia* (Silk-cotton Tree), *Santalum* (Sandal Tree), *Schleichera* (Lac Tree), *Sequoia* (Red Wood), *Shorea* (Sal Tree), *Soymida* (Indian Red Wood), *Swietenia, Syzygium* (Jaman Wood), *Tectona* (Teak), *Terminalia* (Dhaman), *Tetrapanax, Tsuga, Xylia*.

Narcotics, Fumitories and Masticatories

Areca (Arecanut, Betelnut), *Cannabis* (Hemp Resin), *Cola* (Kola), *Datura* (Stramonium), *Erythroxylum* (Coca Leaves), *Gaultheria* (Indian Wintergreen), *Glycyrrhiza* (Liquorice), Hyoscyamus (Henbane), *Illicium, Myristica* (Nutmeg), *Nicotiana* (Tobacco), *Papaver* (Opium), *Piper* (Betel), *Pistacia* (Mastic Tree), *Rivea* (Ololiuqui, Snake Plant), *Vernonia*.

Vegetables

Allium (Onion, Leek, Garlic), *Amaranthus* (Chaulai), *Amorphophallus* (Corm), *Apium* (Celery), *Artocarpus* (Jack Tree or Bread Fruit), *Beta* (Beetroot), *Brassica* (Cabbage, Cauliflower, Knol-khol, Turnip), *Canavalia* (Jack or Sword Bean), *Cichorium* (Chicory, Endive), *Citrus* (Citrus Fruits), *Colocasia* (Taro), *Cucumis* (Cucumber), *Cucurbita* (Pumpkin, Squash), *Cyamopsis* (Cluster Bean), *Cynara* (Globe Artichoke), *Daucus* (Carrot), *Dioscorea* (Yams), *Dolichos* (Lablab Bean), *Entada* (Mackay Bean), *Feronia* (Elephant Apple or Wood Apple), *Fungi* (Edible Mushrooms), *Glycine* (Soyabean), *Hibiscus* (Lady's Finger), *Ipomoea* (Sweet potato), *Lactuca* (Lettuce), *Lagenaria* (Bottlegourd), *Lapidum* (Cress), *Luffa* (Ridged Gourd, Ghia, Tori), *Lycopersicon* (Tomato), *Momordica* (Bitter Gourd), *Moringa* (Drumstick), *Manihot* (Cassava, Tapioca), *Musa* (Plantain), *Mentha* (Mint), *Metroxylon* (Sago Palm), *Pachyrrizus* (Yam Bean), *Pastinaca* (Parsnip), *Petroselinum* (Parsely), *Phaseolus* (Beans), *Pisum* (Peas), *Portulaca* (Common Purslanes), *Psophocarpus* (Goa Bean), *Raphanus* (Radish), *Rumex* (Sorrel), *Sechium* (Chow-Chow, Chayote), *Sesbania* (Agathi), *Solanum* (Potato, Brinjal), *Spinacia* (Spinach), *Thlaspi* (Common Pennycross), *Tragopogon* (Salisfy), *Trianthema, Trichoxanthes* (Snake Gourd), *Trigonella* (Fenugreek), *Vaccinium, Vicia* (Bakhla), *Vigna*, (Pulses), *Vitex, Xanthosoma*.

INDUSTRIAL PRODUCTS FROM PLANTS

Major Industries

Coaltar, cotton mill, Dyestuffs, Jute Mill, Paints and Varnishes, Paper and Paper boards, Pharmaceuticals, Plywood and other wood panel products, Rayon, Rice-milling, Rubber industry, Soaps, Sugar, Synthetic fibres, Tea, Textile industry, Tobacco products, Vanaspati, Vegetable oils Industry.

Medium and Small Scale Industries

Alcohol, Bakery, Beer and breweries, Caffeine, Camphor, Carpentry, and cabinet work, Cigarettes, Cigars and cheroots, Cocoa and chocolate, Coffee, Confectionery, Cordages and ropes, Cotton-ginning and baling, Distilled liquors, Essential oils, Flax manufactures, Flour milling, Glucose, Glue and gelatine, Hosiery, Ink, Jute pressing and baling, Lac, Malt and malt products, Opium and opium alkaloids, perfumery, processed fruits and vegetables, quinine and quinine products, Railway Sleepers, Starches, Vinegar, Wine, Wood-carving, Wood seasoning and preservation, Yeast.

Cottage Industries

Agarbatties, Bidis, Carts, Coir, Handloom, Gur, Match, Pencils, Sago, Saw-milling, Wooden Toys.

PLANT BREEDING AND CROP IMPROVEMENT

The subject of plant-breeding has been scientifically developed to such an extent in recent years that it is now recognized as the best practical method for the improvement of the various crops—cereals, millets, pulses, vegetables, fruits, oilseeds, industrial plants, fodder crops and many other plants of economic value and of aesthetic value as regards their productiveness, quality, colour, size, yield and other useful characters. It has been found possible by the application of this method to combine the desired characters of parent forms and evolve new types of better than the original types in many respects. The subject of plant-breeding has been considered of great importance in agriculture and horticulture. By adopting practical methods of plant-breeding considerable improvements have been achieved in the last few decades; for example, rust resistant and high-yielding types of wheat plants have been evolved, and the milling and bread-making qualities of wheat grains considerably improved. Several new varieties of rice with higher yield and better quality have also been evolved. In tobacco the number of leaves per plant and their size and quality have been enhanced. Pea, bean, vegetable, pulses, oilseeds and condiments have been considerably improved. Fruits like mango, apple, grapes, pomegranate, pecan, pear, banana, plum, orange, litchi, strawberry, etc., have similarly been much improved. In fibre-yielding plants like cotton, jute, flax, hemp, etc., better quality of the fibre, i.e., length, strength and fitness, and also higher yield have already been achieved. In India a considerable amount of work has been done on rice, wheat, maize, millets, sugarcane, pulses, oilseeds, cotton, tobacco, jute, flax, hemp, fruits, vegetables, spices and condiments.

The main methods of crop improvement are as follows:

1. Selection.

2. Hybridization.

3. Plant introduction and acclimatization, and

4. Mutation breeding.

SELECTION

Selection is the choice of certain individuals of propagation from a mixed population where the individuals vary in character. It is the oldest breeding method and is the basis of all crop improvements. Even today it is the most common method of crop improvement among the cultivators. There are two main types of selection, (1) natural selection and (2) artificial selection.

Natural selection. This is a rule in the nature and results in evolution. Here, the fittest can survive and rest wipe out. All the local varieties of crops resulted because of such selection. It remains always operating in nature. It is one of the natural factors which creates variations in the already existing varieties of crops.

Artificial selection. 'Artificial selection is to choose certain individual plants for the purpose of having better crop from a mixed population where the individuals differ in characters'. There are three main types of artificial selection: (1) mass selection, (2) pure line selection, and (3) clonal selection.

Mass selection. 'The selection of a number of plants, heads of seeds phenotypically superior in desired traits from the field population harvesting and bulking their produce together for sowing the next year's crop; and repeating this process till desired improvement is achieved, is known as mass selection'.

The mass selection is followed generally in cross-pollinated crops for producing a new variety. It consists of selection and collection of the similarly appearing best and most vigorous plants from the mixed population of a crop. The selected plants are thrashed together and a mixture of seeds is obtained. The mixture so obtained is sown for raising the new crop from which the selection is made similarly in the next year. This practice of selection is continued till the plants show uniformity in the desired characters and they constitute a new variety. In already uniform population, the mass selection cannot be practised. It means that the mass of selection is based upon the presence of variability in the population. Greater the variability better are the results of selection. The plants are selected on the basis of phenotypical characters. It is the simplest, easiest and quickest method of crop improvement. It is only the method for improving the local varieties to meet the immediate needs of farmers. Mass selection is the most common method of crop improvement among farmers. All the cultivated crops and their local strains are the results of mass selection operating in the nature automatically.

Pure-line selection. 'The process of isolating a desirable homozygous individual from the mixed population and multiplying the same without contamination to release as a new variety is known as pure-line selection'. It consists of the progeny of single self-fertilized homozygous plant and is used for developing variety. It is used in the mixed population of self-pollinated crops and consists of testing the progeny of single individual plants separately. The usual method is to select a large number of single plants, keep them separate, compare their progeny in field trials, and to save the single most valuable progeny as a new variety. In this method the fewer plants are selected and each selected plant is tested separately. The variety developed is genetically more and more durable.

Clonal selection. This type of selection is practised in vegetatively propagated crops such as potato, sugarcane, banana, sweet-potato, citrus, mango, etc. 'All the progenies of a single plant obtained vegetatively are known as a clone' and the method of developing varieties from the clones is known as clonal selection. Clonal selection is the method of selection of desirable clones from the mixed population of vegetatively propagated crops. The superior clones are selected on the basis of their phenotypic characters. The selection is always between the clones and not within the clone. The selected clones are multiplied vegetatively and compared with normal variety.

HYBRIDIZATION

'Hybridization is the method of producing new crop varieties in which two or more plants of unlike genetical constitution are crossed together'.

Kinds of hybridization. The plants which are crossed together may belong to the same species, different species or different genera. According to this relationship between parental plants, the hybridization may be—(1) intravarietal, (2) intervarietal, (3) interspecific and (4) intergeneric.

1. **Intravarietal hybridization.** The crosses are made between the plants of same variety. Such crosses are useful only in self-pollinated crops. In cross-pollinated crops,

where the varieties are genetically heterogeneous. The controlled crossing within the varieties is only useful to maintain and improve the individual varieties.

*2. **Intervarietal hybridization.** In such crosses desired characters can easily be combined. The crosses are made between the plants of two different varieties of the same species and is also known as intraspecific hybridization. This makes the basis of improving self-pollinated crops as well as certain cross pollinated crops. In wheat, tobacco, cotton, tomato, etc., intervarietal crosses have been done to achieve good yield, resistance to diseases, resistance to drought, good quality, nutritive value etc. Most of the hybrid varieties of cereals, have been evolved by this type of hybridization. Hybrid maize is an outstanding practical achievement in plant breeding of this type of hybridization.*

*3. **Interspecific hybridization.** The plants of two different species belonging to the same genus are crossed together. This type of hybridization is between the species and within the same genus and is sometimes known as intrageneric hybridization. All the disease, pest and drought resistant varieties in wheat, tomato, sugarcane, etc., have been evolved by this method.*

*4. **Intergeneric hybridization.** The crosses are made between the plants belonging to two different genera. Raphanobrassica, Rabbage, Triticale, sugarcane-sorghum, etc., are some examples of this type of crossing. Such crosses are generally used for transferring the characters like disease, pest and drought resistance from wild genera into the cultivated plants. Such crosses are difficult to achieve and are of scientific interest.*

Hybridization Procedure. *The steps of the procedure of hybridization are as follows:*

Selection of parents. *The first step is to select the plants which are to be used as parents with all the desired important characters which are not found in good standard variety. The plants must be selected in such a manner, so that the chances of selecting desirable genotypes become more. In the selected variety also the weak and undesirable plants must be rejected, and the healthy and vigorous ones are kept as parents. All the important characters to be combined must be kept in mind and the plants chosen as parents tested repeatedly for these characters.*

Selfing of parents. *The second step consists of artificial self-pollination of parents, which is also known as artificial self-pollination and is essentially needed for eliminating undesirable characters and obtaining inbreds. The selfing of parents is done to obtain homozygosity in desired characters so that they may easily be combined together.*

Emasculation. *This is the third step in hybridization. It is defined as 'the removal of stamens from female parent before they burst and have shed their pollens'. The purpose of emasculation is only to prevent self-pollinating, and therefore, it is adopted only in those crops where there is self-pollination, may be complete or up to some extent and never in unisexual crops.*

Bagging, tagging and labelling. *The fourth step is the bagging, tagging and labelling of males as well as females. The females are bagged to prevent natural cross-pollination and males to prevent the contamination of pollens with foreign pollens and to collect the pollens for crossing. The bagging is usually done in the evening of previous day crossing. After the emasculation the flowers are enclosed in a muslin, paper, plastic, glass, celophane, polyethylene or parchment bags so that foreign pollen may not come in contact with stigma. A tag (tagging) recording the name of the female and male* *parent, date and the name of emasculator (labelling) is tied to the flower. The bags are kept on the females as such till seed setting is complete while in males they are removed as soon as the crossing is over.*

Crossing. *The fifth step is the crossing. It can be defined as 'the artificial cross-pollination between the genetically unlike plants'. In this step the pollens from already bagged males are collected and dusted on bagged females. The crossed flowers are properly tagged and labelled. The labelling is done either on the bag itself or on the labels specially designed for this purpose.*

Harvesting hybrid seeds and raising F_1 generation. *The sixth step is the collection of seeds from the crossed plants after maturity. Such seeds are maintained separately and sown in the next season to raise F_1 generation. The plants so obtained are known as hybrids and may be defined as the 'progenies of cross'. All the plants of F_1, although heterozygous, have similar genetical constitution and look exactly alike. They may or may not show hybrid vigour.*

Hybridization methods. *The seventh step consists of handling of F_1 and subsequent generations by different selection methods of hybridization which are different for self- and cross-pollinated crops. The methods are as follows:*

Hybridization methods in self-pollinated crops. *The well known self-pollinated crops are—wheat, oat, barley, rice, cotton, potato, peas and beans, etc., Every selection method has its application, under some specific circumstances for definite advantages. They are as follows:*

(i) Pedigree method. Here the individual plants are selected from the F_1 population. The plants are selected on the basis of desired characters. The number of plants to be selected depends upon the number of important characters involved, the importance of breeding problem and the facilities available. These plants are harvested and threshed separately, and sown in the separate rows in the next year to raise the F_2 generation. This process is continued up to F_3, F_4 or F_5 generations. At F_6 due to successive self-pollination, most of the lines become homozygous and fairly uniform. The plants uniform in desired characters are harvested and bulked together to constitute a variety. The whole process takes about 10 to 13 years.

This method is well suited to those crops where the characters to be combined in crosses can be easily seen and recognized. The pedigree method is the quickest one and a new variety can be selected and well tested by the time it reaches its ninth generation after cross.

(ii) Bulk method. Here the F_3 plants are not maintained separately but are bulked together to form a single F_3 population. In F_3 again the suitable plants are selected, collected and bulked together. This is done for six generations. In F_6 the desired individuals are selected and harvested separately. The produce of each plant is kept separate. The best performers are released as new varieties. It is a simple, convenient and inexpensive method. It takes much time but minimizes the labour as the plants are not paid any individual attention.

(iii) Back-cross method. In the back-cross method the desirable variety, called as recurrent or recipient parent, is crossed to an undesirable variety, called as donor parent, possessing a character which lacks in the good parents. F_1 plants, instead of permitting to self-pollinate as in pedigree or bulk method, are crossed with the recurrent

parent and, therefore, it is known as back-cross' method. The purpose of backcrossing is to recover the genotype of recurrent parent with disease resistance. The progenies of first backcross designated as BC_1 and containing the good character from donor parent are again backcrossed to the recurrent parent. This process of selection of plants with desired characters and then backcrossing is continued for several generations usually up to BC_5 or BC_6. In each backcross generation, the plants possessing desirable characters of non-recurrent parent are primarily selected. At the end of BC_6, the selected plants are self-pollinated to make the population homozygous in combined characters. The greatest advantage has been in the production of disease-resistant varieties.

(iv) Multiple or composite cross method. It consists in crossing of several pure lines together. The selected pure-lines are first combined into crosses as $A \times B$, $C \times D$, $E \times F$, $G \times H$ and so on. F_1 of these single crosses are then combined into double crosses as $(A \times B) \times (C \times D)$ and $(E \times F) \times (G \times H)$. Finally the F_1s of double crosses are crossed with each other to produce the hybrids $[(A \times B) \times (C \times D)] \times [(E \times F) \times (G \times H)]$. This cross is known as multiple cross and further breeding in these hybrids is carried out according to either pedigree or bulk method. Multiple cross in self-pollinated crop is used when three or four monogenic characters scattered in three or four different varieties are to be combined into one as the resistance to all three rusts of wheat into N.P. 809 variety from different strains.

Hybridization Methods in Cross-pollinated crops. *The inbreds are combined in any of the following crosses and released as improved strains.*

(i) Single cross method. $(A \times B)$, this is the cross between two inbreds such as $A \times B$ or $C \times D$. Its hybrid seed, which is the first generation product, is used for raising the crop.

(ii) Three-way cross method. $(A \times B) \times C$, this is a cross between a single cross used as female and an inbred used as male, i.e., it involves three inbreds. The advantage of a three-way cross is the use of vigorous hybrid of first generation as female in order to maximize the yield of hybrid seed as well as to obtain seeds of normal kernel size.

(iii) Double cross method. $(A \times B) \times (C \times D)$. This is the cross between two single crosses involving four different inbreds. An inbred involved in one single cross must not be included in the another single cross of the double cross parents. A double cross is produced by alternate planting of two single cross plants in an isolated plot. Double crosses are the most widely used commercial hybrids. All the hybrid seeds of maize distributed to farmers for cultivation are double crosses. They give very high yields in small land without any increase in the cost of production.

INTRODUCTION AND ACCLIMATIZATION

'Plant introduction and acclimatization' is the easiest and most rapid method of crop improvement where the acclimatization follows the introduction and both the processes go side by side. "The process of introducing new plants into a locality or introducing the plants from their growing place to a new locality with different climate is known as plant introduction and their adjustment under this changed climate is termed as acclimatization. Both, new crops and new varieties of crops, may be introduced either in the form of seeds or cuttings. In vegetatively propagated crops the cuttings are imported and in sexually propagated crops the seeds are imported. In

the latter case, the cross-pollinated crops are generally introduced since in them there is greater frequency of gene recombinations owing to the frequent cross pollinations and some of the recombinations may be more favourably adapted in the new environment. The crops may be introduced into a locality either from outside the country or from different regions within the country. Introductions within the country are very convenient but for introductions from another country there is a definite procedure. The material desired is demanded from the concerned authority or agency of the foreign country through the plant introduction organization of the country. The material is packed properly and sent by sea. Before entering the country, it is inspected at sea port by the plant protection authorities and, if found fit according to quarantine rules, is permitted to enter the country. In the country, it is handed over to the concerned workers or institutions. There it is grown under local conditions and tested for the acclimatization and the presence of desired characters. If found suitable for both, it is either utilized as such after selection or utilized in hybridization for transferring the desired characters into the local varieties.

This method of crop improvement has been proved of great importance, especially in recent years, as a source of resistance material to some crop diseases.

MUTATION BREEDING

'Mutations are the sudden heritable variations in the plants other than those due to Mendelian segregation or recombination'. These changes are due to rearrangement of genes (gene mutation or point mutation), changes in chromosome size and structure (chromosomal mutation), changes in the chromosome number (polyploidy) and changes in the body of the plant (somatic mutation). They cover up all types of hereditary changes or changes in genotypes of plants and give rise to inexhaustible variations which make the basis of selection and production of new crop varieties in the plant breeding. Mutations may occur spontaneously in nature or may be produced artificially in crop plants with the help of mutagens such as atomic radiations of various types, sudden heat shocks and chemicals. They are X-rays, ultraviolet rays, neutrons and radiations from radioactive isotopes, extreme temperatures and colchicine and other chemicals. With their help the plant breeder can change the genotype and phenotype of the plants according to the needs for production of new superior varieties is known as mutation breeding. This is the latest method of crop improvement and has been responsible for increased rust resistance and baking quality in wheat, higher yield and powdery mildew resistance in barley, superior fibre content and increased yield in cotton, and increased yield of seed and oil in white mustard. In vegetatively propagated plants, selection from somatic mutations has directed to improvement, as in chrysanthemums and dahlias, crop plants like sugarcane, potato and fruit crops.

CHAPTER 21

Plant Breeding Techniques

Process of Emasculation

There is a definite procedure of hybridization in which various steps are involved. **The first step is the selection of parents** from the available material possessing desired characters. **The second step is the selfing of parents** to obtain homozygosity in desired characters so that they may easily be combined together. **The third step is the emasculation** for female parents. A few other steps are also there.

In emasculation the anthers are removed, or killed before they mature and have shed their pollen. The purpose of emasculation is only to prevent self-pollination, and it is adopted only in those crops where there is self-pollination, may be complete or upto some extent, and never in unisexual crops.

Definition. The emasculation is defined as 'the removal of stamens from female parent before they burst and have shed their pollens'.

Purpose. The purpose of emasculation is to prevent self-fertilization, and, therefore it is usually performed a few hours before the anthers ripe, dehisce and self-pollinate their stigmas.

The floral buds or panicles which are expected to open on the following day are selected for the purpose of emasculation and such flowers can be easily recognized by their enlarged unopened corolla still greenish in colour and about half grown in size.

The emasculation is not need in unisexual plants, it is always necessary in bisexual plants of self – as well as cross pollinated crops.

A few methods of this simple operation carried out in different crops have been described here in detail.

1. Forcep or scissor method. It consists in opening of flower and removal of the stamens by using a pair of forceps or scissor. The technique is quite simple and varies from crop to crop. This technique of emasculation is generally used with those plants which bear large flowers such as wheat, barley, cotton, etc.

2. Hot or cold water and alcohol emasculation. In the plants having small sized flowers such as rice, sorghum and pearl millet, the removal of stamens by forcep or scissors is quite tedious. In these the emasculation is being done by dipping the panicles in hot water having a particular temperature for a definite period. In actual practice a thermal jug is filled with water having the desired temperature (45° to 53°C) and taken into the field. The flowers or panicles to be emasculated are immersed in the jug for a definite time (1 to 10 minutes) varying from species to species. In the similar way the cold water or alcohol emasculation is carried out.

3. Male-sterility method. In certain self-pollinated crops such as barley, sorghum, onion and pearl millet, the emasculation operation may be eliminated by the use of male-sterile plants which have sterile anthers and do not produce any viable pollens. The sterility may be due to cytoplasmic and genetic causes. The male-sterility conditioned by the recessive genes is first introduced into the plants to be used as females by backcrossing and the emasculation in theru is then not needed at all.

Male-sterility may also be induced by spraying some chemicals such as 2, 4-D, naphthlene acetic acid (NAA), maleic-hydrazide (MA) and tri-iodobenzoic acid.

Seed Viability Estimation

1. Germination experiment method. In this method the four groups of seeds, each of 100 seeds, are taken from four analytic samples of the same source. Seeds of each group are germinated separately and the germinating seeds are counted. Thus, the germination percentage is calculated for each group and then the average of all the four is taken. This is the germination percentage of the source from which the original sample was taken. It there is more than 10 per cent difference of germination in any two groups, the fresh samples are taken and the experiment is repeated.

The seeds are grown in proper medium under optimum conditions. Seeds of cereals germinate equally good both in sand and filter papers, and those of pulses (legumes) better in sand. In certain cases, soil is also used as germination medium. Filter papers are always put in petridishes and the sand and soil are put in wooden boxes or plates. For germination, optimum conditions of temperature and humidity are provided throughout the testing. Most of the seeds germinate at temperatures between 18° to 22°C and the relation humidity (R.H.) between 70 to 90 per cent. Most seeds germinate easily in diffused light or in the dark. Fresh air is also required to remove CO_2 and to supply O_2 for respiration.

The humidity is maintained by supplying water to the medium from time to time. The temperature is maintained by keeping the petridishes or germination boxes in cold places of freeze or in hot places or oven as convenient. Darkness and light may be provided by keeping the germination boxes or petridishes into darkrooms and sunlight respectively. Provision for fresh air and supply of oxygen is made either by keeping the experiment in open air or by keeping the holes on sides of wooden boxes which may serve the purpose of ventilation without creating drought around the seeds.

The duration of germination test varies from 7 to 28 days depending upon the species under test. Seven days are for those species which germinate very quickly and evenly, and twenty eight days are for those which germinate very slowly. The germinated seeds are counted after definite number of days as the first count is made after 3 or 4 days in case of cereals and legumes, while in grasses after seven days. Each subsequent counting is made after a fixed interval throughout the test.

The seeds are supposed to be germinated when they have produced a healthy root with root hairs and plumule. At each count, the number of germinated seeds is noted and then they are removed. At the end of the experiment, total number of germinated seeds are obtained. Then the figures of all the four groups are added up together and average percentage is calculated. This gives the germination percentage of the seeds.

For example, four groups of wheat seeds, i.e., A, B, C and D, each having 100 seeds gave the following number of germinated seeds (table 21.1).

Table : 21.1. Number of germinated seeds obtained in four groups of wheat seeds separately at each count

Count No.	Group A 100 seeds	Group B 100 seeds	Group C 100 seeds	Group D 100 seeds
1.	10	12	11	13
2.	20	25	19	23
3.	25	25	30	25
4.	20	15	14	15
5.	10	6	10	8
6.	3	4	9	5
7.	2	5	1	3
Total :	90	92	94	92

In this experiment the difference between any two groups of seeds is not more than 4, and, therefore, there is no need to repeat the experiment.

$$\text{Germination percentage} = \frac{(90+92+94+92)\,100}{400}$$

$$= 92$$

This method of germination experiment gives the accurate results of the germination percentage but the experiment takes long time.

2. Biochemical method : Tetrazolium method. In this method a chemical called 2, 3, 5-triphenyl tetrazolium chloride discovered Ray Lakon in Germany is used to judge the viability of seeds.

Concept. The concept behind this method is that the viable seeds are supposed to germinate, and if their number could be counted, the germination percentage could be calculated without conducting the germination experiments.

Method. Hundred seeds are taken at random from an analytic sample and soaked in tap-water overnight. The seeds are then bisected longitudinally. One half of each seed is retained and the remaining hundred halves, each containing some portion of embryo, are placed in petridish and just covered with one per cent aqueous solution of tetrazolium chloride which is almost colourless. They are left as such in petridishes at 20°C for four hours. The seeds are then washed in tap-water and examined.

Observation and inference. Some halved seeds will be found red stained and some will not. This is due to the reduction of tetrazolium chloride by living cells which in its reduced state becomes red in colour. Thus the viable bisected seeds can be distinguished from the nonviable on the basis of distribution of red colour. The viable seeds are counted which directly give the germination percentage of seed sample.

This test gives an accurate idea of germination percentage and could be completed within 24 to 48 hours.

Precautions. In this experiment, close scrutiny of each seed is required which is a difficult task in small seeds, and, therefore, this method is not applicable in cases where seeds are quite minute in size.

Determination of Moisture Content of Seeds

The moisture content is also an important consideration in testing the seeds. The knowledge of moisture content helps the formers and the merchants in storing the seeds for some time before sowing and selling.

A high moisture content may result in rapid deterioration of seed. For example, the wheat seeds with a moisture content of 15 per cent can be stored safely but if the moisture content is more than 17 per cent the seeds will deteriorate rapidly, and if it is 20 per cent or above the seed may become completely useless for sowing.

There are three methods commonly used for the determination of the moisture content of the seeds.

1. *Oven method*; 2. *electrical method* and 3. *oil distillation* method. Among all the three, the oven method is commonly used for routine investigations. The oven method has been described here in detail.

Oven method. Usually three portions, each weighing 5 g. are taken from an analytic sample and weighed out. They are dried at 130°C for 90 minutes in an oven. Again they are weighed after drying and the difference in weight before and after heating will be the amount of moisture contained in seed. The moisture percentage is calculated from this difference on the basis of weight as follows :

$$(M_2 - M_3) \frac{100}{M_2 - M_1}$$

M_1 = weight of petridish with cover

M_2 = weight of dish with cover and seed before drying

M_3 = weight of dish with cover and seed after drying

All weights are taken in grams to an accuracy of 1 mg.

The results of triplicate determinations must not differ by more than 0.2 per cent. If the difference is greater than this, the test must be repeated in duplicate or triplicate.

Precautions. A temperature of 130°C is excessive for tree seeds, and some other seeds such as *Allium* spp., *Capsicum* spp., *Raphanus* spp., etc., which contain volatile oils. In such seeds the temperature is kept at 105°C for 16 hours instead of 130°C for 90 minutes. Both systems are alike except difference in temperature and drying period.

CHAPTER 22

Plant Breeding Exercises

EXERCISE 1

Object : To study the fertility in the pollen grains of the given flower.

Requirements : Acetocarmine, glycerine, sugar, agar, distilled water, heater, gelatin powder, slides, germination chamber.

Method : Several methods are applied to study the fertility of pollen grains, of which two simple methods are mentioned below :

(*a*) *Staining the Pollen Grains* : Take some pollen grains on a clean slide and stain them in a mixture of 1 per cent acetocarmine and glycerine in a ratio of 1 : 1. Wait for about 30 minutes. Only the fertile pollen grains will take stain.

(*b*) *Pollen Germination* : Prepare the Newcomber's medium by mixing and boiling 1 gm sugar, 0.5 gm agar and 25 ml distilled water. Cool the medium up to 35°C and add 0.5 gm gelatin powder. Keep on stirring the medium for some time until the gelatin is completely melted. Keep the solution at 25°C, and smear a thin film of this solution on a clean slide with the help of a needle or finger. Sprinkle some pollen grains on this slide, and keep this slide in a germination chamber. Only the fertile pollen grains will start germination after some time.

EXERCISE 2

Object : To show the artificial induction of polyploidy.

Requirements : Colchicine (0.02 to 0.1% aqueous solution), seeds, glycerin or lanolin.

Method : (Organisms containing the cells with one set of chromosomes in their nuclei are called *haploid*; with two sets of homologous chromosomes in their nuclei are called *diploid*; and with three or more sets of homologous chromosomes in their nuclei are called *polyploids*, and this phenomenon is called *polyploidy* which is of great importance in horticultural and agricultural practices). Polyploidy can be induced artificially also in the plants. Some of the commonly used chemical compounds which are used to induce polyploidy are colchicine, chloral hydrate, actidione, acenaphthene, *etc.* Of these, colchicine is the most commonly used compound.

For artificial induction of polyploidy, colchicine can be used in several ways :

(*i*) Seeds of the desired plants are immersed in desired concentration of colchicine for 2 to 24 hours and then sown. The newly born plants will show polyploidy.

(*ii*) A colchicine paste is prepared by mixing colchicine in glycerin or lanolin. Cotton is soaked in this colchicine paste and young seedlings, specially their growing shoot tips, are treated with this paste. This paste is washed with water after some time. The new tissues, developed after the treatment, will be polyploid in nature.

ARTIFICIAL HYBRIDIZATION TECHNIQUE

EXERCISE 3

Object : To work out the various steps of the process of artificial hybridization.

Requirements : Needles, forceps, scalpel, butter-paper bags, scissor, pocket lens, tag and labels, U-pin, pencil, brush, rectified spirit or ethanol, note-book, *etc.*

Method : The artificial hybridization technique usually involves following steps :

(*i*) Study of floral morphology, (*ii*) Emasculation, (*iii*) Bagging of selected flower, (*iv*) Pollination of emasculated flower, (*v*) Labelling, (*vi*) Harvesting and observation.

Some basic details of these steps are described below :

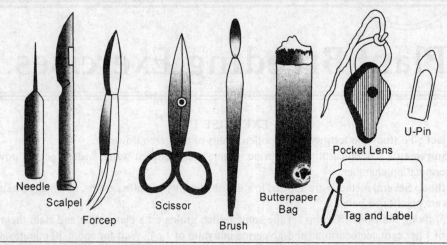

Fig. 22.1. Some instruments used in emasculation technique.

1. Study of Floral Morphology : Before performing the breeding experiment on any plant, the plant breeder should know all the details of the floral morphology of that plant. One should know the presence or absence of sepals or petals or perianth, number of stamens, type and nature of stigma, type of gynoecium, *etc.*

2. Emasculation : Removal of stamens from a bisexual flower is called *emasculation*. Emasculated flower will wither if the removal of stamens is not done with proper care. Before starting the emasculation process, all the instruments (needles, forceps, scalpel, scissor, *etc.*; (Fig. 22.1) as well as fingers should be sterilized with absolute alcohol or rectified spirit. Care should also be taken that only those floral buds or flowers are emasculated in which anthesis has not taken place, *i.e.* there has not been any dehiscence of anthers. Least injury should be done to the flower during the emasculation process.

At the time of emasculation process (Fig. 22.2), unwanted flowers are removed from the twig of the plant, to be emasculated. Calyx and corolla are carefully removed. The stamens of the flower are also removed, leaving only the gynoecium in the bisexual flower. The emasculation process completes when all the stamens are carefully removed. Emasculated flower is enclosed inside a bag under the next process, *i.e.*, *bagging*.

3. Bagging and Protection of Emasculated Flower : Emasculated flower is covered with specially designed oil paper bag or butter paper bag. These bags protect the emasculated flowers from unwanted outside agencies such as insects, pollen grains, dew, dust, rain *etc.* A thread is used to tie the bag to the stem of the plant. If some support is required, a bamboo stick may be used to provide support to the bag. A small hole may be made in the lower part of the bag. CO_2, released during respiration, comes out through this hole and does not harm the emasculated flower.

4. Pollination of Emasculated Flower : As the stamens from the bisexual flower have been removed during emasculation, more food is now available for the gynoecium. Due to this, the gynoecium develops more vigorously and becomes ready for fertilization within one or two days. The desired pollen grains are now brought in contact with the gynoecium by the plant breeder, and this process of shedding pollen grains from the anther up to the stigma of the gynoecium of the emasculated flower is called *pollination.* Thus pollinated emasculated flower is again covered inside the butter paper bag. For the complete success of the process, the pollination process is again repeated after 12 or 24 hours.

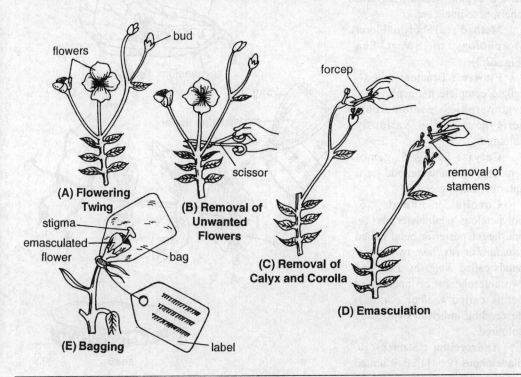

Fig. 22.2. Technique of emasculation and bagging.

If the fertilization has occurred and the entire breeding process has been carried out successfully, the fruits starts developing in each flower within 2 or 3 days.

5. Labelling : A label of hard paper is properly tagged with the help of thread with such flowers in which hybridization technique has been successfully introduced. Some important informations to be mentioned on the tagged label for future reference are : (1) specific reference number, (2) date of emasculation, (3) date and time of pollination, (4) name and family of the plant, (5) date of harvesting, *etc.*

6. Harvesting : The fruits, when mature, are collected along with their labels. The seeds from these fruits are sown in the next season to develop F_1 generation. These F_1 generation plants are called hybrids because they are the progenies of crossed plants. In case these F_1 hybrids do not contain the desired characters, they are crossed again with the desired parent to get F_2 hybrids. When the desired characters have been fully incorporated in the hybrids, their seeds are bulked and sown for developing the crop with desired improved characters.

EXERCISE 4

Object : To emasculate the flower of pea (*Pisum sativum*).

Requirements : Needles, forceps, scalpel, butter-paper bags, scissor, pocket lens, U-pin, pencil, brush, alcohol, tag and labels, note-book, etc.

Method : (*a*) Study of Floral Morphology of Sweet Pea (Fig. 22.2).

Flower : Bracteate, pedicellate, complete, hermaphrodite, zygomorphic, pentamerous, perigynous, cyclic, variously coloured.

Calyx : Sepals 5, gamosepalous, campanulate; odd sepal anterior; hairy, green.

Corolla : Petals 5, polypetalous, papilionaceous (*i.e.* one larger posterior petal called *standard* or *vexillum*, two lateral petals called *wings* or *alae*, and two anterolateral or inner fused petals called *keel* or *carina*); descending imbricate; variously coloured.

Androecium : Stamens 10, diadelphous (9 + 1) *i.e.* 9 united to form a tube and 10th posterior free; dithecous, basifixed, introrse.

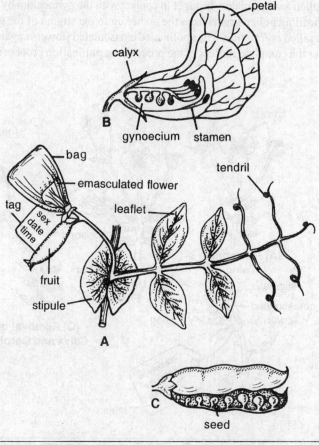

Fig. 22.3. *Emasculation in pea* (*Pisum sativum*).

Gynoecium : Monocarpellary, superior or semi-inferior, unilocular, many ovules in the locule; marginal placentation; style long, hairy, curved; stigma capitate, hairy.

Fruit : A legume

(*b*) *Emasculation* : 1. Select a suitable flower bud, which is expected to open after 2 or 3 days. Hold this bud in left hand with the thumb and forefinger.

2. Keep the standard or vexillum of the corolla towards upper side, and with the help of a needle rupture the keel from base towards upper side. Separate the two halves and press slightly by thumb and forefinger. This will completely expose the staminal tube with its stamens.

3. Now take a forcep in the right hand and remove the filaments of all the 10 stamens one by one. *This flower bud has now been emasculated.*

4. Keep the calyx, corolla and gynoecium in the normal position.

5. Bag, tag and label this emasculated flower bud.

(*c*) *Pollination or Crossing* : After two or three days of emasculation, the pollen grains from the desired male parent are placed on the stigma of the emasculated flower, as explained in detail in Exercise No.3. The emasculated flower has now been crossed. It is again bagged, tagged and labelled.

Precautions : 1. Always select a perfectly healthy bud on a perfectly healthy parent for emasculation.

2. The instruments, to be used in the entire process, should be properly sterilized before emasculation. For this, dip the instruments in the alcohol or rectified spirit.

3. Use sharp forceps and scissor with pointed ends.

4. Remove the anthers with a definite patience, and never in haste. Also count their number after removal.

5. While removing the anthers, the other floral parts should not be injured.

6. Heavy bags and labels should not be used. These should be as light as possible.

EXERCISE 5

Object : To emasculate the flower of Datura (Datura stramonium).

Requirements : Same as mentioned earlier in exercise 3.

Method : (*a*) Study of Floral Morphology (Fig. 22.4) of *Datura stramonium (Solanaceae)* :

Flower : Usually solitary axillary or solitary terminal flowers are ebracteate, pedicellate, complete, hermaphrodite, actinomorphic or slightly zygomorphic due to the presence of obliquely placed carpels, hypogynous and large.

Calyx : Sepals 5, gamosepalous, persistent, valvate or twisted.

Corolla : Petals 5, gamopetalous, trumpet-shaped, twisted, white.

Androecium : Stamens 5, epipetalous, polyandrous, filaments long, anthers dithecous and basifixed.

Gynoecium : Bicarpellary, syncarpous, superior, bilocular, carpels obliquely placed, placenta swollen, false septum provides a tetralocular appearance; many ovules in each locule, axile placentation; style long, stigma dome shaped, ovary wall prickly.

Fruit : Spiny capsule opening by four apical valves.

(*b*) **Emasculation :** 1. Select a young bud expected to open within 2 or 3 days and hold it in left hand with the thumb and forefinger.

2. Make an incision through the petals with a needle. By slightly changing the position of the flower its inner parts are exposed.

3. Take a forcep in the right hand and remove all the five stamens of the flower carefully and one by one. During this process the other floral parts, such as gynoecium, should not be injured. Thus completes the emasculation process.

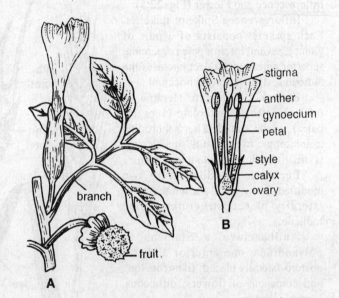

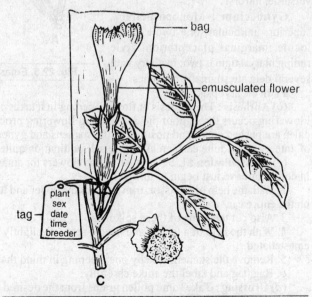

Fig. 22.4. Emasculation in *Datura stramonium*. A, A flowering twig; B, L.S. flower; C, Emasculated flower.

4. The emasculated flower bud, with its other parts (*e.g.*, calyx, corolla and gynoecium) intact, is bagged, tagged and labelled.

(*c*) **Pollination or Crossing** : In this process the pollen grains of the desired male plant are kept on the stigma of the emasculated flower bud after 2 or 3 days of the emasculation. The crossed flower bud is again bagged, tagged and labelled.

(*d*) **Precautions** : Same as described earlier in Exercise No. 4.

EXERCISE 6

Object : To emasculate the flowers of wheat (*Triticum aestivum*).

Requirements : Same as mentioned earlier in exercise 3.

Method : (*a*) Morphology of Inflorescence and Flower (Fig. 22.5).

Inflorescence : Spike of spikelets. Each spikelet consists of a pair of glumes, several inferior palea or lemma, superior palea; each floret encloses the lodicules, stamens and gynoecium.

Flower : Bracteate (lemma or inferior palea), bracteolate (superior palea), sessile, complete hermaphrodite, zygomorphic, hypogynous, small lemma is usually prolonged into a long awn.

Perianth : Reduced into two modified, fleshy, small and white antero-laterally placed structures called lodicules.

Androeciura : Stamens 3, polyandrous, one anterior and two postero-laterally placed; filaments long and come out of flowers; dithecous, versatile, introrse.

Gynoecium : Monocarpellary, superior, unilocular, one ovule in the locule, marginal placentation, style rudimentary; stigmas two, feathery with several delicate stigmatic branches.

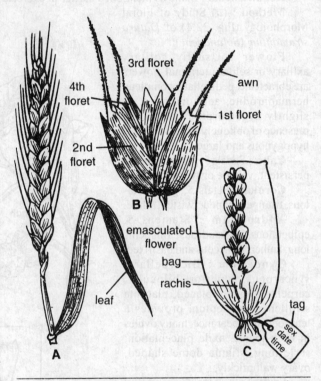

Fig. 22.5. Emasculation in wheat (*Triticum aestivum*).

Fruit : Caryopsis.

(*b*) **Anthesis** : The anthesis or flower opening first takes place in the basal flowers of the spikelets. Flowering occurs throughout the day. During flowering process, the lodicules swell, the lemma and palea are pushed apart, and position of the stamens and gynoecium becomes quite clear. Dehiscence of anthers starts quite early, making the self pollination quite easy.

(*c*) **Emasculation** : 1. Select such young flowers for emasculation in which anthers are still green in colour or have just begin to turn yellow.

2. With the help of a scissor, trim some of the upper and lower spikelets leaving only 6-8 spikelets on the entire ear.

3. Also cut the awns of these spikelets.

4. With the help of a forcep and needle separate slightly the lemma and palea of the florets to be emasculated.

5. Remove the stamens one by one, keeping in mind that other floral parts are not injured.

6. Bag, tag and label the spike carefully.

(*d*) **Crossing** : Take some pollen grains from the desired male plant next morning and dust on the bushy stigmas of the emasculated flowers with a brush. Again bag, tag and label the spike as earlier.

(*c*) **Precautions** : Same as described earlier in exercise 4.

CHAPTER

Laboratory Methods

The practical study of the subject is of immense value. The theoretical knowledge is always incomplete unless and until is supplemented with laboratory work. The laboratory work always adds to the knowledge and discipline. The practical work develops the scientific outlook which is most essential part of life. The science subjects can only be understood when a student works in the laboratory and makes the rational approach based on the facts and figures. The confusions are removed only by practical study of a subject. The practical aspect of the science subject is more essential than other theoretical aspects. Here a student makes the clear cut demarcation between right and wrong.

When one enters in the laboratory to work one should be most disciplined. The student while at working table should follow the laboratory rules. The student is expected to work silently and carefully. If one feels some difficulty in proceeding the work, he should immediately consult the teacher-in-charge. The most essential instruction about the practical work is that things should be signed by the teacher-in-charge, the same day. The cleanliness seems to be most important for practical work. The implements which are provided to you in the laboratory and the instruments which you possess should be clean and in working order. When you leave the laboratory after work, the things should be properly arranged by you.

PRESERVING BOTANICAL SPECIMENS

Preserving specimens for laboratory study. Such specimens may be preserved in alcohol or in formalin, but the latter is by far the most satisfactory. A comparatively weak solution of formalin is suitable for plant tissues. For most plant specimens 4% solution of formalin is recommended, although certain very large, fleshy forms may require a 5 or 6% solution. Plant material preserved in this way will be kept indefinitely and will be available whenever needed for laboratory study.

Green leaves placed in 4% formalin soon lose their green colouring matter (chlorophyll) and become yellowish or whitish. Alcohol presents the same difficulty, but the following solution will preserve the natural green colour in plants :

Phenol	...	20 gms.
Lactic acid	...	20 gms.
Glycerine	...	40 gms.
Distilled water	...	20 gms.
Cupric chloride	...	0.2 gms.
Cupric acetate	...	0.2 gms.

The specimens are merely dropped into this fluid and left there until needed. Usually from 3 to 10 days are required for complete preservation.

Preserving specimens for microscopic examination. For general use the most useful fixative is "F.A.A." This solution is made as follows :

50% Alcohol	...	100 ml
40% Formalin	...	6½ ml.
Glacial acetic acid	...	2½ ml.

This fixative is excellent for most plant tissues. Its usefulness is also due to the fact that tissues may be left in it indefinitely without harm.

A solution which will preserve **green algae** in good natural colour is made as follows :

Potassium chrome alum	...	10 gms.
40% formalin	...	5 ml.
Water	...	500 ml.

This fixative will not plasmolyse such forms as *Vaucheria*, and most algae fixed in it will be well preserved for microscopic examination.

Preserving specimens for display purposes. Green plants intended for display purposes may be preserved in the "ever green" solution mentioned above. After being fixed in this solution the specimens may be mounted in fluid (4% formalin) in glass display jars, or they may be pressed and mounted on standard herbarium sheets.

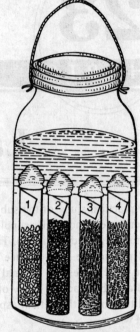

Fig. 23.1. Preservation of small specimens in a larger bottle.

Fruits and Flowers

The natural colours of some of the fruits and flowers may be preserved to some extent, however, by adding 10% of pure cane sugar to the usual (4%) formalin solution.

Fruits such as apples may be preserved in a solution made as follows :

Distilled water	...	400 ml.
Zinc chloride	...	200 gms.
Formalin (40%)	...	100 ml.
Glycerine	...	100 ml.

It is best to dissolve the zinc chloride in hot (distilled) water and filter while hot. Add formalin and glycerine.

INSTRUMENTS

The students while working in the laboratory must possess the following instruments and accessories with them :

1. Practical record book.
2. Pencils (HB, 2H, 4H, etc.)
3. Rubber (pencil eraser)
4. Foot scale
5. Camel-hair brush (No. 3)
6. Dropper

7. Razor with hollow-ground blade

8. Forceps

9. Needles with plastic handles (two)

10. Muslin cloth.

The slides, cover glasses, stains, reagents, mounting media, hone, strop, watch glasses, petri dishes, other glassware and a compound student microscope will be provided in the laboratory.

The following instruments are required, while one is in the field to collect plant materials for laboratory work and to make herbarium of dried specimens.

1. Vasculum

2. Pen knife.

3. Magnifying lens (10 X)

5. Trowel or pick

6. Tough and fair book and pencil

7. Pruning shears

8. Plant presses

9. Blotting papers or waste newspapers

10. Walking stick

11. First aid outfit (Iodine or Burnol)

SECTION CUTTING

In order to reveal the cellular structure of the plant material sections are being cut in various planes.

1. Cross section. Here the section passes at right angle to the material. It is of two types.

(a) *Transverse section.* Here the section is cut at right angle to vertical axis of the plant such as stem and roots..

(b) *Vertical section.* In case of thallus, leaf, etc., the section is cut in transverse plane and is known as vertical section. It is generally applied to the dorsiventral leaf and thallus growing prostrate.

2. Longitudinal section. The section is cut at right angles to the transverse axis. It is of two types :

(a) *Radial longitudinal section (R.L.S.).* It is the section that passes through the radius.

(b) *Tangential longitudinal section (T.L.S.).* It is the section that passes through the tangent, this does not pass through central region, it is transverse to medullary ray.

Method. To cut the thin sections suitable pith material should be used. In case of thalli and leaves, etc., the pith is first divided longitudinally into two equal halves with the help of scalpel and the material is placed in between the two halves of pith. In case of stems, roots, etc., a hole is made in the pith and the material is being fitted in the hole.

During the process of section cutting the students should be cautious so that the material does not dry up in whole operation of section cutting. To avoid this a few drops of water may be put now and then on the material. For cutting the sections the pith is being held in between the fingers and thumb of the left hand and the razor in the right hand. The first two fingers remain at the back of the razor and the thumb remain pressed against the milled surface of thick shank of the blade. The cutting edge of the razor blade should be kept always in horizontal

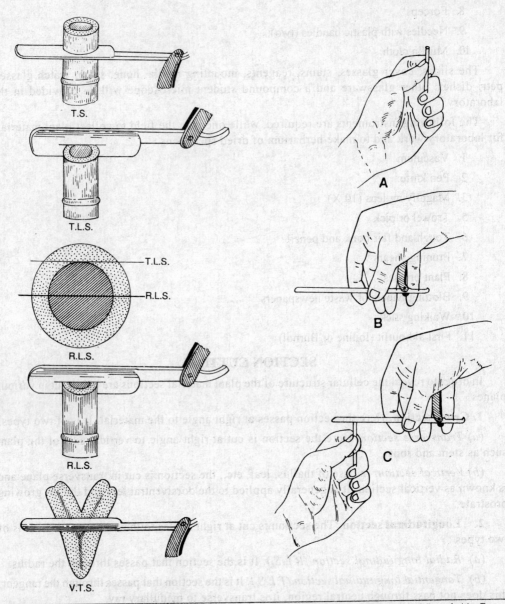

Fig. 23.2. Section cutting. Three planes of a block transverse, radial longitudinal and tangential longitudinal, and vertical transverse sections.

Fig. 22.3. Section cutting. A, holding of pith; B, holding of razor; C, section cutting material is being inserted in the pith.

position so that the uniform and thin sections are cut. The sections should be cut by sliding the razor over the material repeatedly. This process should be repeated several times and then the sections thus cut are transferred with the help of camel's hair brush to a watch glass containing water. With the help of camel's hair brush the thinnest and perfect sections are being selected for staining.

HOW TO PREPARE MICROSCOPE SLIDES OF SIMPLE OBJECTS

Whole Mounts

As the name indicates, whole mounts are preparations of the object entire. Many interesting mounts may be made without cutting sections, and without staining. Fibres of cotton, fern sporangia, the fruiting heads of mosses (if dried first) and pine pollen, may be dropped directly into xylol, placed in a drop of balsam on a slide, and covered.

Free-hand Sections

Free-hand sections of cork, pith and the stems and roots of many of the common plants may be cut. For this purpose the razor must be sharp and free from nicks. Only thinnest sections should be used and they may be placed into 95% alcohol as cut. Subsequent treatment of sections is as follows. Handling should be gentle as possible, using section lifter and camel's hair brush.

1. *95% alcohol - 1/2 hour.*
2. *50% alcohol - 5 minutes.*
3. *Water - 5 minutes.*
4. *Safranin - 4 hours (1% solution in water).*
5. *Water to rinse.*
6. *50% alcohol - 5 minutes.*
7. *95% alcohol - 5 minutes.*
8. *Absolute alcohol - 5 minutes.*
9. *95% alcohol containing 1% light green 1-3 minutes.*
10. *Absolute alcohol - 3-5 minutes.*
11. *Clove oil - 5 minutes.*
12. *Xylol-indefinite.*
13. *Mount in balsam : cover with cover glass.*

The time values given are approximate, and will vary somewhat with the kind of section being stained. Practice on a few sections will teach whether to hasten or retard the process.

MACERATION TECHNIQUE

The various parts of the plants consist of several types of tissues. Such tissues can be studied well by a special technique known as *maceration.* This process involves the separation of a particular cell from a mass of cells. This type of dissociation is brought about by chemical treatment of the plant organ that dissolves the middle lamella and the cells are separated from each other.

Usually three undermentioned methods are employed for the purpose.

1. Jeffrey's method. Take the dried or fresh plant material and make very thin slices of it. Boil the material in water by keeping it in a test tube. After some time when the material becomes air free and settles down in the bottom of the test tube, it is macerated in a solution. The maceration solution may be prepared as follows :

    (*i*) 10% Nitric acid (*i.e.*, 90 ml. water +10 ml. nitric acid).
    (*ii*) 10% Chromic acid (*i.e.*, 90 ml water +10 ml. chromic acid)
        Mix (*i*) and (*ii*) acids.

Now take the material in this maceration solution in a test tube. Heat this solution and separate the material in small pieces by piercing a needle to the material. Stop heating as soon as the material becomes soft and pulp like. Now transfer this pulpy material to a watch glass. Drain out all the maceration fluid. Wash the material several times with water, so that the acid traces are removed completely. Now strain the material with aqueous safranin and mount it in glycerine or glycerine jelly. The material may also be passed through alcohol series for making permanent slides.

2. Harlow's method. Treat the sliced and boiled material with chlorine water for two hours. Now wash the material with water. After proper washing boil the material in sodium sulphite for fifteen minutes. Now transfer this fluid to a watch glass. Drain out the water. Tease the material with the help of a needle for the separation of tissues. Prepare temporary or permanent mounts.

3. Schultze's method. Make thin slices of the material and boil it in water in a test tube. Now fill the test tube with concentrated nitric acid, and add a few crystals of potassium chlorate to it. Heat it gently till material becomes white. Now transfer the fluid to the watch glass and drain out the liquid leaving material alone. Wash the material with water. Tease the material with the help of a needle, so that the cells may be separated from each other. Stain the material and make temporary or permanent mounts.

STAINING

The tissue differentiation is possible only by staining the different tissues with different stains. The stains are the chemical dyes having different reactions with the cell wall of the tissue and thus giving a particular stain to a particular tissue. For example, the acidic dye stains unlignified tissue while the basic one stains lignified tissue.

Single staining. The plant materials having no differentiation of tissues (*e.g.*, algae, fungi, bryophytes) are stained by this process.

Double staining. The plant materials having highly differentiated tissues (*e.g.*, Pteridophyta, Gymnosperms, Angiosperms, etc.) are stained by this process. Double staining involves the use of two dyes, one acidic and other basic. The acidic dye stains unlignified tissues while the basic one stains the lignified tissues. Some important dyes are as follows :

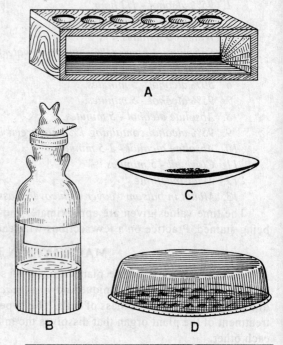

Fig. 23.4. Some laboratory requirements *A*, staining rack; *B*, dropping bottle; *C*, watch glass; *D*, petri dish (petri plate).

1. **Safranin :**

    Alcoholic :

    | Safranin | ... | 1 gm. |
    | Alcohol 95% | ... | 50 c.c. |
    | Distilled water | ... | 50 c.c. |

    Aqueous :

    | Safranin | ... | 1 gm. |
    | Distilled water | ... | 10 c.c. |

    This is mainly used to stain lignified tissues.

2. **Crystal violet or Gentian violet:**

    | Crystal violet | ... | 1 gm |
    | Distilled water | ... | 100 c.c. |

    It is basic violet dye and stains lignified tissues.

3. **Aniline blue :**

   Aniline blue .... *1 gm.*

   Alcohol (95%) of

   distilled water .... *100 c.c.*

   It stains cellulose walls.

4. **Erythrosine:**

   Erythrosine .... *1 gm.*

   Absolute alcohol ...... *5 c.c.*

   Clove oil .... *95 c.c.*

   It is used to stain gelatinous sheath, e.g., Algae.

5. **Eosine :**

   Eosine .... *1 gm*

   Water .... *100 c.c.*

   It stains cytoplasm.

6. **Light green**

   Light green .... *0.5 gm.*

   Alcohol 95% .... *100 c.c.*

   OR

   Light green .... *1 gm*

   Absolute alcohol ...... *2.5 c.c.*

   Clove oil .... *75 c.c.*

   It is used to stain cellulose and lignified cell walls.

7. **Fast green :**

   Fast green .... *0.5 gm.*

   Alcohol 95% .... *100 c.c.*

   OR

   Fast green .... *0.5 gm.*

   Absolute alcohol ...... *25 c.c.*

   Clove oil .... *75 c.c.*

8. **Cotton blue :**

   Aniline blue .... *0.1 gm.*

   Phenol .... *25 gms.*

   Glycerine .... *25 c.c.*

   Lactic acid .... *25 c.c.*

   Distilled water ...... *25 c.c.*

   This is used for staining various fungi.

9. **Basic fuchsin :**

   Solution A

   Basic fuchsin .... *0.3 gm.*

   Alcohol 95% .... *10 c.c.*

   Solution B

   Phenol (melted) ...... *5 gms.*

   Distilled water ...... *95 c.c.*

   Mix solutions A and B.

   This is a nuclear stain and also used to stain bacteria.

10. **Hematoxylins :**

    Heidenhain's hematoxylin.

    Hematoxylin .... *0.5 gm.*

    Warm distilled water ... *100 c.c.*

    Store in a dark place to ripen at least for four days before use.

Delafield's hematoxylin.

1. *Saturated aqueous solution (100 c.c.) of ferric ammonium sulphate.*
2. *1 gm. Hematoxylin + 6 c.c. absolute alcohol.*
3. *Mix 1 and 2 solutions.*

The prepared solution is kept for sufficient time and then used. The solution becomes dark red in colour. It is good nuclear stain.

11. Acetocarmine :

Carmine   ...   *1 gm.*
Glacial acetic acid ...   *45 c.c.*

Dissolve 1 gm. of carmine in 100 c.c. of boiling 45% acetic acid. Cool this mixture and decant. Add few drops of ferric acetate aqueous solution in the mixture. Cool the mixture abruptly by keeping it in ice. Filter the mixture and stock it in a cool place.

MOUNTING MEDIA AND MOUNTING

Mounting Media for Temporary Preparations

1. Glycerine. Prepare the mounting medium as follows - 30 ml. pure glycerine + 70 ml. water. This medium is quite good for the mounting purpose of algae and stained sections.

2. Glycerine jelly. It is prepared by dissolving one part of the gelatin with six parts of water by boiling. Add to it seven parts of glycerine. Also add 10% phenol which acts as preservative. This is a good mounting medium for algae. The slides become semipermanent and can be kept for long.

3. Lacto-phenol. This mounting medium can be prepared by adding equal amounts of phenol, lactic acid, glycerine and distilled water. This makes a good mounting medium to mount various fungi.

Mounting Media for Permanent Preparations

1. Canada balsam. This medium is used for permanent slide preparations. According to need this may be diluted by adding xylene in it. This medium is somewhat yellowish in colour.

2. D.P.X. mountant. This is a good mounting medium for permanent slide preparations. This is perfectly transparent and gives good results.

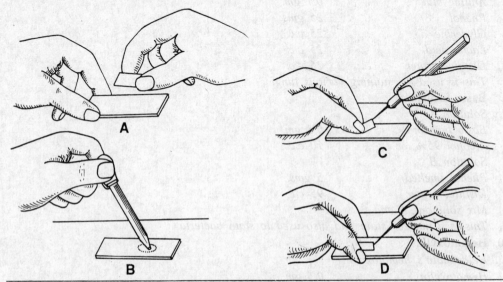

Fig. 23.5. Mounting material after section cutting and proper staining (A—D).

Method of mounting. The stained sections or materials are generally mounted in any one of the media mentioned above. While mounting one should be watchful that the object is being mounted in the centre of the slide. Put a drop of mounting medium in the centre of the slide with the help of a dropper and the material is being transferred in this drop of medium with the help of a fine brush. With the help of forceps or needle the cover glass is kept on the material in such a way that the air bubbles are avoided. The mounting fluid should not flow outside the coverslip. The extra amount of fluid can be removed with the help of a blotting paper.

Labelling. After making the preparation neat and clean it should be properly labelled. The labels should be uniformly pasted on the left side of the slide. Usually the generic and specific names, name of the part and plane of the section are being written on the label. One should also write his name on the bottom of the label.

Ringing. Usually the temporary and semipermanent slides are sealed by cementing material with the help of a ringing machine. By this method only those slides can be sealed which possess round cover-glasses.

HOW TO MAKE LABORATORY DRAWINGS

Accurately made drawings are a very important part of laboratory work. An accurate drawing made in the laboratory from the specimen itself, is a very good indication of the student's grasp of the subject. Every teacher of Biology has heard students say : "I can't draw." However, any student who can follow laboratory directions intelligently and who can be taught to see accurately can make a drawing that will demonstrate his observations. Too often students feel that because their drawings do not look artistic their work is inferior, when as a matter of fact an artistic drawing may be decidedly unsatisfactory from a scientific standpoint. A good drawing is often spoiled by trying to make it look artistic. A laboratory drawing should be as simple as possible, with clean, clear cut lines showing what has been seen and neatly labelled.

Preliminary Study

The most important prerequisite in making a drawing is careful observation. If a laboratory outline is being used, all parts called for in the drawing must be identified in the specimen, and the student must understand the work that he is doing before pencil is put to the drawing paper.

Materials

1. The drawing paper should be heavy enough to permit a good deal of erasing and should have a smooth, hard surface. A heavy, white paper size 8 × 10½ inches, with holes punched to fit the laboratory note book.

2. A hard drawing pencil, 6H preferred. The pencil should not be softer than 4H.

3. A soft rubber eraser.

4. A ruler with the English system on one edge and the metric system on the other. Six-inch celluloid rulers are satisfactory for most work.

5. A very fine sand paper for putting a good point on the drawing pencil.

Size of Drawings

The most common mistake made by beginning students is to make their drawing too small. Since it is almost impossible in every instance for the teacher or for the manual to give the size that every drawing should be, the simplest rule to follow is to have the drawing large enough to show all parts without crowding. If the drawing is one showing a single cell it must be large enough to show clearly and to label all of its parts. Obviously such a drawing need not cover a whole page. The student must learn to judge for himself how large to make the drawing, remembering, roughly speaking, that the greater the number of parts to be shown the larger the drawing should be and also that the tendency is to make drawing too small.

Laying Out the Drawing

The punched holes in the paper should be to the left. Draw on the one side of the paper. The student's name should appear on each sheet, usually at the upper right hand corner. The title of the drawing should be directly over it.

First, determine the size of the drawing and its arrangement on the page. Keep far enough to the right of the punched holes so that no part of the drawing will be obscured when it is placed in the note book. Leave enough margin for labels, one both sides if necessary.

Draw a very faint guideline down the centre of the drawing field. On either side of this line mark the natural divisions of the specimen by means of light dots. Then carefully outline the drawing with very light lines connecting the dots until the proportions are accurately portrayed. Compare the faint outline sketch with the specimen, and erase and sketch until it is accurate. Having obtained an accurate outline erase the guideline and the superfluous light lines, leaving only the faint traces of the outline to be used. Then tracing over this outline makes a sharp, clear-cut line. In doing this use a normal, continuous movement of the hand or finger. The general outline having been completed, the details should then be filled in, sketching lightly at first where necessary to obtain proportion, continually comparing with the specimen to insure accuracy in proper relationship of parts. When the drawing has been completed, every line should be clear and sharp. Any traces of the light lines used in making the outline should be removed by erasing lightly. Every line in the drawing should be there for the purpose of indicating some part of the specimen. Extra line for artistic effect may spoil an otherwise good drawing.

Labelling

When a student has completed his drawing he often feels that the important part has been finished. However, he should give just as careful attention to the labelling as to the drawing. Careless labelling can spoil a good drawing. If possible, all labels should be in a column to the right of the drawing. If there are a great many parts to be labelled, another column to left of the drawing may be necessary.

Neatness

The finished drawing should be neat and clean. Clean hands, and careful procedure at all time will enable the student to make a neat and scientific drawing, against a clean, white background. If the drawing has proved difficult and becomes slightly soiled from much handling, diligent use of the eraser before labelling will usually result in a clean page.

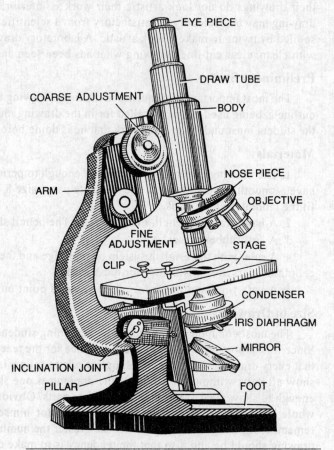

EYE PIECE
DRAW TUBE
COARSE ADJUSTMENT
BODY
NOSE PIECE
ARM
OBJECTIVE
FINE ADJUSTMENT
STAGE
CLIP
CONDENSER
IRIS DIAPHRAGM
MIRROR
INCLINATION JOINT
PILLAR
FOOT

Fig. 23.6. Compound student microscope.

PRACTICAL MICROSCOPY

Illumination

Artificial light is preferable because of its uniformity and availability. For direct observation through the microscope, a desk lamp placed about six inches from the microscope.

Eye Care

Both eyes must be kept open and used alternately while working with the monocular microscope to avoid eye-strain. Microscope illumination may be modified for eye comfort by exchanging the light bulb of the lamp for one of lower or higher watt value, or by interposing a ground glass screen (near the lamp) between the light source and substage condenser. Do not alter the correct position of the substage condenser or the correct opening of the substage diaphragm to reduce light intensity.

To Illuminate the Low Power Objective

(a) Place a suitable object on the stage and while matching from the level of the stage, lower the objective within an eighth of an inch of the slide.

(b) Then, looking, through the 10 X eye piece, direct the light through the condenser with the plane mirror until the field or view is illuminated. Elevate the tube with the coarse adjustment until the object appears in focus. Complete focussing with the fine adjustment.

To Illuminate the High Power Objective

(a) Revolve the high dry-objective into position. If the objectives are parfocal, the image will be approximately in focus. If the objectives are not parfocal, lower the high dry objective until it nearly touches the cover glass.

(b) Then, looking through the eyepiece, focus up. Use the fine adjustment only for delicate focussing.

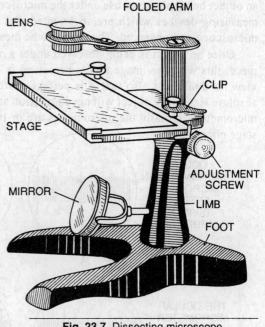

Fig. 23.7. Dissecting microscope.

To Illuminate the Homogeneous Oil Immersion Objective

(a) Place a suitable object slide on the stage. Locate the desired field with a low power objective and centre the light with the plane mirror.

(b) Elevate the microscope tube and place a drop of cedarwood immersion oil on the area to be observed. (Avoid air bubbles)

(c) Lower the oil immersion objective with the coarse adjustment to contact with the drop of immersion oil. Control this operation from the level of the stage.

(d) Raise the objective slightly with the coarse adjustment without breaking the immersion contact.

(e) Then, looking through the eyepiece, focus down carefully with the coarse adjustment until the image comes into view. Complete the focussing with the fine adjustment.

(f) Immersion oil should be removed once a day from objectives when the day's work is complete. It is undesirable to subject the lens surface to excessive polishing. To clean an objective wipe across the lens front with a dry portion of lens paper removing the bulk of oil, then follow with lens paper moistened with xylol, and finally with dry lens paper.

Care of the Microscope

Carry the instrument by the arm - supporting it at the same time by placing the other hand under it. Do not subject the microscope to rapid changes of temperature. The slides of the rack and pinion may be lubricated and cleaned occasionally by applying a small amount of paraffin oil or light grease and wiping it off. Do not lubricate the fine adjustment nor the teeth of either rack or pinion of the coarse adjustment. Keep the microscope covered and protected from dust when not in use. Dust may be removed from lenses with a clean camel's hair brush. Should the front lens of the objective be soiled, wipe it gently with lens paper moistened with distilled water - do no rub.

MEASURING WITH THE MICROSCOPE (MICROMETRY)

The micrometry is the subject in which we have some measurement of the dimensions of an object being observed use under the microscope. The method employs some special types of measuring devices which are so oriented that these can well be attached to or put into the microscope and observed. The object to be measured is calibrated against these scales.

Once an object is being observed under a microscope by the 10 X objective the 10 X eye piece; this way, the image that is perceived is 100 times of the object. We get the magnified view no doubt and also that it is perfect coordination of the dimensions but to find out the absolute size of the object will need precision and which is achieved through the application of micrometers. Usually the micrometers are or two types - the ocular micrometer disc and the stage micrometer.

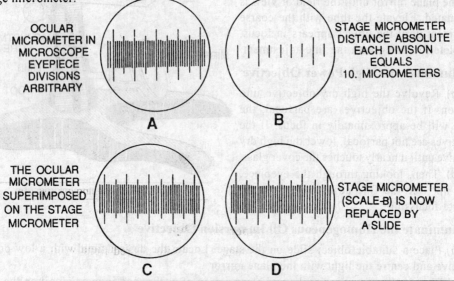

OCULAR MICROMETER IN MICROSCOPE EYEPIECE DIVISIONS ARBITRARY

A

STAGE MICROMETER DISTANCE ABSOLUTE EACH DIVISION EQUALS 10. MICROMETERS

B

THE OCULAR MICROMETER SUPERIMPOSED ON THE STAGE MICROMETER

C

STAGE MICROMETER (SCALE-B) IS NOW REPLACED BY A SLIDE

D

Fig. 23.8.   Micrometry. Standardization of the ocular micrometer and its use in measuring bacterial cells.

The ocular micrometer disc. Before inserting the disc, clean it gently with distilled water and wipe it with a soft lifeless tissue. Examine the disc with a hand magnifier by light reflected from each surface to detect adhering particles and removed them with a clean camel's hair brush. Select the ocular (preferably not stronger than 10 X) and unscrew the eyelens mount. Position the disc over the eyepiece diaphragm with the engraved side down (figures should appear erect), and replace the eyelens. With the micrometer disc in place, insert the ocular into the illuminated microscope and bring the lines into sharp focus unscrewing the upper eyelens for a sufficient distance. There are usually 50 or 100 divisions in the ocular meter which are engraved on the glass.

The stage micrometer. The scale, mounted like a microscope specimen on a glass slide which is generally thicker than a specific slide. The micrometer has a amount of very finely graduated scale. The scale measures only one millimeter and has a least count of 0.01 mm, *i.e.*, 1 millimeter region is divided into 100 divisions. As 1 mm has 1000 μ–one division of stage micrometer is equal to 10 μ.

Method. The stage micrometer is kept in low power under microscope and is observed through the eye piece hang ocular micrometer disc. Suppose we have 10 X objective and 5 X eye piece in the microscope with a tube of 170 mm. length. At this magnification the number of ocular divisions coinciding the stage micrometer are observed and then calculated for microns per ocular division, *e.g.*, 6 ocular divisions coincide 8 stage micrometer divisions

i.e.,   6 ocular divisions = 8 stage micrometer divisions

or   6   „   „   = 0.08 mm.

(since 1 division of stage micrometer is equal to .01 mm.)

$$1 \quad „ \quad \text{division} = \frac{0.08}{6} \text{ mm.}$$

$$= \frac{0.08 \times 1000}{6}$$

$$= 13.3 \text{ μ}$$

Thus the microscope is calibrated for different combinations of eye pieces and objective lens and is kept for record.

Measurement of an object. When the microscope is calibrated, then the object to be measured is kept on the stage of the microscope and is observed through eye piece of ocular. The object is measured in the particular magnification by ocular divisions and then is being changed into micron by multiplying ocular division with calibrated value of one ocular division in that particular magnification, *e.g.*, the length of a bacterial cell is equal to five divisions of ocular that means the length in microns will be 5 ocular divisions X 13.3 = 66.5 μ.

This way the object can be measured in any of the magnification.

COMMON STAINS AND MOUNTING MEDIA

For Algae — Temporary preparations

Stains :   *(i)   Aniline blue (.1% aqueous)*
(ii) Fast green (.5 aqueous)   } *Single staining*
(iii) Safranin (.5% aqueous)

Mounting media   *(i) Glycerine 10%*
(ii) Glycerine jelly.

For Fungi — Temporary preparations

Stains :   *(i) Cotton blue*] *Single staining*
(ii) Aniline blue

Mounting media :   *(i) Lactophenol*
(ii) Glycerine 10%

For Bryophytes — Temporary preparations

Stains :   *(i) Safranin.*] *Single staining*
(ii) Fast green.

Mounting media   *(i) Glycerine 10%*
(ii) Glycerine jelly.

For Pteridophytes

(Temporary and permanent preparations)

Primary stains :	Secondary stains :
(i) Safranin	*Fast green* ⎤
(ii) Crystal violet	*Erythrosine* ⎦ *Double staining*

Mounting media :

(i) Glycerine 10% (for temporary preparations)

(ii) Canada Balsam or D.P.X. mountant (for permanent preparations)

For Gymnosperms :

(Temporary and permanent preparations)

Primary stains :	Secondary stains :
(i) Safranin	*Fast green* ⎤
(ii) Crystal violet	*Erythrosine* ⎦ *Double staining*

Mounting media :

(i) Glycerine 10% (for temporary preparations)

(ii) Canada Balsam or D.P.X. mountant (for permanent preparations)

NOTES

NOTES